UMI
BOOKS ON DEMAND™

UMI
A Bell & Howell Company
300 North Zeeb Road ⋄ PO Box 1346
Ann Arbor, Michigan 48106-1346
800-521-0600 ⋄ 313-761-4700

Printed in 1996 by xerographic process on acid-free paper

THE UNIVERSITY OF VIRGINIA EDITION OF
THE WORKS OF STEPHEN CRANE

VOLUME V

TALES OF ADVENTURE

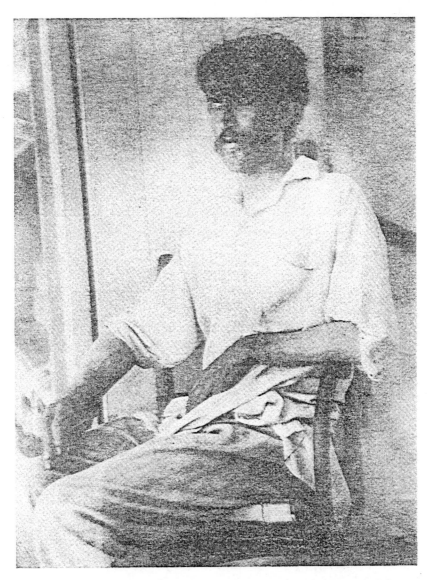

Crane after his rescue from the sinking of the *Commodore* (Yale)

STEPHEN CRANE

TALES OF ADVENTURE

EDITED BY
FREDSON BOWERS
LINDEN KENT PROFESSOR OF ENGLISH AT
THE UNIVERSITY OF VIRGINIA

WITH AN INTRODUCTION BY
J. C. LEVENSON
EDGAR ALLAN POE PROFESSOR OF ENGLISH AT
THE UNIVERSITY OF VIRGINIA

THE UNIVERSITY PRESS OF VIRGINIA
CHARLOTTESVILLE

CENTER FOR EDITIONS OF
AMERICAN AUTHORS
AN APPROVED TEXT
MODERN LANGUAGE
ASSOCIATION OF AMERICA

Editorial expenses for this volume have been supported by grants from the National Endowment for
the Humanities administered through the Center for
Editions of American Authors of the Modern Language Association.

Standard Book Number: 8139–0302–5
Library of Congress Catalog Card Number: 68–8536
Printed in the United States of America

To
Clifton Waller Barrett

FOREWORD

THIS volume brings together a representative group of
Crane's short stories based on the selection he made for
the American edition of *The Open Boat*, which is here
given complete. The additional stories that Heinemann required
to fill out the English edition are mostly sketches that Crane had
on hand at the moment, not what he necessarily wanted collected
with his prime stories found in the Doubleday & McClure volume.
Only one of these—"The Pace of Youth"—has been abstracted for
the present volume. The rest of the "Midnight Sketches," as Crane
called the segregated group of additional material, will appear in
Volume VIII among their own kind. From the 1899 Harper's
Monster, already dipped into for TALES OF WHILOMVILLE, Volume VII of this edition, the printing of "The Blue Hotel" completes
the stories there collected in the American edition; but from the
extra stories in the London edition of 1901 "Twelve O'Clock" and
"Moonlight on the Snow" have been selected to round off Crane's
series of Western tales. Finally, "A Poker Game" has been drawn
from the 1902 *Last Words* for a certain balance that it provides.
These stories are arranged chronologically in the order of their
original composition so far as this can be determined.

The Introduction by Professor J. C. Levenson offers what facts
are known about the circumstances of the composition and publication of the short stories here collected and places these works
in the literary and historical contexts of their time and of Crane's
development as a writer. The Textual Introduction details the
physical forms of the texts, their authority and transmission, and
examines specific problems involved in the establishment of the
texts in their present critical form. The principles on which the
editing has been based are stated in "The Text of the Virginia
Edition" prefixed to Volume I, BOWERY TALES (1969).

Certain special problems are raised by an edition of a group of stories that appeared in a number of different magazines and newspapers and were subject thus to widely varying house styling. The first principle of the editing is that each separate text must be considered as a unit; hence only a few limited efforts have been made to impose any uniformity on their overall details. That is, this is an unmodernized edition of a series of disparate texts in which the present-day theory of copy-text and its treatment operates to establish the words and their forms in each story on an individual basis according to the evidence of the preserved documents for that particular text. In the majority of cases emendation of the accidentals in the most authoritative document chosen as copy-text has been directed toward securing correctness and uniformity within the story itself—this taken to be a desirable objective—but no attempt has been made to produce the overall uniformity expected in modernized popular editions. Thus in one story one may find *mesquite* and in another *mesquit*; in one *whisky* but in another *whiskey*, and so on. Occasionally derived texts may be used to correct inconsistencies within the individual copy-text in a manner that brings these into conformity with Crane's general practice; and considerable freedom has been exercised in this respect in emending the copy-text from texts that are also authoritative for that particular work. However, except in the general substitution (always recorded) of the American forms of accidentals, little or no artificial unity has been attempted between the various stories in the texture of their accidentals.

The two stories in which copies of a master proof were mailed by Bacheller to various newspapers subscribing to his syndicated material present a problem of copy-text. In an ideal sense this proof, insofar as it can be reconstructed from the various newspaper publications radiating from the common copy, should be the theoretical copy-text; but considerations involving the recording of variants force an editor to the simpler procedure of selecting some one typical example of these newspapers as the specific copy-text. The reader should recognize that this procedure is only one of convenience, and that no single newspaper text is technically more authoritative than another except in the rare cases when one newspaper was copied by another which did not use the syndicated master proof. The importance of securing the maximum amount of evidence on which to base the reconstruction in precise detail of the lost common copy for these syndicated newspaper publications has fostered a wide search in likely newspaper files and the uncovering of a number of previously unrecorded places of publication. (New magazine appearances have also been discovered for this volume.) That the newspapers of this country have been exhausted would be an idle hope, and it is to be expected that continuing search will uncover further appearances of the syndicated stories here edited, affording the lost opportunity (for this first printing) of a slightly more refined determination of the most authoritative accidentals. However, for each newspaper story sufficient examples have been found to give confidence that no further variation in the wording in later-discovered copies is likely to reveal hitherto-concealed authoritative substantive readings, although some questions of punctuation about which the editor is at present less than satisfied might be settled.

To assist with the recording of the variants from the larger number of authorities represented by newspaper publication, these newspapers are arbitrarily assigned the generic abbreviation N and are distinguished not by their initials but by superior numbers like N^1, N^2, and N^3, a device that should cause no confusion with the use of numbers to denominate the order of editions such as E1 and E2. In writing of newspapers as a group, the simple N may be used, as "the N text derives from a Bacheller proof." However, for the more exacting collational records a convenient device has been borrowed from descriptive bibliography; this is $, the dollar sign, which means *all* or *every*. Thus if five newspapers N^{1-5} are collated and they all agree in a particular reading to be noted, this unanimous concurrence of every collated newspaper can be expressed as $N. For variations on this convention, see the headnote to the Editorial Emendations listing.

In the Historical Collation sections only the variant paragraphing of substantive editions that have full or partial authority is recorded. A statement of the collated editions is made in the headnote for each Historical Collation, but the status of these editions is provided in the headnote for the Editorial Emendations list, as well as in the Textual Introduction, of course. Regardless of the status of the edition, if the paragraphing variant has been noted under Editorial Emendations it is not included in the Historical Collation. In this respect the recording of paragraph variation in the Historical Collation differs from the treatment given substantive readings. Finally, when certain recorded editions vary considerably from the copy-text in their paragraphing, or in their cutting of the text, the notation of these rejected variants may be presented in shorthand style in a single unit following the Historical Collation, thus throwing into sharper relief the more important substantive data presented in this collation list.

Especially in the recording of newspaper variants, purely typographical errors that do not form recognized words are ignored in the Historical Collation, and also in the Editorial Emendations unless they are copy-text readings.

The expenses of the preparation of the texts in this volume with their introductions and apparatus have been subsidized by a grant from the National Endowment for the Humanities administered through the Modern Language Association of America and its Center for Editions of American Authors, but with generous support, as well, from the University of Virginia.

The editor is much in debt for assistance and various courtesies to Professor Robert Stallman of the University of Connecticut, Professor James Colvert of the University of Georgia, Professor Joseph Katz of the University of South Carolina, and to his colleagues Professors Matthew Bruccoli of South Carolina and J. C. Levenson of the University of Virginia. Especial thanks are due to Professor Bernice Slote of the University of Nebraska whose friendly interest provided several previously unknown newspaper publications. Professor James Meriwether of the University of South Carolina, who examined this volume for the Center for Editions of American Authors seal, made several suggestions. Mr. Kenneth A. Lohf, Librarian for Rare Books and Manuscripts of the Columbia University Libraries, has been of unfailing and particular assistance. The editor is grateful to the librarians of Syracuse University, Yale University, and Dartmouth College for their courtesies in making available unpublished letters in their collections, and to the librarians of Harvard, the British Museum, and the London Library for the use of their collections. Mr. H. C. Schulz of the Henry E. Huntington Library very kindly answered questions about the manuscript of "The Five White Mice." The constant assistance of the custodians of the Barrett Collection at the University of Virginia has been invaluable, and Miss Helen Koiner, Head of Interlibrary Loans, has placed the editor deeply in debt for her help over an extended period. The services as research assistants of Mrs. David Yalden-Thomson and Miss Gillian G. M. Kyles, and of Mr. Alan Day in London, have been essential and much appreciated, for in these days of relatively rapid editorial publication no single scholar can think of assuming the burden of the repeated checking for accuracy of notation enforced by the standards for CEAA editions.

The editor's personal debt to Mr. Clifton Waller Barrett and his magnificent collection at the University of Virginia remains constant and can be expressed only by the dedication of this edition to him.

For permission to use as copy-text the manuscript of "The Five White Mice" and to illustrate it, the editor is grateful to the Director of the Henry E. Huntington Library and to Alfred A. Knopf, Inc.; other illustrations are presented with the permission of the Columbia University Libraries, Yale University, and the University of Virginia. By permission of the University of Virginia, "A Poker Game" is edited from the early typescript in the Barrett Collection used as copy-text.

The general title for the present volume is drawn, at the suggestion of Professor Levenson, from the subtitle of the American edition of *The Open Boat*.

F. B.

Charlottesville, Virginia
January 15, 1970

CONTENTS

To

The late William Higgins

and to

Captain Edward Murphy and Steward C. B. Montgomery

of the sunk steamer Commodore.

1	— The Open Boat	9000	Scribners
6	— Flanagan	6000	London Ill. News
7	— Horses	5000	New Review
2	— A Man and Some Others	7000	Century
3	— The Bride Comes to Yellow Sky	4500	Chapmans
4	— The Wise Men	5500	
5	— The Five White Mice	5000	
8	— Death and The Child	8000	
5	— A Great Mistake	50000	
4	— An Ominous Baby		or in actual count about 53000
7	— The Auction		
9	— A Detail		
6	— An Eloquence of Grief		
1	— An Experiment in Misery		
3	— The Duel that was not Fought		
8	— The Pace of Youth		
2	— The Men in the Storm		

The Open Boat: Autograph dedication and contents list for the English
edition (Columbia)

#	Title	Amount	Notes
1	The Pace of Youth	4000	Bacheller
2	Flanagan	6000	McClure
3	An Open Boat	9000	Scribner
4	A Man and Some Others	7000	Century
5	The Loss of An Arm	1500	Youth's Companion
6	Five White Mice	5000	ms at Hartwood
7	The Wise Men	5000	" " "
8	The Auction	1500	Ms with me
9	An Eloquence of Grief	1000	" " "
10	The Wisdom of the Present	500	" " "
11	The Man in the White Hat	1000	Westminster Gazette
12	Velestino	7000	" "
13	Suda Bay	3000	" "
14	The Men in the Storm	2000	Philistine
15	An Ominous Baby	1000	" "
16	When Man Falls—	1500	The Press
17	The Duel	2000	"
18	The Fire	2000	"
19	An Experiment in Misery	3000	"
20	Bink's Day in the Country	2000	"
21	Christmas Dinner Won in Battle	2000	Plumbers Trade Journal
22	One Dash - Horses	5000	Pocket Magazine
23	The Snake	1000	"
24	A Detail	500	" "
25	Sketches of Nebraska Life	1000	ms to be recovered from Bacheller
26	The Pursuit of the Butter + Eggs Man	500	The Press
27	: The Kid who stole a Lemon	1500	Philistine
28			
29			

Autograph inventory list, about July, 1897 (Columbia)

The Five White Mice
By Stephen Crane

Freddie was mixing a cock-tail. His hand with the long spoon was whirling swiftly and the ice in the glass hummed and rattled like a cheap watch. Over by the window, a gambler, a millionaire, a railway conductor and the agent of a vast American syndicate were playing seven-up. Freddie surveyed them with the ironical glance of a man who is mixing a cocktail. Now from time to time a swarthy Mexican waiter came with his tray from the rooms at the rear and called his orders across the bar. The sounds of the indolent stir of the city, awakening from its siesta, floated over the screens which barred the sun and the inquisitive eyes. From the faraway kitchen could be heard the roar of the old French chef, driving, herding and abusing his Mexican helpers.

A string of men came suddenly in from the streets. They stormed up to the bar. There were impatient shouts. "Come now, Freddie, don't stand there like a portrait of yourself. Wiggle!" Drinks of many kinds and colors, amber, green, mahogany, strong and mild, began to swarm upon the bar with all the attendants of lemon, sugar, mint and ice. Freddie with Mexican support worked like a sailor in the provision of them, sometimes talking with that scorn for drink and admiration for those who drink which is the attribute of a good bar-keeper.

At last a man was afflicted with a stroke of dice-shaking. A herculean discussion was waging and he was deeply engaged in it but at the same time he lazily flirted the dice. Occasionally he made great combinations. "Look at that, would you? he cried proudly. The others paid little heed. Then violently the craving took them. It went along the line like an epidemic and involved them all. In a moment they had arranged a carnival of dice-shaking with money penalties and liquid prizes. They clamorously made it a point of honour with Freddie that he too should play and take his chance of sometimes providing this large group with free refreshment. With bended heads like foot-ball players they surged over the tinkling dice, peeling, cheering and bitterly arguing. One of the quiet company playing seven-up at the corner table said profanely that this row reminded him of a bowling contest at a picnic.

The town was troubled over it. Nobody had been hung in Crazy Cross for months and it seemed unnecessarily harsh that the first victim of the new law should be such a valuable citizen as Snub Parsons

The citizens of War Post were annoyed and dubious. They had not expected that the first man to fall under the shadow of the new rule against promiscuous shooting would be Ignatius Burke, the talented young bar-keeper, the man who had chiefly concerned himself with the passing of the law. It seems that War Post had been getting a bad name. The word had gone among the mountain trails that when the stranger went to War Post there was hardly a known line of conduct which would please that critical town and the stranger usually came away bewildered as well as bandaged. Three-ace Frederickson, a well-known brawler from Fargo City once sojourned in War Post and afterward he often cared to tell his impressions. "They aint no use in being polite with 'em. They dont give a damn whether you're polite or not. Now, look at me. I went over there thinking I'd be nice to 'em an' I was polite as hell. Well, did they do pretty? Git mad! Git mad so bad that after about three fights, I hit the trail. I see there was no good a-stoppin' to reason with 'em when they got mad just b'cause I was polite."

For a long time War Post had taken a high pride in her sinister fame. When abroad, her swaggering citizens said: "I'm f'm War Post" much as they would have said: "I'm the devil himself." They thought it very nice to be known as one of such a justly celebrated collection of desperados.

All went well until certain real estate booms began to strike here and there among the hills. New towns leaped into being

"Moonlight on the Snow": Two early autograph starts (Columbia)

from the direction in which they faced came the dull booming of artillery fire. It sounded in regular measures, like the ticking of some colossal clock, a clock that was counting the seconds in the lives of the stars, it reverberated solemnly, portentously, over the land as if God faced the dial as was counting the moments before the extinction of a planet. These two men slowly threading their way along the bank of the river of peasants found themselves silent in the hearing of this bombardment.

Then suddenly the beats became mingled until a man could hardly separate one from another and with them was the slow rattle of musketry. Suddenly the noise was irritated, silly, infantile. It was so childish this uproar. It forces never reaches to object, to protest against this noise which was as idle as the noise of a penny trumpet by a child. The soldier lifted his arm and pointed. He spoke impatiently as if his irritation followed immediately upon the correspondents words. "There," he said, "If you are looking for war you have a beautiful opportunity.

The young correspondent snapped his jaws in a way that was near to the realing of teeth. "Yes. There is war, there is the war that I wish to enter. I fling myself in. I was not intending to be so strongly a Greek. I find that I am a Greek. I wish to fight my countrys enemies. You know the way. Lead me.

The soldier smiled inscrutably. There was pity in it, there was pride in it — the vanity of experience — there was a slight contempt in it. "Very well," he cried, "If my company is in the thick of the fight I shall be glad for the honor of your companionship. If my company is not in the thick of the fight I will if you like send you on to when

"Death and the Child": unique page of early version dictated to Cora Crane (Columbia)

"[I will] not go away" said Renigan "until I hear the [story] of this business. Who has threatened you? If any man has troubled you I will take care of him. This is my house and I won't allow any peacable man to be troubled here." He cast a terrible look upon Jimmie, the cowboy and the Easterner.

"Never mind Mr Renigan, never mind. I will [go] away. I do not wish to be killed." He moved toward the door which led upstairs as if his intention was to at once [get] his baggage.

"No, no" shouted Renigan peremptorially but the white faced Swede slid by him and disappeared. "Now" said Renigan to the others in a very cold and deadly tone "What does this mean?"

Jimmie + the cowboy chanted "Why we didn't do nuthin' to him." Renigan was dangerously suspicious. "No" said he, "you didn't?"

Jimmie swore a deep oath. "Why this is the craziest... I ever see. We didn't do nuthin' to him at all. We were just sittin' here playin' cards and he —"

Renigan interrupted with a question to the Easterner. "Mr Blanc" he asked "What has these boys been doin'?"

After a deliberation the Easterner answered quietly "I didn't see the slightest thing wrong."

"But what does it mean?" howled Renigan. He stared ferociously at his son. "I have a mind to lather you for this my boy."

Jimmie made a gesture that denoted he was... "Well what have I done?" he bawled at his father.

"The Blue Hotel": unique page dictated to Cora Crane (Columbia)

Crane in his study at Brede Place, September, 1899 (Roger Frewen)

Crane in 1899 (reproduced from *Napthali*, by C. L. Hind)

INTRODUCTION

STEPHEN CRANE learned—from publishers, from agents, and most decidedly from the reading public—that collections of short stories are not as well received as full-length novels. Yet his story collections, though they never matched the success of *The Red Badge of Courage,* better showed the range of his sensibility and the variety of his talents. Moreover, the loosely organized book of stories really suited his conception of experience. As he saw it, men know only parts of the world, life is made up of mere episodes, the most intensely felt events are but minor conflicts occurring within the unfathomable multiplicity of nature. To render intensely felt episodes with artistic fidelity made a clarification within the general confusion, a limited order which could be valued justly if it were not overstated. So he conceived the artistic aim which Henry Adams called "running order through chaos" and which Robert Frost saw as providing "a momentary stay against confusion." This motive found its best expression, for Crane, in the short story, but he did not think that even for him this was the only way to organize experience. He wanted to make an order not only in his stories but also in his books. He tried, except when intuition, economics, or accident intervened, to make his collections hang together. A number of stories in the present collection he first set in a group when, in November, 1896, he drew up instructions for his literary executors; he classified the tales based on his 1895 trip to the West and Mexico among his "sketches of outdoor life" and hoped they would make a book if the executors "thought that they were up to my standard." [1] Most of this early Western harvest went into *The Open Boat and Other Tales of Adventure,*

---

[1] Stephen Crane to William Howe Crane, Jacksonville, Fla., Nov. 29, 1896, in Joseph Katz, "Stephen Crane, 'Samuel Carlton,' and a Recovered Letter," *Nineteenth-Century Fiction,* XXIII (September, 1968), 223.

along with some of the great stories of 1897. "The Blue Hotel," had it been a little earlier in the writing and a lot luckier in its publishing history, might best have been grouped with these; instead, it went into the 1899 volume headed by "The Monster," his earliest Whilomville story. Two more "tales of western American life," which in 1899 Crane hoped might turn into a book-length series,[2] went to fill out the London edition of *The Monster*, not published until 1901. On the other hand, "The Pace of Youth" was one of the "Midnight Sketches" with which Crane filled out the London edition of *The Open Boat*, though the others in the group were New York City stories. A fine example of his early, stylish newspaper realism, the story in some ways anticipates the later antiromance "The Bride Comes to Yellow Sky." "Death and the Child," which Crane from the beginning put into the *Open Boat* collection, is different from his other war stories not only in its being about Greece, but in its being more literary in its origins than most of the others. Like "The Blue Hotel," written just after, it belongs with the other tales of that remarkable year which followed Crane's shipwreck off Florida and the thirty-hour ordeal in an open boat. "A Poker Game," which Crane never published at all, came out in the posthumous miscellany *Last Words* (1902). In his own lifetime and ever since, collection making has illustrated the point that beyond the limits of the work of art the unities of experience are tentative and limited.

Crane's vision of an enormous, multiple, indifferent, undeified universe underlies his early stories and late, but it comes to crucial expression in "The Open Boat" (1897). In that story the unpredictable not only occurs within the action but is the given starting point of everything that happens—"Shipwrecks are *apropos* of nothing." On this point of what the world is ultimately like, there is a radical difference between Crane's realism of truthfulness and Howells' realism of truthfulness and probability: "In a ten-foot dingey one can get an idea of the resources of the sea in the line of waves that is not probable to the average experience, which is never at sea in a dingey." But Crane did not start with a fully developed idea of the resources of the sea or of

---

[2] Crane to James B. Pinker, Brede, England, [August, 1899], in *Stephen Crane: Letters*, ed. R. W. Stallman and Lillian Gilkes (New York, 1960), p. 214. On the dating of this letter, see note 113 below.

the universe. The principles of his imagined world, in the early fiction, are usually principles of an inner world—the chaotic, unpredictable flux of subjective experience. In *The Red Badge* or "One Dash—Horses" the stream of consciousness psychology is more evident than the sense of fortuitously arranged, morally neutral objective nature, but both are surely there. In "The Open Boat" and "The Blue Hotel" the emphasis seems to be reversed, but again both are surely there. Between the chaos within and the chaos without, the individual personality is hard pressed. If, in Scott Fitzgerald's phrase, "personality is an unbroken series of successful gestures," [3] the making of the self is threatened by a tendency to meaningless casualness within the mind and in the world. Identity is almost as fragile as life itself. So, between his metaphysics and his psychology, Crane established a realm of dramatic interest in which living is a series of adventures, and survival a wonder, and obliteration the end of which all men must take account. In all these things, such was the intelligence of his art, he was as consistent as if he were a philosopher. And yet characteristically he did not put these ideas in abstract terms. His imaginative processes tended, even more than with most other artists, to go on subconsciously—and to require more time than he could always give them. But his method of work, subject to inner and outward vicissitudes, can be traced to some degree after the fact, and even where it seems to have been unpredictable, it may conform to a recognizable pattern of meaning. Thus his first trip west, which supplied materials for a number of the stories in this volume, included one episode of more representative character. In young Crane's meeting with the even younger Willa Cather can be seen the accidents and pressures to which he was subject and, emerging from that complicated background, clues to his method and his personal drama.

Boyhood dreams apart, Crane first planned to go west as a journalist and writer in August, 1892, almost at the beginning of his career. For the next two and a half years, however, he stayed home to good purpose. In that time he wrote *Maggie, The Red Badge of Courage*, over a score of newspaper articles and stories,

[3] *The Great Gatsby* (New York, 1925), p. 2.

and his first book of verse, *The Black Riders.* With this exhausting spate of work behind him and with book publication and critical recognition of *The Red Badge* still in the unknowable future, the twenty-three-year-old writer began his travels in January, 1895. Officially he was a correspondent for the Bacheller Syndicate, but official status did not mean smooth arrangements. He had to delay his scheduled departure for Nebraska for two weeks until he got money for his railroad ticket. He must have got exactly that and no more, for when he reached Lincoln at the beginning of February, he had to wait day by day at the office of the *Nebraska State Journal* for the rest of his promised expense money. Though he had known poverty before, now for the first time he learned what it was to be forced to wait passively upon circumstance, in a strange place, without friends to turn to or the means of helping himself. Worst of all, his inner fatigue matched his outer circumstance. Usually noticed for his good looks and a neatness that bespoke pride, discipline, composure, he arrived in Lincoln looking "gaunt and unshaven . . . shaggy and unkempt." Yet even now he had a recognition that would not let him be in his isolation and his gloomy silence. Willa Cather, a twenty-one-year-old student at the University of Nebraska and a part-time helper at the newspaper, knew who the young man was who had turned up at the newspaper office looking like a tramp printer. Her own youth saved her from thinking him too young to be important, and her discernment made her one of the few people in the world to guess how important he was. She had found out about his being a serious artist, the story goes, by correcting his grammar as she edited the syndicate copy of *The Red Badge* for the *Journal.* Unlike the veteran reporter who had quickly dismissed the book for its fractured English, she saw through the minor errors to the novel. With the wisdom of her years, she recognized the artist in the work, and when Crane himself later appeared at the *Journal,* she determined to find the artist in the man. She would not be put off by his slovenly appearance or his difficult mood. Crane, usually so courteous, turned aside every line of inquiry. When the girl tried to get him started with a question about Maupassant, he came out with a sarcastic "Oh, you're moping, are you?" On another occasion she asked about the theory of the short story and got the reply, "Yarns aren't done by mathematics." But while her patient tactful questioning seemed to get nowhere, Crane was gradually coming to a view of himself. When at last he began of his own accord to talk about his writing, he seemed to regard his career as one long experiment in misery. "In all his long tirade," Miss Cather recorded, "Crane never raised his voice; he spoke slowly and monotonously and even calmly, but I have never known so bitter a heart in any man as he revealed to me that night. It was an arraignment of the wages of life, an invocation to the ministers of hate." The writer's conception of his destiny was complex in much the same way as the imagined destinies in his fiction are complex. First of all, he brought it on himself; his commitment to writing was his own responsibility. But beyond his personal control was the blank fact that his writing brought him so little money. The syndicate payment for *The Red Badge,* for example, had come to about ninety dollars. At that rate, it was simple enough to conclude that he must learn to write fast, and he even claimed to have adopted "a double life; writing in the first place the matter that pleased himself, and doing it very slowly; in the second place, any sort of stuff that would sell." Such calculated prudence, however, did not put him in control of circumstance, for he was by nature the very opposite of the born journalist: he lacked the gift for writing in immediate response to an event. The constitutional need to work slowly was the final irony of his fate. Yet as he gave the account of his entrapment, Crane described his fatal slowness in words which Willa Cather was to remember the rest of her life: "The detail of a thing has to filter through my blood, and then it comes out like a native product, but it takes forever." The brilliance of his language stood out against his bitter logic, and the figure of his work as a native product, filtered through the blood, expressed a positive value as well as a bitter truth. Beset as he was, he found the words which affirmed his identity as an artist and retrieved a clarification of self from his exposure to the flux of consciousness and circumstance.[4]

"The Pace of Youth" bears a title that is appropriate to its bril-

[4] Willa Cather, "When I Knew Stephen Crane," *Library* (Pittsburgh), I (June 23, 1900), 17–18; reprinted in *Prairie Schooner*, XXIII (Fall, 1949), 231–236.

liant young author as well as its subject, but it also illustrates what Crane meant by a slow process of filtering through his imagination. The story came out in the New York *Press* on January 18 and 19, 1895, on the eve of his departure for the West, but its literary history reaches back to the summer of 1892 when he first planned that journey and beyond that, less definitely, a lot further. It is about Asbury Park, the New Jersey seaside resort that he had known from the age of twelve when his widowed mother moved there from Newark. This was the scene of his boyhood summers and, thanks to his brother Townley's having the New York *Tribune* agency there, of his earliest literary apprenticeship. He began helping out with anonymous news items when he was sixteen and in the course of four years worked up to the point where a number of pieces are unmistakably his own. He was twenty, in the summer of 1892, when he first used the special scene of "The Pace of Youth." In "Joys of Seaside Life" he described a merry-go-round such as would reappear in the later story, "loaded with impossible giraffes and goats, on which ride crowds of joyous children, who clutch for brass rings"; but he had not yet caught, in the early sketch, the color, the detail, and the wonderful variety of the painted animals or the plainness of the people who tended the machine. In another bit of seaside correspondence, "On the Boardwalk," he focused on the "summer girl and golden youth business that goes on" and began working out the ironies between summer-resort illusions and everyday facts. Remarking that the golden youth was "not the same steady and, perhaps, sensible young man who bended all winter over the ledger in the city office," Crane made his reader aware that this was indeed the same young man, brightened for a moment by "his somewhat false hues." And he saw the summer girl come into view as "a bit of interesting tinsel flashing near the somber hued waves." Even before he lived among the young painters of the New York art world, he had begun combining his defiationary realism with his sense of the dazzle of appearances. Though he did not yet render visual impressions as vividly and directly as he would later, he already grasped the relation between his passion for truthfulness and his fascination with the look of things. He told the story of seemingly dazzling people who stood out against the somber natural scene, or of ordinary representative people for whom the colorful backdrop seemed accidental and irrelevant. Either way, he understood that it was the brilliant hue which commanded immediate belief and that the contrast which undercut the reader's expectations might actually intensify the effect of brilliance.[5]

Crane's most famous dispatch, that summer before he was twenty-one, worked the ironies of scene and story so well as to breach the conventions of newspaper reporting. In the New York *Tribune* of August 21, 1892, he reported the parade of the Junior Order of United American Mechanics, a working-class patriotic organization which had met in Asbury Park to reaffirm the principles of restricting immigration and keeping the Bible in the schools. Crane saw the dusty marchers against the background of lace parasols and boater hats. Once he had noted the indifferently smiling onlookers, he turned a sharper eye on the men themselves: "Their clothes fitted them illy, for the most part, and they had no ideas of marching. They merely plodded along, not seeming quite to understand, stolid, unconcerned and, in a certain sense, dignified—a pace and a bearing emblematic of their lives." [6] The pace of labor, like the pace of youth in his later piece, is, in Crane's rendering, a more durable and respectable characteristic than the changeful hues of mere surface. But the marchers did not take it so. Where the story indicated sympathy for the bedrock plainness of these "slope-shouldered" and "spraddle-legged" men, they themselves saw the contrast with the colorful vacationers and resort promoters as invidious. Moreover, they made their opinions felt. They rightly guessed that their complaints would be taken seriously by a paper whose publisher, Whitelaw Reid, was running for Vice-President on the Republican ticket. The incident drew an editorial apology, and later enough so as to obscure the line of causation, it was followed by termination of Townley Crane's career with the *Tribune*. In any case, the end of the resort season led to Stephen

---

[5] "Joys of Seaside Life," New York *Tribune*, July 17, 1892, in *Stephen Crane: Uncollected Writings*, ed. Olov W. Fryckstedt (Uppsala, Sweden, 1963), p. 17; "On the Boardwalk," New York *Tribune*, Aug. 14, 1892, in *Uncoll. Writ.*, pp. 25–26.

[6] "On the New Jersey Coast," New York *Tribune*, Aug. 21, 1892, in *Uncoll. Writ.*, p. 29.

Crane's leaving his Asbury Park apprenticeship for free-lance newspaper work in New York and serious application to the writing of fiction.

In the first winter of his destitution he did not yet find poverty bitter. He lived among other struggling young men who were making their way into journalism, attending medical classes, or painting, and he did not blush sometimes to live off them. He found that illustrators like writers confronted the two necessities of mastering one's medium and making good in the world of editor and publisher. Besides understanding, his friends kept him from being a stranger in New York by offering light but real links with his past. The painter Louis Senger was a boyhood pal from Port Jervis, New York, where Crane had lived for five happy years when his father was still alive. The newspaperman Post Wheeler had been a friend from the time when the two of them as youngsters had accompanied their mothers to a convention of the W.C.T.U. While Crane learned enough about hunger and cold so that he could fully imagine lostness, he was not at all lost. And though he was to learn a good deal of the seamier side of Bohemianism, he was mostly among generous and loyal friends and shared with them a spirit of play that fell far short of wildness. Louis Senger's cousin C. K. Linson was one of these, a painter-illustrator who gave Crane a standing invitation to use his studio for a roof over his head and who used his influence with S. S. McClure to get Crane his first magazine assignment. Linson, in his invaluable memoir of those days, caught his friend's easygoing gaiety at the same time as he recorded the filtering through of the Asbury Park materials. For Stephen's company he gladly made the long trip uptown to 1064 Avenue A, where Crane had rooms in the spring of 1893:

My knock at his door was answered by a short, "Come in!" By a far window sat Stephen, with a towel turban-like about his head. An ink bottle was on a chair beside him, sheets of foolscap on his knees, and with no further ceremony he continued his work. Presently pages were tossed to me, "The Pace of Youth" written at the top of one. Certain "indomitable whiskers" caught my eye, then a "young tarrier" and a girl named Lizzie, and I was lost. Steve had nearly finished, and when I stopped he handed me more and stretched wearily back. I read on to the end. "Like it?" he asked laconically. Of course I liked it. That girl in a red dress—it would be red!—"crawling slowly like some kind of spider on the fabric of nature"—Stimson going out to smoke and revel in himself—the symbolism of the old horse that became "intent upon his aged legs and spread them in quaint and ridiculous devices for speed" pursuing "the eager spirit of a young and modern horse"—the little glass eye of derision in the rear of the elopers' buggy. That vehicle was "youth, with youth's pace; it was swift flying with the hope of dreams." Of course it escaped, as youth eludes age; Stimson was defied by the derisive eye, by the universe; he suddenly became conscious that his bald head was hatless. Well, he was not responsible for the "smiles that were soft and prayerful caresses," nor for the careening gay paper lanterns that "sang a chorus of red and violet and green and gold; a song of the mystic bands of the future." Not responsible for any of it but that one little sign, "Cashier," which, "hanging upon the silvered netting behind which the girl sold tickets got directly in range and interfered with the tender message." Responsble only for interference, and that was as impotent as age itself.

"How do you feel all the people so long after you've seen them? It's months since you were down there." He smiled. "Can't you make sketches from memory? Of course. Well, haven't I known these types since I was a kid? Certainly." That was it. . . .

"A bird of a story, Steve!"

He warmed to my appreciation, while through his cigarette smoke I studied his headgear. "Yeh, the towel? This thing got me going and I couldn't sleep, so I got up. Been at it all night. A wet towel cools the machinery all right. And I work better at night. I'm all alone in the world. It's great!" [7]

Crane's outlandish costume, with a towel turbaned round his head, proclaims "It's great!" as surely as his tramp printer's slovenliness announced the opposite when he arrived in Lincoln, Nebraska, almost two years later. Except for his deliberate Bowery experiment in flophouse misery, Crane was known among his friends for "the cleanly grooming of a wild animal," in contrast to his notoriously unkempt alcoholic brother Townley, who had started downhill well before the *Tribune* episode put an end to his career. [8] The three occasions in his life when Crane appeared slovenly and unkempt—on his arrival in Lincoln, in the

[7] *My Stephen Crane*, ed. Edwin H. Cady (Syracuse, N.Y., 1958), pp. 27–29.
[8] Post Wheeler and Hallie Erminie Rives, *Dome of Many-coloured Glass* (New York, 1955), p. 99.

aftermath of the sinking of the *Commodore* and the "Open Boat" episode, and during the Spanish-American War—bespoke crises of spirit that were, respectively, minor, crucial, and simply debilitating. But the wet towel round his head was not slovenly. In 1893 his youthful imagination easily converted the meager materials of his poverty into style. Moreover, what was true for his person was true also for his career: he knew how to make the most of his disadvantages. Inability to sell his work had its cheerful side, since it freed him from pressure to publish quickly and let him stretch out the process of composition to suit himself. Unlike his regularly active newspaper friends, he could let his subject filter through and then take still more time for critical testing thereafter. R. G. Vosburgh, one of the painters he knew then, gives his version of Crane's working intensely through the night and then goes on to describe the next stage of the process: "After writing a story he would put it away for two or three weeks, and work on something else until his mind was thoroughly clear for a fresh consideration of it. When the story was taken out for revision it would be turned over to his friends for criticism, and Crane would argue with them about the objections they would make." [9] Even after critical scrutiny of every incident and every word, in the instance of "The Pace of Youth" at least, he did not rush into print. There was a long lapse between the spring of 1893 when he wrote the story (or, for that matter, the spring of 1894, if Linson misremembered the year) and its newspaper appearance in January, 1895. Since he had fairly sure access to the *Press* for his sketches beginning in the spring of 1894, the delay must be partly explained by his carelessness or his indifference. Certainly it was not revision that held matters up, for even after retouching for the book version of 1898, the story remained substantially the same. Linson, with his vivid recall of particular phrases, was to declare, " 'The Pace of Youth' appears, unabridged, as I read it that morning in New York, in Heinemann's English edition of *The Open Boat*, 1898." [10] Attention to niceties did not disturb the casual vivid-

---

[9] "The Darkest Hour in the Life of Stephen Crane," *Book-Lover*, II (Summer, 1901), 338.

[10] Linson, *Crane*, p. 29. Linson's vivid recall of particular phrases was assisted, however, as Professor Fredson Bowers points out to me, by his having the Heinemann edition conveniently at hand.

ness which had been got essentially right in the first concentrated effort.

Phrases like the ones Linson fastened on were the authentic sign of Crane's mastering his craft, for looked at closely, they disclose the way that disparate materials are worked together in the story. With the "indomitable" whiskers belonging to the proprietor of Stimson's Mammoth Merry-Go-Round, the author was adding something of his own to the thing seen, projecting his own interpretation. On the other hand, with the horizon view of the girl in the red dress "crawling slowly like some kind of a spider on the fabric of nature," he deliberately added nothing to the optical image, and in the absence of perspective, the eye's seeming independence of the judgment makes a conventionally far-fetched simile plausible. Both the subjective coloring of narrative and the objective rendering of how things appear serve to undermine the assumptions, as they do the method, of common-sense realism. In an interview with William Dean Howells in the fall of 1894, Crane made clear, perhaps unconsciously, how difference of style made a difference in kind between his acknowledged master and himself. In his New York *Times* report, the older writer comments on just such a trick of perspective as the interviewer might have introduced into the conversation. Crane's Howells, though what he says is in character, talks Crane's language:

It is the business of the novel to picture the daily life in the most exact terms possible, with an absolute and clear sense of proportion. That is the important matter—the proportion. As a usual thing, I think, people have absolutely no sense of proportion. Their noses are tight against life, you see. They perceive mountains where there are no mountains, but frequently a great peak appears no larger than a rat trap. An artist sees a dog down the street—well, his eye instantly relates the dog to its surroundings. The dog is proportioned to the buildings and the trees. Whereas, many people can conceive of that dog's tail resting upon a hill top.[11]

The dog's tail resting on the hilltop sounds like Crane because it honestly gives the appearance of things; it is the evidence of things seen and not of revision according to formula. Yet he was

[11] "Fears Realists Must Wait," New York *Times*, Oct. 28, 1894, in *Uncoll. Writ.*, pp. 80–81.

perfectly sincere in believing that Howells' ideas of fiction were
identical with his own, and to a certain extent, he was right.
With his highly visualized style he conveyed the distortions,
emotional and optical, which made it hard for his characters to
see how events worked themselves out almost independently of
appearances. He also held that truth to the underlying logic of
the action was the highest motive of the writer. Though he was
faithful to ironies of experience which Howells scarcely recognized, he agreed with his master in seeking this underlying
truthfulness, and he drew a number of the same corollaries from
this first principle. Like Howells he despised sentimentality and
highfalutin romance. With a Howellsian instinct for the commonplace, he saw his Asbury Park story not in the colorful
summer visitors but rather in the merry-go-round people themselves, the proprietor's daughter in the ticket booth and the
attendant who courted her silently with glances over the heads
of the crowd. He charted the ups and downs of emotion with
painstaking accuracy, but the careful record of young love conveyed a sense of realism much less interesting than his notation
of the unconventional obstacles between the lovers: the brightly
colored wooden animals and the noisy children, the wire front of
the ticket booth and the gold-lettered sign "Cashier" that occasionally swung into their line of sight, the vigilance of the indomitable Stimson. (If it were not for those whiskers, the irate
father might be detected as a rather conventional figure of romance.) In having young love triumph over forbidding age,
Crane was like Howells restoring the comedy of sentiment by getting rid of sentimentality: he presented a situation which was superficially the opposite of romantic but actually emphasized the
rightness of the heart's free choice. Notwithstanding appearances, he made his plot conform to the proportions of middle-
class realism. Like Howells, finally, he became aware of other
norms only as the world of chance impinged on private destinies
and predictable behavior. He developed a sense of that other
world much sooner and much stronger than the older writer, to
be sure, and even in "The Pace of Youth" proportions almost
collapse when Stimson, outraged at the elopement of his Lizzie,
plays the indomitable father almost too well, calls for his revolver, and presses the chase like a military pursuit. With the

momentary suspense, Crane showed the possibility of violence that lies just behind the commonplace romance or the conventional role. But he managed his comedy with finesse, so that when the role of indomitable authority does not work and the astonished father finds that his universe fails him, he gives a shrug and turns his concern to the hat that he forgot to wear. He finds it embarrassing not to be properly attired.

Crane's heading west in January, 1895, was not altogether a new departure. However close he may have been to Howells' realism in his early fiction, he had his differences—differences important enough so that he seemed to move quite naturally in the direction of the Western tale. In "The Pace of Youth," for example, he worked with ironies that he was to use again in "The Bride Comes to Yellow Sky." In both stories the would-be violent are so caught by convention that the unexpected can undo their purpose, and in both stories the triumphant lovers are so colorless that they bleach all romance out of the happy ending. Insofar as one literary experiment may prompt another along the same line, the Asbury Park tale is at least as much a source for "The Bride" as any experience Crane had in the West. Moreover, his use of Western story conventions did not depend on his travels. The young man who wrote *The Red Badge of Courage* obviously felt no timidity at rendering what he had not seen. Certain that he understood conventional illusions about war and the emotional logic of battle, he had confidence enough to undertake Western subjects too. In his sketch "Billy Atkins Went to Omaha" he portrayed hobo life in bitter detail. Compared to the Bowery derelicts he was then studying at first hand, the Western tramp, he guessed, was a little less demoralized. His Billy Atkins can sustain over several days his purpose of going somewhere, but clearly he is the victim of his own absurd and changeful will as well as of railway trainmen and society in general. The logic of indignity is the same with both types. Crane's other early use of Western materials occurs in the New York sketch "In a Park Row Restaurant." Entering such a restaurant in the noon rush, a former Nevada sheriff recaptures the "fever and exhilaration" that he had been used to in his early career, and the incidents of the melee prompt a series of tall-tale reminiscences that have the ring of authentic Western humor.[12] This sketch, which saw print on the very same day as the interview with Howells, offers the most striking evidence of how Crane's technique was differentiating him from his master. For the younger writer, conventions are not obstructions to right seeing which must be got rid of, nor are they merely useful means for apprehending reality which may require correction. The storytelling sheriff claims more interest than the Park Row waiters and the restaurant crowd, and to get rid of the disproportionate interest would be to destroy the sketch. To put the aspect of realism most strongly, one may say that Crane's irony implied that New York was much like Nevada and that the backdrop of appearance made little difference to the transaction of human destinies. But his evident relish for Nevada literary conventions bespoke a range of artistic taste beyond that for which a Howells could account. This taste, less obviously characterized by high seriousness than an orthodox American realist might wish, led him to write tales of adventure, of the West, of the sea. The categories to this day suggest escapism. But to become involved with these subjects and their storytelling conventions, and yet not lose critical detachment, was to enlarge the possibilities of realistic fiction. Just as stories of growing up or courtship affirmed the norms of middle-class culture, stories of adventure suggested another world of values. When these subjects were treated with the same critical seriousness as romantic affections, say, or domestic vicissitudes, they were no longer escape stories even though their realism was not the same as Howells'. Crane's irony often cut in two directions, criticizing both the conventions of popular literature and the assumptions of domestic felicity. This complexity of subject, working to the same effect as his complexity of style, created a kind of realism which, better than the simpler orthodoxy, would nourish writers to come.

Crane's West was first of all the Wild West of literary convention, which he had a knack of taking seriously when for others it might seem a question of play. When he was sixteen, Thomas Beer relates, he "begged five dollars from his mother to start a lost cowboy back to Wyoming and the man gave him a real

[12] New York *Press*, May 20 and Oct. 28, 1894, in *Uncoll. Writ.*, pp. 52–58, 82–85.

revolver alleged to have slain six Indians." [13] One anecdote after another tells how often thereafter he was the man with the revolver, from the time when the nightshirted boy in the college fraternity stood off the hazing party until, established in the English countryside, he affected cowboy boots and deigned to prove his marksmanship to Ford Madox Ford. He took it to the West and Mexico when he went, and his later tales testify that he could imagine himself using it. Playing cowboy became a deadly serious game when the revolver was taken into account. In the West more readily than in Asbury Park, the peaceful social order turned into a fragile illusion when this remarkable engine transformed the scene.

Violence and destruction had their part in Crane's West, but he was not so gloomy as to think that once the orderly city of popular middle-class conception was left behind, a man was sure to face the red-handed mob and meet his plotted end. In the first place, it was not simply a matter of geography. The East had its own essential insecurity, which Crane could evoke simply by thinking of Asbury Park without the tinsel summer girl: "Without her the men would perish from weariness or fall to fighting. . . . The crowd on the boardwalk would be a mob without the smile of the summer girl." [14] On the other hand, he would later deflate the notion that the West was different: "Where then can one expect cowboys if not in Kansas City? . . . Nebraska has come to an almost universal condition of yellow trolly-cars with clanging gongs and whirring wheels, and conductors who don't give a curse for the public. . . . Galveston is often original, full of distinctive characters. But it is not like a town in the moon." [15] States of mind were more important than physical places in differentiating Crane's West from the usual Howellsian scene. Once the security of routine labors and usual pleasures was left behind, he conceived that a man entered, not necessarily a realm of terror, but a world of chance. The test of manhood was to keep one's nerve in the face of the unexpected and the unpredictable. Here the coolness of the gambler rather than the inventive-

[13] *Stephen Crane: A Study in American Letters* (New York, 1923), p. 54.
[14] "On the Boardwalk," in *Uncoll. Writ.*, p. 26.
[15] "Galveston, Texas, in 1895," *Westminster Gazette*, Nov. 6, 1900, in *Uncoll. Writ.*, p. 145.

ness of the maker was the virtue most to be prized. Crane no longer lived in the old middle-class universe of Benjamin Franklin; poker, not handiwork, was his hobby. And as soon as he was able to pay his own way at meals with his artist friends, he took to rounding off his dinners with a little recreation of shooting dice. He never shot for high stakes or made himself a very accomplished poker player, and he never became a compulsive gambler, but he enjoyed gaming. It was for him a kind of stylized play, a symbolic model of human experience. The poker playing and dice shooting in Western literary convention allowed him to use gambling in his stories directly as well as to transpose the emotions of games of chance into his plots. Just as he claimed to have learned the emotions of *The Red Badge* on the football field, he might have claimed to derive the psychology of his tales of adventure from what he knew of poker and dice.[16]

Going west was but one of Crane's exploratory journeys into the territory beyond that security and order from which he started as a minister's son, a small-town boy, and a conventionally reared citizen for whom the more smiling aspects of American life were the expectable. When he found his expectations illusory, he turned to other worlds which might be worse, and might also be better, than the world he had first assumed. Thus his West was in its darker aspect "a state of warfare and a game of chance, in which each man fights and bets against fearful odds." But this phrasing is that of William Dean Howells, describing "our competitive civilization" as he found it to be beneath its placid appearances.[17] Crane would have accepted Howells' statement, but he would not have made it in just that way. If he seemed less radical than Howells in not directing his criticism upon the established order, he was in fact far more devastating to middle-class assumptions in that he conceived the state of warfare and game of chance to be the way things are in the universe, not just in a society which had gone wrong some-

[16] A fair sample of the poker enthusiast is Crane to Willis Brooks Hawkins, [New York, October, 1895, or early April, 1896]: "Can—will—you bring the boys over for a little fiesta de poke tonight" (*Letters*, p. 123; see also p. 123 note). The customary dice after dinner are described in Henry McBride, "Stephen Crane's Artist Friends," *Art News*, XLIX (October, 1950), 46.

[17] Howells to Edward Everett Hale, Little Nahant, Mass., Aug. 30, 1888, *Life in Letters of William Dean Howells*, ed. Mildred Howells (Garden City, N.Y., 1928), I, 416.

how and needed correction. In his far-reaching vision of ultimate chaos, he had less to do with reform than Howells and more to do with changing the tacit assumptions of American culture. But the terrors of his imaginary West existed side by side with pleasures, for one aspect of getting away from orderly routine was that of "moral holiday." (When William James invented that term, in *Pragmatism,* he identified his own philosophic cast of mind with the toughs from Cripple Creek rather than "Bostonian tourists.") [18] The foremost popular spokesman for this point of view was Theodore Roosevelt, who as New York police commissioner was soon to be Crane's friend and then his enemy. He told the readers of the *Century* about his adventures "In Cow-boy Land" and described with relish a model of Western character:

One of my valued friends in the mountains, and one of the best hunters with whom I ever traveled, was a man who had a peculiarly light-hearted way of looking at conventionally moral obligations. . . . He saw facts as they were, and could tell them as they were, and he never told an untruth unless for very weighty reasons. He was pre-eminently a philosopher, of a happy, skeptical turn of mind. He had no prejudices. He never looked down, as so many hard characters do, upon a person possessing a different code of ethics. His attitude was one of broad, genial tolerance. He saw nothing out of the way in the fact that he himself had been a road-agent, a professional gambler, and a desperado at different stages of his career. On the other hand, he did not in the least hold it against anyone that he had always acted within the law. . . . He did not often refer to his past career at all. When he did, he recited its incidents perfectly naturally and simply as events, without any reference to, or regard for, their ethical significance. It was this quality which made him at times a specially pleasant companion, and always an agreeable narrator.[19]

Crane, who did not have to go west to learn about violence or chance, also knew this other, more smiling aspect of Western life back in the East. In fact, the man responsible for his Western trip was a fine exemplar of easygoing bonanza temperament. Irving Bacheller did not have the checkered career of Roosevelt's cowboy friend, but he had the expansiveness and casual freedom

[18] (New York, 1907), pp. 78, 13.
[19] XLVI (June, 1893), 277–278.

that go with the ideal type. Like Crane, he came from a small town in upstate New York. In 1884 he founded the first newspaper syndicate in America and struck it rich in a modest way. His success was imperfectly genteel from the established literary point of view, for he purveyed moral-holiday literature rather than belles-lettres. The newspapers he catered to, and the Sunday supplements in particular, provided recreation for men and boys in contrast to such magazines as the *Atlantic* or the *Century* which supplied authentic culture to American womanhood. Even without the highest credentials of feminization, it was of course possible for the syndicate owner and the writers who worked for him to be well within the limits of conventional respectability. Bacheller, with some other newspapermen including Stephen Crane, founded the Lantern Club so that they could have someplace more temperate than the Press Club where they might lunch congenially. There they proved that the literary estates were not rigidly separate; they entertained representatives of the highbrow monthlies and of belles-lettres generally, including Howells himself and that renegade newspaperman Mark Twain, "At the Sign o' the Lanthorn," even though the flavor of the working press predominated. The friendly and hospitable man who headed the group was to prove that he could endure ups and downs of fortune almost as rapid as if he were on the mining frontier: when he sold out his syndicate, he lost his small fortune even quicker than he made it, and then he went on to strike it rich again as the author of popular novels. In 1894, when he met Crane, he was still at the height of his first success. He readily listened to the young man who could claim Howells' approval for his work. He took home the offered manuscript, read it that same night, and without delay accepted *The Red Badge* for condensed serial publication. Although he did not make the young man rich at half a cent a word, he did kindly fetch him down to the offices of the Philadelphia *Press* one cold December afternoon so that the editor, Talcott Williams, and his staff could offer the young novelist their congratulations. And when he found out about Crane's desire to see the West, he pledged his backing so convincingly that Crane got ready to leave at once, before he finished proofs for *The Black Riders* or completed arrangements for book publication of *The Red Badge*.

Bacheller's openhanded intentions outreached his care for detail, as Crane's ten-day delay in New York and his ten-day stranding in Lincoln testify. But he was as easygoing with Crane as with himself and never complained about not getting his money's worth despite rather meager returns on the syndicate's investment. As he calmly expected, everything evened out in the end: Bacheller the syndicate executive may not have received sketches enough to warrant his expense, but later Bacheller the magazine editor got several tales which germinated from the imaginative seeding of 1895. This friendly man, for whom comradeship and sympathy came readily and money and power mattered little, was the appropriate sponsor of Crane's trip west.[20]

Crane's being broke and demoralized was not, despite Willa Cather's memory, the whole story of the young man who arrived in Lincoln about the first of February. He did research by day into the effect of the last summer's drought. As the friend of Hamlin Garland, he informed himself painstakingly—and in despite of any Wild West visions he may have entertained— about the plight of farmers on the sod-house frontier. He did night research also, after his own fashion, and one evening in a Lincoln barroom he tried to break up a one-sided fight. "But thus I

[20] The dichotomies of newspaper *vs.* magazine, lowbrow *vs.* highbrow, audience of men *vs.* audience of women and children, foul and deadly facts *vs.* censored subject matter are well illustrated in Howells, *Criticism and Fiction* (New York, 1891), pp. 159–161.

Bacheller's autobiographical statements are sometimes factually incorrect. He was in and out of publishing more times than he could remember, and he began writing novels a decade before he reckoned the beginning of his writing career. (His usual account has him coming to fiction for the first time with his *David Harum*–style best seller *Eben Holden*, 1900.) But he conveyed essential truth in his good-natured recollection of windfalls alternating with reversals. In the absence of a biography, the best guide to Bacheller chronology is the article in *American Authors, 1600–1900*, ed. Stanley J. Kunitz and Howard Haycraft (New York, 1938), pp. 188–190. "An Interview with Irving Bacheller," in Robert van Gelder, *Writers and Writing* (New York, 1946), pp. 249–250, connects Bacheller's birth in a log cabin on the Adirondack frontier with his sanguine making and losing of fortunes.

Bacheller's *Coming up the Road* (Indianapolis, 1928), pp. 276 ff., tells of his relations with Crane and the founding of the Lantern Club. Bacheller to Cora Crane, Canton, N.Y., July 13, 1900, *Letters*, pp. 298–299, and Bacheller to William Hamilton Osborne, [n.p.], Nov. 2, 1921, *Letters*, pp. 322–323, supply more of Bacheller's testimony on his relations with Crane. Wheeler and Rives, *Dome of Many-coloured Glass*, pp. 98, 101, bear witness to the temperance of the Lantern Club in general and Stephen Crane in particular.

offended local custom," Beer quotes him as saying. "These men fought each other every night. Their friends expected it and I was a darned nuisance with my Eastern scruples and all that. So first everybody cursed me fully and then they took me off to a judge who told me that I was an imbecile and let me go; it was very saddening. Whenever I try to do right, it don't." [21] When this episode filtered into "The Blue Hotel," the Eastern scruples were crossed with fear and the ludicrous misreading of local custom turned into a gruesome absurdity. But at the time Crane's sense of comedy had just been freshly restored: he got word from Appleton's that they would like to publish *The Red Badge*, with some revisions, and he received funds from Bacheller and could get on with his travels. He headed into drought country just as it was undergoing a new desolation, this time from fierce winds, sheeting snow, and eighteen-below-zero cold. From this snow-storm, he sensed how dust storms must have reduced the country to "a condition of despair." His image of the Nebraska small town was a fit scene for pitifully vulnerable man whether in fact or in the fiction to come: "The buildings straggle at irregular intervals along the street and a little board sidewalk connects them. On all sides stretches the wind-swept prairie." [22] In a gloomy setting like this he changed trains once, according to Beer, and was struck by the sight of the local hotel incongruously painted blue. Beer, who may have half-imagined the incident, called the blue of the hotel dreadful, lugubrious, loathsome, and portentous of "some dire action." But in Crane's imagination, long after his trip to the storm-stricken prairies, the dash of color was more like the flash of tinsel against the somber-hued ocean. In "The Blue Hotel" he described the onset of the storm upon the town and commented: "One viewed the existence of man then as a marvel, and conceded a glamour of wonder to these lice which were caused to cling to a whirling, fire-smote, ice-locked, disease-stricken, space-lost bulb. The conceit of man was explained by this storm

[21] Beer, *Crane*, pp. 113–114.

[22] "Nebraskans' Bitter Fight for Life," Philadelphia *Press*, Feb. 24, 1895, in *Uncoll. Writ.*, pp. 122, 127. The town with the straggling buildings and board sidewalk is Eddyville, Nebraska. However, Bernice Slote in her definitive article "Stephen Crane in Nebraska," *Prairie Schooner*, XLIII (Summer, 1969), 197, suggests that Kearney is the most important contributor to Crane's composite picture and that the fictive name "Fort Romper" may derive by association from "Fort Childs," the original name of Fort Kearney.

to be the very engine of life. One was a coxcomb not to die in it."
It is hard to guess why the Blue Hotel should have given its
name to the story if it did not somehow symbolize the conceit of
man and the engine of life. But Beer may have been right about
Crane's first reaction, for there was time for many changes of
attitude between the experience of February, 1895, and the
drawing off of the filtered material in December, 1897.[23]

With Bacheller's money in his pocket, young Crane quickly
recovered his mobility and his morale. The enthusiastic traveler
inspected the storm area, doubled back to Lincoln and Kansas
City, then veered south to Hot Springs, Arkansas, and New
Orleans. There the manuscript of *The Red Badge* arrived, as he
had requested, at the end of February, and in barely a week he
sent back revised copy to Appleton's. He had also begun sending
sketches to Bacheller fairly regularly. His spirits were high as
he began making his way west and south to Texas and Mexico. By the time he got to San Antonio, he could not resist
playing a Wild West character after his own generous design:
the literary convention which made room for natural violence
and human brutality in the world also gave men the chance to
practice other virtues besides Howellsian prudence. In the
shadow of the Alamo, Crane put on his imaginary spurs and,
meeting a young runaway from Chicago, a stranded would-be
cowboy of sixteen who sat on the curbstone and wept, fed him
and funded him and put him on the train for home. He was
bighearted down to almost his last dollar, and shortly after
helping Edward Grover this way, he was himself broke and
stranded. This time he was able to take his situation in stride or,
more correctly, in style. When Grover telegraphed back the
money, he acknowledged the return with a letter that was at
once jaunty and kind:

Dear Deadeye Dick:
  Thanks for sending back my money so fast. The hotel trun me out,
as my friends of the Bowery say and I was living in Mex diggings with
a push of sheep men till my boss in New York wired me money.
  Now, old man, take some advice from a tough jay from back East.
You say your family is all right and nobody bothers you. Well, it

---

[23] Beer, *Crane*, p. 113. Miss Slote finds "no evidence of a blue hotel anywhere
but in Crane's story" (*Prairie Schooner*, XLIII, 198).

struck me that you are too young a kid and too handsome to be free and easy around where a lot of bad boys and girls will take your pennies. So better stay home and grow a mustache before you rush out into the red universe any more.

Yours sincerely,
· Stephen Crane [24]

At twenty-three this veteran of the tough world had more than his mustache to prove his right to talk so. One evidence of his maturity was the use he now made of being down and out. Thomas Beer is authority for tracing a later story to the San Antonio incident:

In that Mexican lodging house he met a blushless rogue who, peddling illicit drink to the thirsty soldiers of Leon Springs in 1917, called himself Keenan. This man had charms; he was a Bowery boy who had wandered away from police and friends. He told Crane a tale of shooting down some Mexicans who tried to drive his sheep from a waterhole. The slaughter was a simple gesture of carelessness for at once he sold his sheep to them and retired from the pass. Crane sent him, in 1897, a copy of the *Century Magazine* with "A Man and Some Others" and Keenan hated Crane ever after for spoiling the point of the story.[25]

This callous little anecdote, like the incidents in Nebraska, was to be changed by time, but a spontaneous friendship which began in San Antonio would make its way into Crane's later fiction more directly. In a couple of tales Crane was to appear as the "New York Kid" whose inseparable companion was the "San Francisco Kid." Crane may, as John Berryman plausibly suggests, have "split his personality into Eastern and Western," but there is little characterization to distinguish the two and no exploration of that eerie psychological phenomenon, the sense of the double. What the pair mostly convey is the pleasure a young man may feel in sharing experience, for better or for worse, with a friend—once again a subject that was excluded by Howells' middle-class realism with its atomistic preconceptions. Crane seems at least in part to have modeled the fictional comradeship

---

[24] [San Antonio, March, 1895], *Letters*, p. 54.

[25] Beer, *Crane*, p. 116. R. W. Stallman, *Stephen Crane: A Biography* (New York, 1968), p. 149, mistakenly transfers this Mexican lodginghouse from San Antonio and postpones the incident by a month.

on his acquaintance with Charles Gardner, the Chicago engineer with whom he traveled from San Antonio into Mexico. Together they discovered the color and poverty of the Mexican countryside. Together they explored Mexico City, where the tourist and business section abounded in American businessmen and American tourists and cafes with American bartenders. In his newspaper sketches Crane sometimes wrote from the point of view of "two Americans," identified as a "capitalist from Chicago" and an "archaeologist." Gardner, playing the capitalist from Chicago and as much affected by the air of gallantry as the self-styled archaeologist, gave Crane a handful of opals. Crane saved these through all his Mexican adventures and got them safely back to New York, where he gave two away according to premeditation and handed the rest out to friends at the Lantern Club party celebrating his return. The precious stones quickly disappeared, but the gift of friendship carried over from actuality to the fiction.[26]

It was on his solitary travels, however, that Crane found himself actually living a tale of adventure. With a guide named Miguel Itorbide, he set off by horseback into the back country. One night when he and his guide had gone to sleep in the back room of an adobe tavern, experience caught up with imaginings. A local bandit, Ramon Colorado, drunk and looking for trouble, thrust aside the curtain between the two rooms and peered into the dark for the rich American. Crane sat up in his blanket, instinctively grasped his revolver under the covers, and stared stonily at the man who wanted to rob and probably kill him. That silent stare, whether of fear or courage, halted the intruder just long enough to make time for a change of mind. The arrival of girls and music and the calling of his gang diverted the bandit from his intention for the moment anyway, and the prolonged moment subsided at last into drunken sleep. At first light Crane and his guide slipped to their horses and got the start of the bandits, but almost at once they were the quarry of a deadly chase and they finally reached safety only by luck, when they

[26] John Berryman, *Stephen Crane* (New York, 1950), p. 112; "Mexican Sights and Street Scenes," Philadelphia *Press*, May 19, 1895, "Ancient Capital of Montezuma," Philadelphia *Press*, July 21, 1895, in *Uncoll. Writ.*, pp. 149, 156; Beer, *Crane*, p. 119; Linson, *Crane*, pp. 88–89.

happened upon a troop of rural militia. The facts of the incident were to go more or less literally into "One Dash—Horses" but the self-interpreting form of the event—the silence that covers possible panic, the terrible wait for the odds to change and for the nerve to rally, and the all-or-nothing run for life—took time to filter through.[27] A language equal to conveying the intensity of the experience came naturally enough: when Crane related the incident to Linson shortly after his return to New York, his friend remembered the occasion as a proof that his vivid style was not "a mere trick of writing." The horses' hoofs as "flying leaves in the wind" and the guide's eyes as "the eyes of fear," phrases that came out in the oral narrative but did not appear in the story, testify to the easy brilliance that Linson asserted.[28] But full control of the story was another matter. When, the following September, Crane was actually writing about his encounter with the bandit, he alluded to it in a letter simply as "my personal troubles in Mexico." And when the tale came out in January, 1896, and he sent it to the girl in the world whom he most wanted to impress, he remarked only that it "celebrates in a measure my affection for a little horse I owned in Mexico."[29] The intensity of the youthful adventurer gave way to the understatement of the veteran as the writer came to know himself the master of his materials. A measure of the difference is suggested by the title, for Crane the lover of horses was shifting attention from himself to his mount. This was especially true when he canceled the Americanism "One Dash" for the English edition of

---

[27] Beer, *Crane*, pp. 116–117. The anecdote in Beer is very close to the story, and such details as the names of the guide and the bandit lend it credibility. Though Beer leaves the date vague, the incident took place in April or May, 1895. A letter at the end of March (Crane to Wickham W. Young, Mexico City, March 30, 1895, *Letters*, p. 55) indicates that Crane was then still in the sight-seeing and archaeologizing stage of his visit. During the first half of April his movements are unknown, but a receipted bill from the Hotel Iturbide in Mexico City places him there from April 16 to April 30 (MS in Columbia University Libraries). In May he went off alone for at least a week and perhaps for as long as three weeks. If the incident took place in early April, its first literary consequence may have been a kind of displacement effect. Berryman, *Crane*, p. 107, suggests that "A Mystery of Heroism"—a story in which Crane treated courage as the almost fortuitous product of inner and outer circumstance —was written in Mexico City.

[28] Linson, *Crane*, pp. 87–88.

[29] Crane to Willis Brooks Hawkins, Philadelphia, Sept. 18, [1895], *Letters*, p. 63; Crane to Nellie Crouse, New York, [Jan. 26, 1896], *Letters*, p. 103.

The Open Boat and the story appeared simply as "Horses." [30] But the canceled phrase of the original title, as it appeared in print and in Crane's private listings, tells something more. A "dash," as the *O.E.D.* tells us, is American sporting language for a race run in one heat. It is also a slang term, not listed in any of the dictionaries of Americanisms, but used by Crane in another of his Mexican stories where the meaning comes out clearly. In "The Five White Mice," which is full of colloquial dialogue, the opening scene concentrates on Americans festively playing dice in a Mexico City café. The man who calls the last game uses the phrase: "Three dashes—high man out!" "One dash," then, would mean an all-or-nothing roll of the dice, and Crane's original title speaks for him as a gamesman as well as a horseman. For the hero to learn that a good animal can be relied on in a race for life, he must first be willing to stake everything. The argument of Crane's tale runs parallel to that of Pascal's wager, though on a different road. His hero must act in a world where the event cannot be foreknown, and when he sees that he cannot count on himself alone to make the event he wants, he takes the risk of counting on something outside himself. In his version, however, the fable has less to do with the will to believe than with the readiness coolly to make one's bets.

The interval between the incident and the writing of "One Dash—Horses" was an active time as well as a period of quiet filtering through. During May, Crane continued his solitary wandering east and south from Mexico City. He became so easy in the local surroundings that he felt himself gradually blending in, face sunburned "the color of a brick side-walk" and "nothing American about me save a large Smith and Wesson revolver." Then one day in the town of Puebla he saw a young American girl in a new spring gown who resembled the girl he had most recently fallen in love with back home. The girl in Puebla, like the summer girls of Asbury Park, stood for the world of properly

[30] "Table of Contents," MS in Columbia University Libraries.

When the story was first published in England in February, 1896, the editors of the *New Review* made the same deletion—apparently for the same reason of not wanting to confuse readers with an American expression. The manuscript Table of Contents shows that Crane consciously accepted such reasoning, but the retention of the full title in the McClure edition shows that he preferred where possible to keep the notation of personal intensity and risk as well as the tribute to the "little horse I owned in Mexico."

ordered appearances; if it were not for her, society might fall apart, but a single glimpse could recall a man to his appointed role. Without so much as meeting her, Crane reported, "I ran to the railroad office. I cried: 'What is the shortest route to New York.' I left Mexico."[31] He arrived in New York City by May 16, and after seeing friends and dispensing opals, he continued his journey upstate to Port Jervis, where his brother William lived, and from there to his brother Edmund's place at Hartwood in the nearby hills. Edmund's was to be his headquarters more than anywhere else during the next year and a half, but he was not quick to settle down. He spent much of June and July in New York City, and he gave himself an August vacation in Pike County, Pennsylvania. Then in September he went down to Philadelphia, where Talcott Williams of the *Press* had received him so enthusiastically the previous December and where his friend Frederic Lawrence was starting out in medical practice. Williams' enthusiasm had turned to conviction: since last seeing Crane, he had printed seven of the sketches sent back to Bacheller as well as "A Mystery of Heroism." He now wanted to make a place for the young writer as dramatic critic, but at the last minute the business manager of the paper said no. Economically speaking, Crane was at loose ends once more, but Philadelphia was not like Lincoln. He wrote Willis Hawkins in New York what had happened: "Dear old man: Things fell ker-plunk. Stranded here in Phila. Don't you care! Nice town. Got lots of friends, though, and 23,842 invitations to dinner of which I have accepted 2."[32] The friends persuaded him to stay on, and it was from here on September 18 that he announced himself as "engaged at last" on his Mexican troubles.[33] The story first saw print in the *Press*, but not until January 4 and 6, 1896. Though it was written virtually under the eye of the editor, the story could make its way to him officially only by way of the Bacheller Syndicate in New York. The delay was worth while. Besides arranging for co-ordinated syndicate publication in the United States, the Bacheller firm seems to have acted as agent and to have placed the story in England, where it appeared in the *New*

[31] Crane to Nellie Crouse, Hartwood, N.Y., Dec. 31, [1895], *Letters*, p. 86.
[32] Philadelphia, [Sept. 10, 1895], *Letters*, p. 63.
[33] Crane to Hawkins, Philadelphia, Sept. 18, [1895], *Letters*, p. 63.

Review in February, 1896. When it came to American magazine publication, Bacheller figured in yet another way. He had become editor of *Pocket Magazine,* the first inexpensive all-fiction monthly, and made Stephen Crane one of his regular authors, using "One Dash—Horses" in his third issue in June. If Bacheller had been neglectful at the start of Crane's Western trip, his casual way of doing business with a friend proved to be a good enough bet for the long run.

After the productive stay in Philadelphia, Crane returned briefly to New York and then, as he said, skipped to the country where he was better able to work. During this period his energies are pretty well accounted for by his rapid writing of *The Third Violet* and a series of war stories for McClure. He finished the novel in December, 1895, and was not satisfied with it, and even before he finished "The Little Regiment" in February, 1896, he was ready to say, "Hang all war-stories." There followed an abortive journalistic trip to Washington in March and another spell in New York; then he was ready for rustication again. On May 29, 1896, he wrote: "I have again taken to the woods and I shall try to remain here for I am certainly unable to withstand the fury of New York." In the easy atmosphere of Hartwood, during the late spring and summer of 1896, he returned to his Mexican materials and wrote "The Wise Men," "The Five White Mice," and "A Man and Some Others." [34] These three stories

---

[34] Crane to Nellie Crouse, Hartwood, Feb. 5, [1896], *Letters,* p. 111; Crane to Ripley Hitchcock, Port Jervis, N.Y., May 29, [1896], *Letters,* pp. 124–125.

The dating of the first two of these stories is partly a matter of inference. They were definitely written before November, 1896, and the manuscripts left at Hartwood with his brother Edmund (see p. liii below). June and July, 1896, are the best of the few possible choices of when Crane could have written them between his return from Mexico in May, 1895, and his departure for Florida in November, 1896. Though they could possibly have been written a year earlier, in June and July, 1895, in Hartwood and New York, there are good reasons not to think so: (1) *George's Mother* was high on Crane's agenda when he got back from Mexico in May, 1895. The *Bookman* for that month (I, 230) mentioned the novel, which Crane had first pronounced complete the previous November, as being read by publishers, but the reference to it by its early title, "A Woman without Weapons," suggests that the text as well as the title was subject to revision. Since he had written the book in New York and presumably left the manuscript there, this period of late spring and early summer of 1895, when he was spending much time in New York, would be the most plausible for further work on it. There would be no other chance before the novel was published the following spring. (2) Crane corresponded with Copeland and Day, publishers of *The Black Riders,* in the early summer of 1895 about another possible book for them. He mentioned his early Sullivan County sketches but gave no hint that he

complete the first series of tales to come out of his Western trip, and all three have a directness and spontaneity which are strikingly youthful compared to the tales Crane would be writing the very next year. Yet they also show how he was moving experimentally but surely toward the artistic complexity of his greatest works.

"The Wise Men" and "The Five White Mice," written in its earliest version immediately after, present the companionable world of the two Kids, from New York and from San Francisco, and the subtitle of the former story, "A Detail of American Life in Mexico," indicates the simplicity of narrative conception from which they start. But even with "The Wise Men," the claim of simplicity is deceptive, for the wisdom of the inseparable companions is paradoxically bound up with a signal lack of conventional prudence. Mexico City is for them a holiday realm where they may indulge—innocently—in vices that American small-town respectability proscribes. Crane, as the son of a Methodist minister, relished the discovery that drinking or betting might be play rather than corruption—and not only in his eyes, but in the world's. His youths "were very wicked according to report, and

might be doing a Western series. (3) His Mexican sketches were coming out in the Philadelphia *Press* during this summer of 1895. Had he been doing more along this line—that is, short stories as well as journalistic articles—the strong likelihood is that he would have sent the work to Bacheller and had it published promptly. (4) Crane's note to Hawkins of Sept. 18, 1895, reporting himself "engaged at last on my personal troubles in Mexico," has the ring of a man who is starting *at last* on a subject that his friends and listeners have wanted him to set down on paper for some time. (5) In a note to Hawkins from Hartwood on Nov. 25, 1895 (*Letters*, p. 77), he claimed to "have been frantically hustling of late to make some money." In such a juncture, he would hardly have kept stories of this quality off the market while selling—and sometimes not being able to sell—inferior work.

As for the possibility that the stories were written later than the summer of 1896, the blank spaces in the Crane biography during September and October prove to be well accounted for by (1) the Dora Clark affair, beginning Sept. 16, in which journalist Crane's gallant defense of an accused prostitute against false arrest led by rapid complication to something like full-scale war between Crane and the New York police; (2) the Amy Leslie affair, in which Crane's emotional and financial entanglement with the slightly daft forty-year-old divorcée, theater reviewer, and sometime star of the musical stage, led to her accusations of jilting and embezzlement and to her legal attachment of his royalties at Appleton. Given these pressures, he made at least one tactical withdrawal to his friends in Philadelphia and showed a readiness for out-of-town assignments that led to a couple of football trips in early November before his more or less permanent departure later that month to cover the Cuban revolution for Bacheller.

yet they managed to have it reflect credit upon them." (Of course sex is a proscribed area which they do not explore, and their grossest sensuality is the passion one of them has for eating salads.) The young men are discerning enough and reckless enough to believe an old bartender's claim to be a great runner even though he scarcely looks like an athlete: "The buttons of his glittering white vest formed a fine curve, so that if the concave surface of a piece of barrel-hoop had been laid against Pop it would have touched each button." They arrange a race between him and a much younger American bartender, and sustaining the bravado of an initial fifty-dollar bet, they coolly proceed to take all bets. As they are obviously getting in so deep that they could be ruined by a loss, they draw the warnings of friends and the caution from Pop that "nobody can ever say for sure" that he will win. They thank their friends, reassure their runner, ignore the contempt of the surly Benson who pronounces them a couple of asses. And they win their bet. Their wisdom, however, is not so much in their discernment or their luck as in their style. Two bits of dialogue, one from before the race and one from after, illustrate that style:

"Say, this is getting interesting. Are you in deep?" asked one anxiously of his friend.

"Yes, pretty deep," said the other stolidly. "Are you?"

"Deep as the devil," replied the other in the same tone.

They looked at each other stonily and went back to the crowd. Benson had just entered the café. He approached them with a gloating smile of victory. "Well, where's all that money you were going to bet?"

"Right here," said the Kids, thrusting into their vest pockets.

.   .   .   .   .

The Kids, grinning, said: "How much did you lose, Benson?"

Benson said defiantly: "Oh, not so much. How much did you win?"

"Oh, not so much."

In the midst of purported vice, Crane presented the test of self-discipline for which the proper rhetoric is understatement.

Understatement seems to be the ruling principle of "The Five White Mice," the last sentence of which is "Nothing had happened." But this is not simply the understatement of bravery, coolness, or tacit understanding of a common code. It is a comment on the equivocal ways in which the incident may be regarded: Has anything happened if the witnesses are unaware? Is there value to the moral effort which prevents violence rather than performing it? The story illustrates how Crane's fiction could become more complex and yet not lose the concentration of the short-story form. Instead of elaborating plot or character in the traditional sense, the tale exposes more facets of the single intensely rendered episode. The story opens with the New York Kid among the wicked, drinking and gambling. Even with his fancifully inventive gambler's imprecation to the "five white mice of chance," he loses at dice and has to take the winners off as promised—to the circus. The chances connect with consequences: after the performance the Kid is sober when he joins his pal from San Francisco and Benson; on their way home a sidewalk jostling puts them face to angry face with three fiercely aggressive Mexicans; in a "crescendo of provocations" the two drunken Americans invite a fight, and the sober Kid realizes that the Mexicans' knives are about to flash home and make a quick end to the uneven contest. Thinking of death, he is weak, but forcing his almost giddy mind to think how to draw his revolver, he gradually summons the energy to try. When he draws it and points it at his enemies, he suddenly sees them jump back: "The cry and the backward steps revealed something of great importance to the New York Kid. He had never dreamed that he did not have a complete monopoly of all possible trepidations." The lesson he has learned more than qualifies any pride he may feel in his own courage, for the universality of fear is one main reason why a single man may be able to act effectively even though subject to trepidations himself. He does not make the circumstance in which action is possible, and he does not even understand how he happens to generate the will to act. Though his companions have learned nothing, not even that he has saved them, and though there is no adventure to this tale of adventure, something has happened in the consciousness of the protagonist. Attaining grace under pressure like Hemingway's heroes to come, the Crane hero learns so much about pressures on the mind that he is truly humble about making any claim to grace. In the sickening moment of fear, "a combination of honorable manhood and inability prevented him from running away." The combination of bravery and weakness makes the honest man wary of saying very much about bravery. In the event more generally considered, the combination of casualty and self-reliance—to use John Berryman's terms—makes it impossible to simplify the conceptual universe in which the incident takes place. Although Crane made no overt metaphysical statement, the world of his fiction was becoming a pluralistic universe in which chance, will, and general laws all had room to exist.

With the complex world which it projects, "The Five White Mice" suggests the continuity of Crane's career before and after the turning point of "The Open Boat," and the manuscript evidence bears this out. The revisions in the surviving manuscript, a fair copy of the 1896 story which Crane made in England in December, 1897, bespeak his readiness to leave it essentially unchanged.[35] He gave no sign of wanting to alter his plot, characters, or theme. He would not have called his concern for style minor, but when he made improvements of language, he almost always left the cleaned-up sentences grammatically and semantically the same as they were. So, at the beginning, as the mysteries of cocktail making are described, the bartender's spoon whirls merely "swiftly" instead of tritely "like a top," and the hum and rattle of the turning ice sounds "like a cheap watch" instead of vaguely "like a bit of mechanism." Having decided that there was no point in talking about "the saloon" without giving it a name, Crane tried "Cafe" and "Maison" and finally thought himself back to Mexico and settled on "the Casa Verde." With his sharp eye for clichés, he caught "glimmering rays" and

[35] The copying and revision of "The Five White Mice" probably took place in the first half of December, 1897, between Crane's forwarding "Death and the Child" to his agent, Paul Revere Reynolds, and his setting aside his proposed Greek novel in order to turn to "The Blue Hotel." While working without an advance for his novel, he was under severe financial strain, and yet the letter which went with "Death and the Child," despite an anguished cry for all the money that the agent could raise, did not mention the Western tale (Crane to Reynolds, [Oxted, December, 1897], *Letters*, 156–157). In his next letter to Reynolds he promised to hold "Death and the Child" off the English market until he received further instructions from the agent about possible sale to an international-copyright magazine, and he went on, "The Five White Mice however is on the market here," speaking of the story as if Reynolds also had a copy. In the same letter he first mentioned his working on "The Blue Hotel" (Oxted, Dec. 20, [1897], typed copy in Syracuse University Library).

The manuscript was given by Crane to Joseph Conrad (Crane to Conrad, Oxted, March 17, [1898], *Letters*, pp. 176–177). In 1912 it was acquired by John Quinn; it is now in the Henry E. Huntington Library.

a "loud roar" and sensibly deleted the adjectives. When the adjective was not superfluous in an instance of "mild surprise," he vivified the drunken Benson's reaction to the man he accidentally jostled by having him gaze in "gentle" surprise. As the encounter became more tense, he had written of the New York Kid, "He ceased to breath[e]"; rejecting the obvious overstatement, he now tried a stylish indirection: "In this test, the lungs of the Kid still continued to perform their duty." Gentle surprise and lungs that do their duty come from the same fanciful play of mind that made five white mice the object of the gambler's incantation. The incantation had to have been there in the earliest version to give its name to the story, and yet it too may have been retouched, for of the two cancellations in the manuscript, one seems to have been a slip and the other a slip back to an earlier form. The story gives the ditty twice. The Kid recites it when he is about to roll the dice, and he thinks it when he is about to draw his revolver and, with everything riding on the success of his move, make "a new game" of the night encounter:

> "Oh, five white mice of chance,
> Shirts of wool and corduroy pants,
> Gold and wine, women and sin,
> All for you if you let me come in—
> Into the house of chance."

In the first instance Crane wrote "Dust" for "Gold" and then deleted it; if, as it seems, he was changing "Dust of gold" to "Gold and wine," he multiplied temptations and at the same time got rid of any verbal hint that sin, in this story, would draw the conventional wages. On the second occasion Crane wrote "Into the temple of chance." In this case the inconsistency, corrected by another hand, was apparently caught by an editorial eye other than his own, but his intention could be taken for granted: though he had accidentally reverted to an earlier draft, he presumably meant to get rid of the near-cliché and sharpen his mock invocation.

But the youthful brilliance of the story came through without need of many such polishings. The jaunty irony of the incantation—"if one was going to believe in anything at all, one might as well choose the five white mice"—carried a suggestion of nursery rhyme: "Three Blind Mice" and "Hickory Dickory Dock" seem relevant without being analogous; like the best of nonsense verse Crane's almost makes sense, but not quite. The colloquialisms—"dashes" for dice throws, "scragged" for drunk, "scummed" for swept along out of a crowd—add color, in the musical sense, to the language. The most brilliant effects, if not literally colorful, are indeed visual. In the climactic scene the Kid sees his antagonist's face "as if he and it were alone in space —a yellow mask smiling in eager cruelty, in satisfaction." With the same kind of unrationalized vision, the Kid's consciousness fixes on images which are absurd to common sense and yet ironically close to the literal plot. Dwelling on the revolver at his hip, "he recalled that upon its black handle was stamped a hunting scene in which a sportsman in fine leggings and a peaked cap was taking aim at a stag less than one eighth of an inch away." [36] This image uncorrected by common-sense perspective was not, like the dog's tail in the Howells interview, simply a playful foray against comfortable assumptions. Crane was prefiguring what the Kid must act out in pointing the revolver at close range against men. By rendering the psychological narrative with sharp intensity, he broke through the melodramatic convention of the Wild West plot and made the usual gun-drawing scene into a horrifying absurdity. The imaged style was more than a rhetorical technique; it was Crane's medium for expressing his grasp of the inner life. And when the medium was inadequate to his conception, he changed it. He understood that when the presence of death was acutely felt, fear and self-pity generated images so fast that the analogy of painting could not work. So, in getting the Kid from his first fantastic conception of pointing a gun to the grim act of doing so, he resorted to a modern figure: "These views were perfectly stereopticon, flashing in and away from his thought with an inconceivable rapidity until after all they were simply one quick dismal impression." He had to invent moving pictures, so to speak, in order to render the mind of this young man under stress. Whatever his formal

[36] The manuscript originally had a "black rubber handle" on the revolver, but Crane canceled "rubber"; except for the deletion of the irrelevant though accurate descriptive term, and the corrected spelling of "it's," the sentence of the final text follows the manuscript.

knowledge of dynamic psychology—probably nil—he had in fact invented long since a strong working conception of the stream of consciousness. This is the logic that underlies the rhetoric. That the image happens to be utterly without color tells something important about the acknowledged brilliance of Crane's early fiction, that it is due not simply to the high palette he frequently used, but mainly to the immediacy with which he presented his characters' inner experience. He was developing other, presumably solider, qualities, but the intimate subjectivity of *The Red Badge* or "The Five White Mice" would occur rarely in the later work.

Detachment rather than intimacy prevails in "A Man and Some Others." One difference is that between the one-dash encounter with death, which may be exciting and suspenseful, and the sustained encounter against fearful odds, which evokes the calm of certainty. Instead of a struggle with fear or self-pity, the story is one of learning to look steadily at what is, and to see it whole. The given situation is simple: the sheepherder Bill hears himself threatened off the range and almost automatically defies the murderous José who speaks for himself "—and the others." Though his word to the emissary is "Well, you tell them to go to the devil!" Bill knows that to hold out for his rights is to assure his own doom. The personal history which has led to this dead end begins to put the incident in context, but it is given in so arch a style that it is less morally repellent and much less lurid than an intimate account might be. A poker game began things by reducing Bill from a mineowner and a great man in Wyoming to a cowboy "more weirdly abandoned than if he had never been an aristocrat." Bill remembered the single night's gambling rather than the long downward road of brutalization whereby, as cowboy, railroader, bouncer, a killer once and more and more often a fighter, he came at last to southwestern Texas and sheepherding. Yet after so much he still has the decency to warn away the tenderfoot stranger who asks to share his campfire, not to "let him in for no such game" as he expects that night. The stranger, who stays to be the naïve observer and initiate of knowledge, finds that to get the whole bitter truth of the event is hardly a steadying experience. He starts in comic fatuity, asking Bill why he doesn't get the sheriff. Before the end he learns the meaning of the wilderness—the message that is said to be in the crackle of the campfire as in the boom of the sea—namely, the "inconsequence of individual tragedy," the inconsequence, as the phrase recurs, "of human tragedy." Beween the extremes of naïveté and knowledge, however, the initiate attains certain truths. He seems to have entered both outward and inner chaos in which the "lightning action" of the final attack appears as "the fabric of dreams," "a happening of the night"—

And yet afterward certain lines, forms, lived out so strongly from the incoherence that they were always in his memory.

He killed a man, and the thought went swiftly by him, like the feather on the gale, that it was easy to kill a man.

Moreover, he suddenly felt for Bill, this grimy sheep-herder, some deep form of idolatry. Bill was dying, and the dignity of last defeat, the superiority of him who stands in his grave, was in the pose of the lost sheep-herder.

The three modest statements—on the forms that live out from the incoherence, on the fragility of life, on the dignity of death —show what Crane's steady contemplation of the event could yield. But the three short paragraphs are dramatically assigned to a character within the story, that is, they do not exist separately out of time and out of context but are integrally part of a continuous action. They occur at the moment when the horror of killing and the absoluteness of death are more important than the fear of dying, when the intensity of self-regard has given way to the perception of truths. The revolver which had been wildly brandished in "The Pace of Youth," seriously drawn and pointed in "One Dash—Horses" and "The Five White Mice," had finally gone off. Crane could go no further in imagination. In experience and in art he would hereafter build on what he had done in his early Western tales.

The three Western tales Crane wrote in 1896 had a various history before they appeared in the *Open Boat* volume of two years later. He left the manuscripts of "The Wise Men" and "The Five White Mice" at Hartwood and, under the pressure of events, did not send for them for a year. "A Man and Some Others" he brought down to the city with him, and he showed it or told about it in detail to his new friend and enthusiastic admirer Theodore Roosevelt. On August 18 Roosevelt wrote him, "Some day I want you to write another story of the frontiersman and the Mexican Greaser in which the frontiersman shall come out on top; it is more normal that way!"[37] That hearty Philistine criticism from the New York police commissioner, so much like the comment of the sheepherder who provided the germ of the story, shows how Crane transcended the popular convention, but it also foreshadows his losing his popular audience.

What Crane himself was aware of, however, was his beginning to reach a new audience, of which Roosevelt must have seemed the prize example. In the summer of 1896 Irving Bacheller had introduced him to Paul Revere Reynolds, the first American literary agent, and Reynolds offered him the chance of breaking into the high-paying monthlies like *Century* and *Harper's*, the quality trade. He had his own access to less highbrow —and less high-paying—magazines, especially after the success of *The Red Badge* gave publicity value to his name: *McClure's* brought out two of his stories in 1896, and Bacheller's *Pocket Magazine,* founded in the spring of 1896, printed seven Crane stories in its first eight issues. He did not need to pay commissions to be published with them. So when he left his first story with Reynolds on September 9, he specified: "Don't go to Bacheller or McClure." The story was "A Man and Some Others," and Reynolds was pleased to have it. He promptly reassured Crane that he could sell the story as quickly and lucratively as the writer wished and especially that he could handle the English rights.[38] But the flurry of activity and of writing to a London agent gave way to the simpler solution of selling the story to the *Century*, an international monthly that published a simultaneous London edition and paid accordingly. He was enough encouraged by preliminary negotiations so that when he submitted the manuscript on October 2, he set a price of $500 for English

[37] New York, Aug. 18, 1896, *Letters*, p. 128; compare Beer, *Crane*, cited p. xxxvi above.

[38] Crane to Reynolds, [New York], Sept. 9, 1896, *Letters*, pp. 130–131; Reynolds to Crane, New York, Sept. 11, [1896], TLS in Columbia University Libraries. The Reynolds letter, directed to "Stephen Crane, Esq., Sullivan County, N.Y.," indicates that Crane was back in Hartwood briefly—probably for the last time in his life.

and American rights. There was evidently no difficulty over the price, but the editor, Richard Watson Gilder, did raise some questions about the text.

The censorship of the genteel public through the instrumentality of the highbrow monthlies showed its vague but real power in Gilder's letter to Reynolds of October 24:

My dear Mr. Reynolds:

I am truly obliged to Mr. Crane for getting out that hackneyed "crown of thorns."

You may think me over anxious, but I am particularly sorry he did not change "B'Gawd." It is difficult to know what to do with swearing in fiction. When it appears in print it has an offensiveness beyond that of the actual word; and it is never true or "realistic" because, if the actual oaths were printed just as the swearer swears it would be as unendurable among men as among gods.

I am a sincere well-wisher of the author, and I am anxious that this story should not attract unfavorable criticism in any details; so I particularly ask him through yourself to omit that expression, for his sake as well as yours.

Sincerely,
R. W. Gilder

This is the sentence: " 'B'Gawd,' said Bill, speaking as from a throat filled with dust, 'I'll go after 'em in a minute.' "

Reynolds replied at once:

My dear Mr. Gilder,—

I have your letter of to-day about Mr. Crane's story. I will communicate with him and see if he is willing that you should change the word that you object to. Of course you know how sensitive authors are about their literary children, and how much they dislike any change in them. I will see what I can do and let you know.

The agent was right about Crane's resisting, but he did not worry that sale of the story would be endangered: as he knew, the story was then or shortly would be set up in type. Skilled in his business, he was equally calm in the face of mislaid proofs. He wrote Gilder on November 10:

Unless I am very much mistaken and I don't think I am, you received the proofs back from Mr. Crane. You wished him to modify one sentence where he had used the word "gawd". I have been trying to see Mr. Crane for the last week, but we have missed each other. I have now written to him about the matter and will let you know what he says.

Reynolds' unhurried communication, if it ever reached Crane, probably did not make him feel any urgency to change his story. But Gilder eventually won—he might have said compromised— by printing the sheepherder's oath less offensively as "B'G—." [39]

Censorship of another sort indirectly affected publication of "The Wise Men" and "The Five White Mice," for while the sale and bowdlerization of "A Man and Some Others" were going on, the career of Crane the New York journalist supervened on that of the rising young writer from Hartwood. Less than a week after he had left his manuscript with Reynolds and retreated to the country, Crane fled in turn from rural peace and resumed his studious observation of city life. On September 16 at 2 A.M., outside a Broadway nightclub, he stepped forward to save a girl from false arrest for soliciting. Despite her record as a prostitute, he stood by his commitment and appeared in court not only in her defense but even in her countersuit against the harassing policeman. His sense of justice and gallantry conflicted with popular notions of law and order: Roosevelt's friendship, for example, turned to hostility and contempt forever after. Since the incident and the two trials were well publicized by the yellow press, at least once with Crane's own by-line, the effect on priggish sensibilities could be guessed. In fact, Thomas Beer was to report that Gilder demanded of Reynolds: "What does Crane mean by getting into such a mess when he's sold a story to us?" and that he held up publication of "A Man and Some Others" until the newspaper scandal passed. [40] As it happened, Gilder did not see the manuscript until two weeks after the Dora Clark affair had broken in the papers, he accepted it while the furor was at its height, and he conducted his single-minded campaign for verbal decency at a time when Crane's misadventure was still alive in the press though he took no notice of the event.

[39] Reynolds to Mr. Buel, New York, Oct. 2, 1896, TLS in New York Public Library; Richard Watson Gilder to Reynolds, New York, Oct. 24, 1896, in Frederick Lewis Allen, *Paul Revere Reynolds* (New York, 1944), p. 49; Reynolds to Gilder, New York, Oct. 24 and Nov. 10, 1896, TLS in New York Public Library. Reynolds added a somewhat less phlegmatic postscript to the Nov. 10 letter in his own hand: "Mr. Johnson certainly had the corrected proofs."
[40] Beer, *Crane*, p. 137.

Yet there is a kind of poetic truth to the Beer account. One reason Reynolds could not find Crane was that he was making himself scarce in town. While the police were making New York too hot for him, Crane's sensitivity to small-town views—keener than Gilder's—evidently kept him from taking refuge in Port Jervis or Hartwood. His friend Lawrence reports that he visited him in Philadelphia again, and a couple of football assignments also took him out of town. Even when Bacheller was arranging for him to go and cover the Cuban Revolution, he found no time for a last visit home—and thus no chance to pick up the manuscripts of two stories which he had every reason to think were highly salable. From Jacksonville on November 29 he wrote his brother William, excusing his evasion: "The very thing that I apprehended came to pass in a violent manner and I was off to Cuba before I had a chance even to inform you of it from New York." He and his lawyer brother had been discussing wills, and having lost the will which his brother had drawn for him, he repeated the terms as he remembered them in the hope that the letter might have some legal weight. As for literary executors, he was confident that Howells, Hamlin Garland, his friend Willis Hawkins, and his Appleton editor Ripley Hitchcock would be willing to serve. His instructions concerning his literary affairs centered on collecting stories into book form—"there are some of them which I would hate to see lost." After the "Midnight Sketches," his first care, he thought of culling from the list he had left at Hartwood the "sketches of outdoor life," among which he put "One Dash Horses" and "The Wise Men," and the story which *Century* would be bringing out in January or February, "A Man and Some Others." Finally he touched upon the recent scandal:

I forgot to mention the Dora Clark case. If I should happen to be detained upon my journey, you must always remember that your brother in that case acted like a man of honor and a gentleman and you need not fear to hold your head up to anybody and defend his name. All that I said in my own article in the Journal is absolutely true, and for my part I see no reason why, if I should live a thousand years, I should ever be ashamed or humiliated by my course in that matter.

Temperamentally there were plenty of reasons—his romantic idealism, his Bohemian irresponsibility, and his realistic tough-mindedness—why he might have taken a detached view of the moralism which censors and gossips try to enforce. Yet he also felt an impulse to popular conformity strong enough to keep him away from Port Jervis and Hartwood, as it turned out, for the rest of his life.⁴¹

Crane's abandoning the manuscripts of his unsold Western stories is one measure of how much he shared the popular culture which he stood out against in his life and work. What the culture censored, he concealed, more or less. The Dora Clark affair was only the beginning. Later, after the Florida episode and after his coverage of the Greek-Turkish War, it was his settling down in England with Cora Stewart. His domestic arrangements, however unconventional, involved some conventional responsibilities, and so sometime in the late spring or early summer of 1897 Crane made a survey of his capital resources. This list of stories, with word count and place of publication or location of the manuscript, could have been the basis for making up book-length collections. Only the two Western tales are recorded with the notation "Ms at Hartwood." ⁴² Some time thereafter he wrote to his brother Edmund: "Can you find among my possessions a story called 'The Wise Men' and another story called 'The Five White Mice'? If so send them to me as soon as possible." Characteristically he gave his return address in care of his London publisher, misspelled "William Heinaman"; not until January, 1899, did he give either of his brothers his English home address. When Edmund sent him a shipment of manuscript together with what must have been a solicitous letter, Stephen replied on September 9, from Schull, Ireland, with a more circumstantial report of himself. Of himself alone. Though he reported a carriage accident which befell him and

⁴¹ Frederick M. Lawrence to Thomas Beer, Philadelphia, Nov. 8, 1923, *Letters*, p. 332; Crane to W. H. Crane, Jacksonville, Nov. 29, 1896, *Nineteenth-Century Fiction*, XXIII, 222-223. Crane, though he used a dash in his title elsewhere, left it out and wrote "One Dash Horses" here and in the original, canceled listing for the Table of Contents of the London edition of the *Open Boat* volume, discussed below.

⁴² MS at Columbia University Libraries. The list runs from early New York sketches to the latest Greek dispatch which appeared in the *Westminster Gazette* on June 18, 1897, and it is in random order. After the first twenty-five entries Crane put down a running total of 73,000 words, making an error in addition of 1,500 words against himself. As he became more hard-pressed, he began to add more carefully. The list is reproduced in the illustrations following p. xiv.

Cora and the trip to Ireland which they made with Harold Frederic and his mistress, the letter read "I was thrown . . . I was shaken up . . . so Frederic and I have come down here . . . ," and it concluded by saying that his address would "continue to be at Heineman's." The Western tales appeared in this letter also: "The ms you mailed to me was not the one I wanted but I was glad enough to get it. Any odd bits of writing you find at H please mail to me. Some of them will come in handy." He did not say handy for what: secrecy about his domestic life added obscurity to his conduct of business.[43]

Presumably the right stories came from Hartwood in due course, and the last phase of their manuscript history illuminates another side of Crane. He revised "The Five White Mice" in December and sent a copy to Reynolds. In January, 1898, he informed the agent that the story was sold in England and thus must not go to "one of the three big fellows," the international monthlies, but no English periodical publication has been found. Then in February he advised Reynolds that the story was to go to the "McClure book." Having failed to find a magazine buyer, Reynolds finally let the story go to the New York *World* for its Sunday supplement of April 10, just eight days before copyright application and deposit were made for the *Open Boat* volume. In England there was no such last-minute sale. Rather, on March 17 Crane sent the story to Joseph Conrad with a little note: "I am enclosing you a bit of original ms. under the supposition that you might like to keep it in remembrance of my warm and endless friendship for you." [44] The fortunes of "The Wise Men"

---

[43] *Stephen Crane Newsletter*, I (Spring, 1967), 7–8. The first of these letters is ascribed by the editor, Joseph Katz, to June, 1897, because Crane's Oxted address was firm in July and would have obviated the use of Heinemann's address. It could have been written, however, any time up to Aug. 16, the date of the accident which Crane mentioned for the first time in his letter of Sept. 9. The emphasis on the singular personal pronoun in the Sept. 9 letter is my own.

The renewed correspondence with Edmund evoked a friendly letter from William also, to whom Crane replied on Oct. 29. In this letter, written from "c/o William Heineman" once again, Crane gave a circumstantial account of his calamities, adventures, achievements, and projects, but made no mention of a wife (*Letters*, pp. 146–148). After William already knew, he finally mentioned being married in a letter of early 1899 (see Vol. VII, TALES OF WHILOMVILLE, p. xxxviii).

[44] Crane to Reynolds, Oxted, Dec. 20, [1897], typed copy in Syracuse University Library; same, [Oxted], Jan. 14 and Feb. 7, [1898], *Letters*, pp. 169, 171; Crane to Conrad, [Oxted], March 17, [1898], *Letters*, pp. 176–177.

went the opposite way. This story, too, was part of the *Open Boat* volume. In England it made a last-minute appearance in the *Ludgate Monthly* of April, 1898; in America it ended in the friendly hands of Irving Bacheller, the original sponsor of Crane's Western travels. Bacheller used it as the leading piece of *The Lanthorn Book*, an undated, uncopyrighted memento of comradeship and newspaper days, which included work originally read by various members at the Saturday dinners of the Lantern Club. Both stories, rightly enough, give evidence in their publication history of the open, easygoing generosity which Crane thought of as belonging to the Western type. The quality appears more often in literary types than in actual men and women, but his friends had no trouble recognizing it in him.

Crane's hasty appointment of literary executors on November 29, 1896, was not a gloomy act. He liked having sudden orders to leave town, and not just because his complicated personal affairs were well worth leaving behind. Whatever his personal motive for escape, the escapism of popular culture gave him another reason to be off. He sought adventure even beyond what the West had offered, and he had set his heart on it for a long time. As early as December, 1895, he was, he said, "considering a start very shortly to some quarter of the world where mail is uncertain." [45] To get beyond the world of daily appointed rounds, his means once more was a journalistic assignment, but this time he went as a star reporter. Though he did not play that role as flashily as a Richard Harding Davis, his celebrity as the youthful author of *The Red Badge* and the obscure poet of *The Black Riders* supplied glamour enough to make him, according to formula, front-page news as well as a front-page reporter. Bacheller, who had done well enough with him when he was unknown, was eager to try again. Crane was, in fact, the last best hope of the Bacheller Syndicate, the one big-name reporter who might help that modest jobbing enterprise to survive in competition with the new and powerful mass-newspaper combines of Pulitzer and Hearst. Saying nothing of his economic troubles, Bacheller played his chances coolly as he knew his "last, great,

---

[45] Crane to Ripley Hitchcock, Hartwood, Dec. 27, 1895, *Letters*, p. 83.

shining star" would do. Some time after Crane reported the Princeton-Harvard football game of November 7, 1896, Bacheller gave him the assignment of covering the Cuban Revolution and, for expenses, a money belt containing seven hundred dollars in Spanish gold. Crane was to leave at once for Jacksonville, the major port for Cuban filibusters and contraband arms shippers, and "seize the first opportunity to get across to Cuba." [46] He took the first step promptly, establishing himself at the best hotel in Jacksonville and making contact with fellow reporters and their local sources of information. But the next step required time. Without letting other newsmen or government agents know, he had to find a ship that could slip past the American naval patrol and carry him to his destination. In his hurried letter to William Crane on November 29, he sounded as if he might embark at any moment. In fact, however, he had another month to wait, and the interval was not simply a time of frustrated haste.

Early in his canvass of saloons, restaurants, and other spots where newspapermen hung out, he discovered the Hotel de Dream, a nightclub-brothel presided over by the redoubtable Cora Howorth Stewart. [47] No visitor to the club ever confused the proprietress with the girls who worked there, for the handsome young woman from Boston had a commanding look that taught discrimination to the coarsest patrons. Blonde, thirty, full of figure, she made up for lack of prettiness by her vitality. "Virtue," she confided to her notebook, "never yet atoned for wrinkles, men ask us to be forever young and pretty. Though a woman must be rather more than pretty—and may be rather less—to attract a fin de siècle man." Her worldly wisdom had not saved her from making two rash marriages, the second to a British officer who refused to give her a divorce, but it did help her accommodate to the somewhat tawdry grandeur of the Hotel de Dream. Still, having drifted so far from her cultivated mid-

---

[46] Bacheller, *Coming up the Road*, pp. 292–293.

[47] It is perhaps important to distinguish niceties that are unavailable in the current American idiom. By the coarse definition of *Webster's Seventh New Collegiate Dictionary*, a brothel is "an establishment in which prostitutes are available." Cora Stewart was a hotelkeeper and not an employer, and her conduct was sanctified by the laws of real estate, common carriers, and ordinary commerce. In the grim years after Crane's death she did become a bawd in order to support herself, but at this stage she was still technically genteel.

dle-class background, she was more than gratified by the attentions of a twenty-five-year-old fin de siècle man. She knew how to respond with intelligent sympathy as well as pleasure, admiration, and charm. Before long the warming friendship was marked by Crane's presenting her a copy of his recent novel, *George's Mother,* with the inscription "To an unnamed sweetheart." At the same time he gave her a melancholy little note, an arty fin de siècle memento as she must have recognized: "Brevity is an element that enters importantly into all pleasures, of life, and this is what makes pleasure sad; and so there is no pleasure but only sadness." [48] The sad pleasures of Jacksonville went on and on, and Bacheller's checks kept coming in, until Crane finally got passage on the *Commodore*. Officially on the ship's roster as an able seaman, he set sail on December 31 along with a load of munitions and a band of Cuban insurgents, and the voyage was almost what it then seemed—the end of the interlude.

There was a fog when the *Commodore* went down the St. Johns River that New Year's Eve, and despite Captain Edward Murphy's precaution of having a local pilot at the wheel, the ship struck a sand bar. At dawn it was towed free by the revenue cutter *Boutwell,* a patrol ship whose mission was not to help but to stop contraband and insurgents that put out from American bases. Though he was an excellent captain, Murphy did not inspect for damage after the grounding. Despite an excellent chief engineer, no leak was noticed during the first day at sea, and pumping did not begin on the night of January 1 until so much water had been shipped that the vessel was doomed. Such contradictions betoken what Crane thought of as the nature of things beyond the boundaries of routine, security, and comfortable illusions: the historical puzzles stand for what he saw as

[48] Lillian Gilkes, *Cora Crane: A Biography of Mrs. Stephen Crane* (Bloomington, Ind., 1960), pp. 21–22; *Letters,* p. 132. Both the inscription and the note "To C. E. S." are dated Nov. 4, 1896; unless Crane shuttled to Jacksonville between the two Harvard football games he reported, found Cora, and swooned into love at once, this is an impossible date. The editors' conjectural date of Nov. 14 would require less of a dash to the train but just about the same emotional lightning. Nov. 24 or, better still, Dec. 4 would be more plausible emotionally. Dec. 4 would imply only a common slip of dating, and coming so soon after his testamentary letter home of Nov. 29, it would account for Crane's thinking so solemnly about the brevity of his Jacksonville pleasures.

cosmic mysteries. When the mysteries supervene on normal experience, a man's only option may be to face disaster the best way he knows how. In this case, Captain Murphy tried first to head back to land, and then when the failure of pumps and engines made it clear that the ship was foundering, he ordered passengers and crew to the boats. Crane himself, who had earlier kept a panicky sailor from the lifeboats and had joined the bailing crew in the hot, half-flooded engine room, stood by the captain until the last boat. It was said of him, as the newspapers later reported, that "his nerve greatly encouraged all hands," that he was a "brave little gentleman" and "the spunkiest fellow out," that he "behaved like a born sailor." Certainly he needed all the spunk he could muster, for he and Captain Murphy, who had injured his arm in the lifeboat operation, the cook Montgomery, and the oiler Billy Higgins were left with a small dinghy which they had to manage in high seas. Moreover, their ordeal began in horror. The mate's boat had capsized, and the seven men from that boat returned to the fast-sinking *Commodore*. Standing off at voice distance, the captain instructed them how to make life rafts, though only three of the men were enough beguiled by hope to try. Even those rafts were too heavy for the dinghy to tow and soon capsized. One of the drowning sailors tried to pull himself by the towrope to the little boat which was about to swamp, so that the cook had to let go the line and watch his fellow sailor drop astern. What impressed Crane in the whole of this nightmare was the wordless fortitude of the men involved—"no shrieks, no groans, but silence, silence and silence, and then the *Commodore* sank." [49]

[49] The basic documents of the episode are reprinted in *Stephen Crane: An Omnibus*, ed. Robert Wooster Stallman (New York, 1958), pp. 448–476; these are six dispatches from the *Florida Times-Union* and the New York *Press* as well as "Stephen Crane's Own Story."

Further details are available in Stallman, *Crane: A Biography*, pp. 245–254, 548–550. Stallman seems to have established that the number of men in the dinghy was four, that the seas were indeed rough, and even that there was no treachery involved in the sinking. However, he argues the seaworthiness of the ship and the competence of the officers so urgently as to invite the question of how the accident could have happened at all except by treachery. He also dismisses the cook's mention of five men in the dinghy on the ground that to take that evidence seriously "impugns Crane as a journalist" (p. 249); but he himself refers to the "disingenuousness" of "Stephen Crane's Own Story" and impugns both Crane and Captain Murphy by accepting the cook's report of "heartrending" cries over the testimony of the other two (p. 251). The testimony

The first two of the ship's boats made it to shore at ten A.M. and noon on Saturday, January 2. At four o'clock that afternoon the dinghy came within half a mile of a beach, though cut off by a surf that would have swamped the boat had they tried a landing. The captain fired his pistol to signal the people on shore, and the dinghy waited outside the surf for a rescue craft that never came. So, for a second grueling night, the men rowed for their lives against the imminent danger of being swamped. On Sunday morning off Daytona Beach, with no one to be seen on shore, they decided to use their last strength and try to row through the breakers. When the boat overturned, they had to swim for it, and the exhausted Higgins went under. A man who happened to be walking upon the beach, one John Getchell, or Kitchell, saw the men in the surf and ran to their aid. He pulled Montgomery and Crane to safety, and when the captain waved him to the body of Higgins—already washed onto the sand—he tried to revive him. But it was too late.

Crane, suffering from exhaustion and exposure, was unable to take the train from Daytona to Jacksonville that day and was still very weak when he did go on the next day, January 4. Two more days passed before he filed his story, which appeared in the New York *Press* on January 7. For a story of well over three thousand words, this was quick work. Though the story helped Bacheller, whose syndicate business, he said, was "in constant need of sky-rockets," it did not help enough. Bacheller lacked the funds to replace the seven-hundred-dollar money belt that had gone to the bottom of the sea; he therefore released Crane from his contract. But as one member of the Lantern Club bowed out, others came forward. Willis Hawkins wired Crane money as soon as the newspapers told that he had been saved, and Edward Marshall, now an editor of the *Journal*, found a place for him on the Hearst payroll. Nevertheless, Crane was to do no reporting of the Cuban Revolution that year; after the well-publicized event, his attempts to get illegal passage were too well watched. So he

---

for heart-rending cries comes, as it happens, from the one newspaper report which Stallman discredits on account of its claim for a fifth man, saved from drowning by Crane. But there is perhaps no need to call anyone disingenuous about the supposed cries: apparently Crane and the Captain refer to the men from the foundered lifeboat who stayed on board the *Commodore* as she sank, and the cook refers to the men who tried the rafts and foundered a second time.

had the chance to follow up what he had said in his first dispatch: "The history of life in an open boat for thirty hours would no doubt be instructive to the young, but none is to be told here and now. For my part I would prefer to tell the story at once." He did so, and in the course of the next month produced his masterpiece "The Open Boat." [50]

Crane's newspaper friends were not the only sponsors of the tale. Cora Stewart, in a flurry of telegrams, had let him know her anxiety and then her joy as the news came in. She took the train to Daytona to bring him back, and in the time between trains she seems not to have let him out of her arms. Though Crane returned to his quarters at the St. James, he held court thereafter in Cora's private apartment at the Hotel de Dream. A doctor who was invited up one evening to provide conversation later recalled the scene, and in his thoroughly unromantic report of a vividly romantic episode, he recorded some suggestive details. First, the ordeal at sea had traumatically brought back the Nebraska mood, and the usually well-groomed Crane, deeply identified with the helpless sufferings of men against the sea, had yielded control of appearances:

He was right young; he talked slow; and if he ever said anything pleasant about anybody, it was not while I was around. He was rather slouchy; speaking as a medical man, I think that a clean shirt would not have hurt him. No, sir, it would not have hurt his looks at any rate, not for a full week before I ever even saw him.

The doctor also observed that the morose castaway played other roles. The writer who mixed his account of bitterest reality with allusions to popular literature and children's sentiments was himself both the hero in a trite scene of reunited lovers and—the doctor's eye was sharp—the waif of the sea restored to the big-bosomed maternal blonde:

She and Crane were up there, starting in on some quail on toast, and some watercress salad, and two or it might have been three bottles of champagne; and I just joined in with them. It was on the house, Cora said. She was about the happiest thing I ever saw, that night. I mean, a quiet sort of happiness, not a bit like the way she carried

[50] Bacheller, *Coming up the Road*, p. 292; "Stephen Crane's Own Story," New York *Press*, Jan. 7, 1897, in *Omnibus*, p. 475.

on when Cora was drunk. So Crane and I got to talking; and what with the champagne and all, we kept on talking with Cora filling up the glasses and just patting him every once in a while right like a mother whose boy has come home with a Sunday-school prize, until seven in the morning.[51]

One other Jacksonville scene pertains to the writing of "The Open Boat" and the contributions made by others. The subtitle of the work is "A Tale Intended to be after the Fact: Being the Experience of Four Men from the Sunk Steamer Commodore," and while the wording suggests among other things that reflection has taken place since the experience, its main intent is obviously to say that the author has tried to be accurate, to give an account in accordance with what really happened. Crane believed more strongly than ever that accuracy had to be the basis of truth in a story. Hitherto that term had meant the logic of events or plausibility of character, but in this case he wanted, far more literally than even Howells had ever done, to make his fiction an interpretation of reality and in the strictest sense a criticism of life. The effort to verify his story, which has occupied a number of scholars over the years, began with Crane himself. He went over his manuscript with Captain Murphy, as his friend and fellow journalist Ralph Paine bore witness: " 'Listen, Ed. I want to have this *right*, from your point of view. How does it sound so far?' 'You've got it, Steve' said the other man. 'That is just how it happened, and how it felt.' " [52] In writing this piece, the reporter in Crane won precedence over the castaway or the waif. Appropriately, the author appears in the story unidentified except as he is called "the correspondent."

In one sense, the correspondent is unobtrusive, and "The Open Boat" is justly singled out for the immediacy with which it presents objective fact. The famous opening sentence—"None of them knew the color of the sky"—is the simplest possible rendering of direct experience. The concentration of the men in the boat on their problems of small-boat navigation could serve as a metaphor for any almost total intensity of stress. Joseph Conrad

---

[51] Branch Cabell and A. J. Hanna, *The St. Johns: A Parade of Diversities* (New York, 1943), p. 281.
[52] Ralph D. Paine, *Roads of Adventure* (Boston, 1922), p. 168.

was to recall Crane's visiting him once when both men were beset, each utterly preoccupied with the problems that harassed him. The one way to break the long depressed silence in which they sat, Conrad decided, was to quote that line, and the touchstone of preoccupation was that Crane started as if he found the words familiar but "failed to place them at first." The words which pleased Conrad for their universality—"like a symbolic tale," he said [53]—mattered to Crane because they were the right words for one specific situation. He cared little that the words might function interchangeably for other experience because the drama for him had been in finding words that would function rightly for this. Immediacy and objectivity did not easily come together. Immediacy meant giving honestly what circumstance evoked in the consciousness, like the concentration on navigating a dinghy. But what came to mind at any moment might not have so simple a relation to the facts at hand. More often than not the words, the feelings, and the ideas that memory casually brought to awareness were wrong. Or not wrong, but so weakened by sentiment, by overuse, and by generality that it took a specific objective event, intensely and precisely felt, to provide meaning where the language by itself might not:

To chime the notes of his emotion, a verse mysteriously entered the correspondent's head. He had even forgotten that he had forgotten this verse, but it suddenly was in his mind.

> A soldier of the Legion lay dying in Algiers,
> There was lack of woman's nursing, there was dearth
>   of woman's tears;
> But a comrade stood beside him, and he took that
>   comrade's hand,
> And he said: "I never more shall see my own, my
>   native land."

In his childhood, the correspondent had been made acquainted with the fact that a soldier of the Legion lay dying in Algiers, but he had never regarded it as important. Myriads of his school-fellows had informed him of the soldier's plight, but the dinning had naturally ended by making him perfectly indifferent. He had never considered it his affair that a soldier of the Legion lay dying in

---

[53] Joseph Conrad, "Stephen Crane," in *Last Essays* (Garden City, N.Y., 1926), p. 103.

Algiers, nor had it appeared to him as a matter for sorrow. It was less to him than the breaking of a pencil's point.

Now, however, it quaintly came to him as a human, living thing. It was no longer merely a picture of a few throes in the breast of a poet, meanwhile drinking tea and warming his feet at the grate; it was an actuality—stern, mournful, and fine.

The debris which floats on the stream of consciousness contrasts ironically with the problems of small-boat navigation which give the physical basis of the story. Caroline Norton's sappy and very popular ballad *Bingen on the Rhine*, also a tale of adventure, confirms the value to "The Open Boat" in being founded on fact. Conversely, it argues the near worthlessness of the prevailing culture as an instrument for finding the actual and reacting to it with the right emotions. Pointing up the discrepancy between popular daydream and stern actuality, Crane stands squarely in the line from Mark Twain to Ernest Hemingway. Like them he scorns the poetic throes of the safe, the comfortable, and the sentimentally bemused. In fact, he scorns the childish longing for woman's nursing or woman's tears with an insistence that suggests firsthand acquaintance. At any rate, it is not only in the direct hit at popular culture that childish appeals become mixed with hard facts. The correspondent sees the waves as "most wrongfully and barbarously abrupt"; the captain, when he reassures the men, is "soothing his children"; in a moment of hope, the four of them ride "this wild colt of a dingey like circus men"; they are "the four waifs" and "the babes of the sea, a grotesque rendering of the old babes in the wood." The mock pathos which runs through the story both satirizes and, with qualification, uses the sentimental conventions. What the mind casts up from its cultural store bears all the marks of tears and flapdoodle, but irony and intelligence establish a relation between the subjective coloring and the objective facts. As near clichés, the childish appeals indicate the inadequacy of popular culture for dealing with the world beyond the cheerful, grate-warmed living room; but they indicate an absurdity not only of the cultural, but also of the metaphysical, situation. Critically qualified by the ironic context, the childlike images provide bitter emblems of man's triviality and weakness when, having ventured from the safety of the living room, he makes his way through the chaos of the actuality beyond.

But the quaint figurative language of "The Open Boat" is secondary to the underlying logic of the story. In the first stages of the struggle, as the castaways discover the "subtle brotherhood of men," the half-bantering ironies reflect the élan of that discovery. When they have made their way almost to safety and then been kept off by the surf, the childlike imagery expresses frustration, resentment, and even self-pity. Then as the ordeal goes on and gradually wears down their powers of endurance, the feelings within count for less and less and the mind begins to comprehend the serene indifference of nature. The quality of the imagery changes. Thus, when he had his waifs curl up to rest in the cold comfortable sea water at the bottom of their boat, Crane mocked the comfort of poets or readers who sipped tea and warmed their feet at the grate. But the mockery subsides as "bodily depression" comes to prevail, though something like the same fantasy recurs. Instead of imagining that one might tumble comfortably upon the soft mattress of the sea, the correspondent, when the boat has capsized and he is actually struggling in the water, thinks that "when one gets properly wearied, drowning must really be a comfortable arrangement, a cessation of hostilities accompanied by a large degree of relief." It is not any power within himself that keeps him from yielding to such comfort; circumstance, not will, wins out over circumstance. But in the chance reversal, circumstance prompts the mind to a renewed play of style—and illusion: "Then the correspondent performed his one little marvel of the voyage. A large wave caught him and flung him with ease and supreme speed completely over the boat and far beyond it. It struck him even then as an event in gymnastics, and a true miracle of the sea. An overturned boat in the surf is not a plaything to a swimming man." Though the correspondent may be said ambiguously to have *performed* his little marvel, the wave and not the man has controlled the event. With another wave, another chance, the event might permit no such coloring of fact. In contrast to the correspondent who seems to perform his marvel, Billie the oiler, the one character of the tale who is identified by name, is last

seen as "a still and dripping shape" which is "carried slowly up
the beach." [54] At the end of the story the vanity of life and the
somber reductiveness of death exist together. The equivocal affirmation of the one and the unenhanced dignity of the other are
true at once to "how it happened, and how it felt."

In the complex art of "The Open Boat," Crane managed to
fuse the most external and the most inward of narrative forms,
the tale of adventure and the fiction of consciousness. The adventure itself, no matter how honestly or brilliantly told, might
easily have remained a mere episode. Billie in this story, like Bill
in "A Man and Some Others," attains the dignity of last defeat.
But he attains tragic stature even less than that namesake from
the earlier story: given Crane's view of the way things are, his
story offers no occasion for crucial choice or self-determined act.
In the adventure tale, taken by itself, everything is to be endured
and nothing is to be done. With a tale being told *after* the fact,
however, what is immediately presented is the consciousness
going over the facts of memory and trying to find some order,
some meaning by which to interpret the event. In this respect,
the plot of "The Open Boat" is—for the survivors, for the correspondent who provides the controlling point of view among the
actors in the tale, and for the storyteller who tries to comprehend
the whole—a movement toward understanding. Technically, the
fiction of consciousness simply makes dramatically immediate
the way things felt, and the constantly shifting point of view in
the story is a device for rendering how it felt in all its multiplicity. Formally, beneath the brilliantly changing surface of experience, there are cumulative changes whereby men, though they

[54] As the revision of "The Five White Mice" indicates (p. xlv above), Crane
did not leave people or places nameless except to serve his literary purpose. So,
too, in writing out his dedication of the English edition of *The Open Boat and
Other Stories*, he did not hesitate to identify his fellow survivors of the ordeal at
sea along with the oiler, who is individualized by both his character and his
fate. The manuscript dedication, on the same sheet as the manuscript list of
stories for the Heinemann edition, reads:

To
The late William Higgins
and to
Captain Edward Murphy and Steward C. B. Montgomery
of the sunk steamer Commodore.

(MS in Columbia University Libraries. The McClure edition in New York kept
this wording, but the Heinemann edition changed the first line to "To the
Memory of.")

cannot control what happens, can at least come to a rational perception of their fate. At the beginning these men who bear no names and have no history are utterly the creatures of their given situation. Engrossed in the now, they scarcely note the existence of a world beyond the gunwales of their ten-foot dinghy—not even the color of the sky. But their experience of man's relation to man, to nature, and to imminent death expands their vision. In contrast to the famous negation of the story's opening line, the last section begins: "When the correspondent again opened his eyes, the sea and the sky were each of the gray hue of the dawning. Later, carmine and gold was painted upon the waters. The morning appeared finally, in its splendor, with a sky of pure blue, and the sunlight flamed on the tips of the waves."

Crane had come a long way since the day when Howells told him that an artist does not see a dog's tail resting on a hilltop but puts things in proportion. Had he started with Howells' certainties, he too might have made corrections automatically when appearances and received truths did not jibe. Instead, he had gone his own way with the conviction that "a man is born into the world with his own pair of eyes, and he is not at all responsible for his vision—he is merely responsible for his quality of personal honesty." [55] He conceived a world in which people lived by what they saw, not what they were supposed to see, and that discrepancy, which prompted the most interesting experiments in fiction of his time, was his starting point also. He took seriously both terms of the not quite congruous relation. His emphasis on consciousness never led him to suggest that reality was constituted by the eye of the beholder or the language of the artist. He did not relinquish the common-sense idea of objective reality, as the last section of "The Open Boat" may illustrate. In the large view of the morning sky, for example, the sunrise does not stand for more than itself. If the correspondent made it into a symbol of personal promise, he would be distorting his vision through naïve self-centeredness. He has, rather, learned to look with detachment "as one who in a gallery looks at a scene from Brittany or Holland." Freedom from self and sentimentality affects not only vision but language. Compare the similar refrains

[55] Crane to John Northern Hilliard, [n.p., n.d., possibly January, 1896], *Letters*, p. 110.

which occur at the center of the narrative and at the end. The first, which articulates the reflections of the men, runs for a dozen sentences beginning: " 'If I am going to be drowned—if I am going to be drowned—if I am going to be drowned, why, in the name of the seven mad gods who rule the sea, was I allowed to come thus far and contemplate sand and trees? Was I brought here merely to have my nose dragged away as I was about to nibble the sacred cheese of life? It is preposterous.' " The stylized fancy, so much like the youthful imprecation in "The Five White Mice," is given a realistic variation in the final scene. In the latter version it is simpler and it is individualized. The correspondent is caught in a current he cannot swim against: "He thought: 'I am going to drown? Can it be possible? Can it be possible? Can it be possible?' Perhaps an individual must consider his own death to be the final phenomenon of nature."

The expansion of consciousness leads at last to the encounter with that absolute finality, the extinction of consciousness. The progress from self-engrossment to clear vision, from fanciful outrage to puzzled acceptance, is a growth of moral intelligence which does not simply come from within. The encounter with reality has made a crucial difference. From it the men *learn*— and not just about themselves. A younger Crane might have emphasized their exultation in survival, or acknowledgment of chance, or conquest of fear. The youthful author of *The Red Badge* focused on personal feeling and concluded concerning his hero that "he had been to touch the great death, and found that, after all, it was but the great death." [56] In "The Open Boat" the last one sees of an individualized character is the still, dripping shape being carried up the beach. Then, in the objective scene, there are only the phenomena of nature: "When it came night, the white waves paced to and fro in the moonlight, and the wind brought the sound of the great sea's voice to the men on shore, and they felt that they could then be interpreters." Self-knowledge and self-mastery come only with the capacity to interpret the world outside oneself. For Crane, therefore, it was natural that he should found his narrative on literal reality. His function as a writer was not to invent incidents but to elucidate what

[56] In a still more youthful earlier version, Henry Fleming had found that it was but the great death "and was for others."

happened. To find out how comradeship and courage, finalities and continuities, were realized was to create value in an otherwise meaningless universe. Honesty of vision required that he do justice to the contradictions with which experience disrupted common sense, and imagination enabled him to discern in the experience a logic of its own. To his worst encounter with the anarchy of the universe—"Shipwrecks are *apropos* of nothing" —he responded with his greatest effort at making an imaginative order.

Not all of anyone's life is convertible to lucidity and order, as the later history of "The Open Boat" makes clear. Crane finished the story sometime in February and then may have sent it to Bacheller. Bacheller was later, on two different occasions, to recall getting the tale and even to approximate the price it brought, but his recollections in the 1920's are not authoritative: as early as 1900 he had left his syndicate business far behind, account books and detailed recall alike. But the possibility is worth noting for two reasons. First, on March 11, 1897, Crane wrote his brother William that he had left Jacksonville for the Indian River swamp country over a month before, and even allowing for exaggeration, the lapse between Crane's departure and Reynolds' receipt of the manuscript can be most simply accounted for by such a transaction. Also, the informal co-operation of syndicate proprietor and literary agent would set a rough general precedent for the arrangement with S. S. McClure which Crane was presently to make. On February 24, at any rate, Reynolds sounded out E. L. Burlingame of *Scribner's Magazine* about the story. The next day Burlingame replied expressing interest, and by March 5 he was ready to offer $300 for it. Reynolds tried further negotiation without avail, and when on March 9 Burlingame stood fast on his original terms, the agent accepted. Topicality helped to speed publication—*Scribner's* brought out the story in June—but Crane's own rapidity of movement probably kept him from seeing proofs. For on March 11, before the news of the agreement lost its glow, Crane recorded his decision to leave Florida. As he told his brother, the United States Navy was not giving him a second chance to elude antifilibuster patrols; so he would head for Crete and cover the revolution there instead.

Evidently Hearst had arranged his passage, for he already knew that he would sail from New York for England on March 20.[57]

During the week which he had in New York, he concluded some agreements of his own. He called on S. S. McClure, who had given him his first magazine assignment three years before and had shown a constant interest in his work, and he came away with some six or seven hundred dollars. In return for the cash he bound himself to give McClure his next book, a set of stories to be centered on "The Open Boat." He also agreed to regard the money as a loan rather than an advance on royalties. To pay the loan, he undertook to give *McClure's Magazine* first option on serial publication of his next stories. If McClure published them, he understood that the price would be taken off his debt. What he did not anticipate was that if McClure did not publish them, he might hold them for collateral. Finally, he was to start working off his debt at once.[58] On March 16 he wrote to his brother—on McClure's letterhead—that he would have to cut his visit home to Port Jervis to a couple of hours "as I am in the middle of a story which I am bound to finish before I leave." In fact, he never got home at all, but he did presumably deliver to McClure his second Florida story, "Flanagan and His Short Filibustering Adventure." The failure of the one intention and the presumed accomplishment of the other presaged the future. During his one last stay in New York hereafter, he would once again miss seeing William. On the other hand, the rush to

---

[57] Crane to W. H. Crane, Jacksonville, March 11, 1897, *Stephen Crane Newsletter*, 1 (Winter, 1966), 8. This letter establishes Crane's movements in Florida, his decision to leave there and go to Greece, and his intended date of departure from New York.

Bacheller to William Hamilton Osborne, [n.p.], Nov. 2, 1921, *Letters*, p. 323; Bacheller, *Coming up the Road*, p. 293. Although Bacheller in these instances testifies that he received and sold "The Open Boat," a letter of Bacheller's to Cora Crane (Canton, N.Y., July 13, 1900, *Letters*, pp. 298–299) indicates his vagueness of memory and lack of access to supporting documents.

Allen, *Reynolds*, pp. 50–51.

[58] Crane to Reynolds, [Oxted, October, 1897], *Letters*, pp. 144–145, explains the debt to McClure—"about $500"—and the McClure holding of stories as collateral. Crane there states: "As for my existing contracts there are only two. I. To write an article on an engine ride from London to Glasgow for the McClures. II. To give them my next book." The plural reference included S. S. McClure's younger brother, Robert, who headed the firm's London office. Crane to Reynolds, [Oxted], Jan. 14, [1898], *Letters*, p. 168, indicates that when Crane thought his debt paid off, McClure still delayed in releasing "The Monster" for publication elsewhere.

complete the story was evidently imposed by McClure's financial caution rather than an urgent need for copy, for the story did not come out in *McClure's Magazine* until October.[59] In Crane's own mind, getting money from McClure before setting off to the wars may have been like providing himself with a money belt when he left for his Florida adventures. But it was now a different game. His friend Bacheller, with full knowledge of the odds, had risked the money of a dying business, and when he had to cut his losses, he did so good-naturedly and could turn to something else. With the new arrangement, McClure was taking virtually no risk whatever while Crane unthinkingly staked his future ability to produce.

Though Crane was on the eve of one of his most productive periods, "Flanagan" showed what could happen when he worked hurriedly under pressure. The story tells of a ship's master who signs on for a filibustering voyage "just for fun, mostly." He must evade American patrols to load his ship off Florida, and he must evade Spanish patrols to get it unloaded off Cuba. He can quell mutinous stokers by brute force and can escape a Spanish gunboat by daringly and skillfully doubling back to cross under her bows. But a moment's slip by his helmsman allows the *Foundling* to carom off her pursuer, and the seams which are weakened by the smash are opened later by a squall. The captain's anguish at losing his ship—he sobs and he swears—is set against the indifference at the resort hotel on the Florida shore, where dancers put on their wraps to go watch the lifeboats come in and decline to entertain the idea that men may drown. Despite the acid ironies and the colorful Crane style, the story is a tale of adventure and nothing more. The technical devices enhance the narrative at every point but add little to the significance of the whole. The incidents define a world no bigger than

[59] Crane to W. H. Crane, New York, March 16, 1897, *Stephen Crane Newsletter*, II (Fall, 1967), 9. Edmund Crane's daughter twice stated to his biographer and offered evidence that Crane did not return to Port Jervis or Hartwood after the Florida episode (Edith Crane to Thomas Beer, Poughkeepsie, N.Y., Dec. 30, 1933, Jan. 14, 1934, ALS in University of Virginia Library).

"Flanagan and His Short Filibustering Adventure" also appeared in the *Illustrated London News* of Aug. 28, 1897. There is no documentary evidence as to whether McClure's London office or Crane himself, back in England after the Greek-Turkish War, arranged the English publication and provided copy. But lack of co-ordination with *McClure's* October publication suggests that the latter was the case.

the scene in which they take place. The story, as a response to the *Commodore* incident, was as good as might have been predicted—but it might have been predicted. Still, the falling off at this time meant only that a writer cannot always be at his best.

Crane sailed as planned on March 20, 1897, spent a few days in London, and set off for Greece by the first of April. As he put it, "I am going to Greece for the *Journal*, and if the Red Badge is not all right I shall sell out my claim on literature and take up orange growing." The closer he got to the scene, the more anxious he became over his lack of languages. "Willie Hearst has made a bad bargain," he worried. But Hearst had in fact done well, and though one of Crane's functions was to be a celebrity for other Hearst writers to cover, he held his own as a war correspondent. By the time he got to the battle zone he was slowed down by dysentery, and he had little knack for being at the right spot at the right time; but he saw enough of slaughter and starvation to write about them with authority. He did not miss the lesson in perspective: "From a distance it was like a game. No blood, no expressions of horror were to be seen; there were simply the movements of tiny doll tragedy." But his great skill lay in conveying the truth that the actors of the drama were people. When his ship the *St. Marina* carried eight hundred of the wounded to Athens, his eye caught the sleeping soldier "with his head pillowed on the bosom of a dead comrade" and his ear caught the shouting crowd on the Piraeus docks, "Hurrah! Hurrah for war!" Back in England after the war he was prepared to say, *"The Red Badge* is all right." [60]

The little joke about orange growing as his alternative to literature became less obscure when he returned to England with the lady from Florida. From the time of Crane's shipwreck he and Cora Stewart had become more and more deeply caught in each other's lives. The month in the Indian River country, despite a certain amount of hide-and-seek with the United States Navy and its hired detectives, had been a honeymoon of sorts. Crane's emotional commitment, though slightly tentative, was

[60] Berryman, *Crane*, pp. 174, 184; Beer, *Crane*, p. 154; "Stephen Crane at Velestino," New York *Journal*, May 11, 1897, in *Uncoll. Writ.*, p. 259; "Stephen Crane Tells of War's Horrors," New York *Journal*, May 23, 1897, in *Uncoll. Writ.*, p. 266.

genuine. In New York on his way to the Greek war, he told his old friend C. K. Linson—without names—that there was a woman in Jacksonville whom he wanted to marry. "She could sail on the same steamer and be married in England," Linson recalled. "But there were tongues. 'The weasels would draw blood anyhow.' He hated to leave her alone, but his job was to go on to Greece and come back when the stew was over. 'What would you do, CK?' " [61] Linson agreed that he must go on, and Crane sailed alone. Cora for her part was a woman of decision not given to waiting. She followed Crane in a few days, caught up with him in London, and traveled much of the way with him to Greece. There she became the world's first woman war correspondent and Crane's gay comrade in arms. On their return to England, they established themselves, after a brief search, at Oxted about twenty miles south of London and settled down as man and wife. With his new domestic responsibility, Crane now made his inventory of literary resources and, writing from his publisher Heinemann's London address, sent to Hartwood for "The Five White Mice" and "The Wise Men." He also got down to work on new stories, of which the first was to be "The Monster." Setting this tale in Port Jervis (the Whilomville to which he came back in a later series of stories), he put some of his special feelings toward his home town in minor characters like the weasel gossips and in a protagonist who is cut off from his fellow townsmen by his gallant but unpopular loyalties. But the topical suggestions of the tale are far less important than the controlling vision. Crane presented with considerable sympathy that common life which he knew that Howells recommended as a subject, and at the same time he showed the world beyond the safe bounds of comfort and routine where chance and violence are as natural as life itself. He proved, in the writing, that he did not need a battlefield or an open boat for subject in order to imagine a state of warfare or a game against fearful odds. Able to use literal fact or literary convention with the freedom of a master, he now turned again to the Wild West.

September 9, 1897, when he announced completion of "The Monster," sets the date when Crane was first free to start "The

[61] Linson, *Crane*, p. 101.

Bride Comes to Yellow Sky." His writing home to ask again for his unpublished Western tales indicated the way his mind was turning. His not mentioning his domestic state was equally suggestive. Though he had just tried out the expression "my wife" in a letter to a young friend—"after practicing nine days I can write that without a jump"—he stuck to the first person singular in his letter home.[62] His qualms, which were to deepen into compulsive evasion over the next fifteen months, were still only qualms, and they may well have provided the germ of the tale. The initial situation of "The Bride" arises from the failure of Jack Potter, the town marshal, to consult or even to inform Yellow Sky about his marrying a young woman from San Antonio. The anxiety which besets the marshal on the long railroad trip home and makes him want to slip into town unnoticed is of the common masculine lot. It is certainly not founded on guilt. His "heinous crime" is not to have made his intention known to his friends or to the small-town constituency of gossip. If "cowardice" has kept him from telegraphing home after the event, what he fears is the brass band with which the citizens are likely to escort the couple to their marriage bed. This is a bridegroom story from the hand of a writer who had recently yielded the freedom of his bachelorhood. Except for a sense of the anonymity that comes with distance—"At San Antonio he was like a man hidden in the dark"—Crane touched on nothing special to his own domestic arrangement.[63]

The bride of the story, although she is like Cora in being neither pretty nor very young, is very different in everything else. Her most obvious quality is her commonplace background: "she had cooked," and patently she would be at home in a kitchen all her life. She is awkward and, in her simple way, demure. Her going unnamed is partly due to Crane's habit of

[62] See pp liv–lv above. Crane to Edmund B. Crane, Schull, County Cork, Ireland, Sept. 9, [1897], *Stephen Crane Newsletter*, 1 (Spring, 1967), 8; Crane to Henry Sanford Bennett, Paris, Sept. 2, 1897, Beer, *Crane*, p. 158. Berryman, aware that Crane was in Ireland at the time, first called attention to the fact that the letter to Bennett, if genuine, represented an effort to concoct a "marriage" for a friend to whom the matter would be important (*Crane*, pp. 189–190).

[63] He did make an unconscious slip, however—a slip of his artistic wariness rather than his psychic defenses. Speaking of the marshal's unannounced marriage, he wrote that "spurred by his sharp impulse, he had gone headlong over all the social hedges." His recent settling among the hedgerows of Surrey betrayed him into momentarily forgetting the Texas landscape.

reducing his characters to something like archetypal simplicity, but it is also a function of the marshal's untutored formality. He calls her "girl" on the trip home and softens to "dear" as they approach his house, but he is not yet at ease with a first name. In her naïveté she does venture to call her husband "Jack" even though she rarely says much else. She is just the person to whom the slightly more experienced marshal can show the splendors of the parlor car and the "big lay-out" of a dollar meal in the diner. Both wife and husband are simple, but they are individual characters. The careful specific notation keeps the bride-and-groom situation from imposing stock roles upon them.

Such realism breaks through the conventionality of stock Western melodrama also, for the would-be villain of the piece is comically baffled when he encounters people instead of fixed roles. The town outlaw, Scratchy Wilson, is a leftover from the days of Wild West gangs. Though his costume out of the sweatshops of New York proves his connection with the everyday reality of his countrymen, he does not know that he has been absorbed by progress. Drunk and on a shooting rampage, he challenges the silent town and, for want of takers, finally seeks out his traditional adversary, the marshal. At the marshal's house he meets the returning bridegroom, who is unarmed, though Scratchy cannot at first believe it. " 'If you ain't got a gun, why ain't you got a gun?' he sneered. 'Been to Sunday-school?' " Facing the drunken gunman, Jack Potter coolly explains. Except for one fleeting recollection of the just-finished wedding journey, his inner consciousness does not come to the surface. Physical courage is the automatic reflex of the experienced man: as he stands up to the brandished revolver, we learn, his heels do not move backward in the sand by so much as an inch. The easy switch he makes into his official role signifies a readiness for the unexpected, no matter how violent, no matter what the odds. But the convention-bound outlaw, since marriage is outside the range of the ordinary melodrama, is undone by the marshal's news: " 'Married?' said Scratchy. Seemingly for the first time he saw the drooping drowning woman at the other man's side. 'No!' he said. He was like a creature allowed a glimpse of another world." The glimpse of another world, in Crane's fiction, is usually an initiation into chaos. When a figure of random violence catches a glimpse of social order, the shock is equally great, but the plot has been turned toward comic affirmation. Crane's humor, however qualified by irony, issued for once in a comic masterpiece.

It was still true, however, that Crane could not order his literary affairs half so well as he could his world of imagination. He was sure that "The Bride" was a "daisy," but he was to have no say in the price it might bring since it went to McClure as part payment on the loan-advance of the previous March. He seems to have sent the manuscript by way of Robert McClure, the publisher's younger brother who had charge of the McClure Syndicate's London office; at any rate, he continued to check Robert concerning "The Monster," which S. S. McClure was still holding as collateral in New York. Robert McClure may also have placed "The Bride" with *Chapman's Magazine*: the story came out in February, 1898, in both *McClure's* and *Chapman's*, and the only previous time Crane had had a story published simultaneously in American and English magazines was when *McClure's* and *Chapman's* brought out "The Little Regiment" in June, 1896. But the business proceeded slowly,.and in October, 1897, when he could not get "The Monster" released to Reynolds for sale even though it was too long for McClure, and when he had received no word about "The Bride," he took a positive step toward putting his affairs in safe and efficient hands. He converted his casual relation with Paul Reynolds into an exclusive agency. Reynolds was to get all Crane's work that was not yet contracted for, plus a number of Crane's problems that he may not have fully expected, mainly, the extrication of the McClure collateral and the clearing up of an allegedly overdrawn account with Hearst. The businesslike tone with which Crane entered on his agreement with Reynolds was somewhat deceptive; characteristically he forgot to date the letter. And the last topic he brought up was a reckless proposal to found a one-man syndicate at a special rate of commission and to do a series of sketches modeled on some newsletters he had helped Cora to write. The proposal foreshadows some of the farmed-out journalism that Crane was eventually to do in *Great Battles of the World*, but it has more immediate significance. It is the first mention of Crane's learning to dictate, and it reveals his practice of sending handwritten manuscript for the agent to have typed. Dictation was a step toward rationalizing and speeding literary production at one end of the process, but the reference to typewriting expenses showed that he was not yet interested in cutting costs by means of home industry at the final stage of manuscript preparation. The illusion of getting rich quick and the chummy tone that does not ring true were signs of the economic hysteria that was close to the surface even when Crane was being most businesslike:

> You might go to Curtis Brown, Sunday Editor of the Press and say how-how from me. Then tell him this *in the strictest confidence,* that a lady named Imogene Carter [Cora Crane's pseudonym] whose work he has been using from time to time is also named Stephen Crane and that I did 'em in about twenty minutes on each Sunday, just dictating to a friend. Of course they are rotten bad. But by your explanation he will understand something of the manner of the articles I mean to write only of course they will be done better. Ask him if he wants them, signed and much better in style, and how much he will give. Then if he says all right you might turn up a little syndicate for every Sunday. You can figure out that I should get about £10 per week out of it. Then—you do the business—I do the writing—I take 65 per cent and you take 35. The typewriting expenses in New York we share alike.[64]

If Crane had helped Cora with a certain amount of dictating, she now began to help him by taking dictation. "Death and the Child," which he started to write about the time of this letter to Reynolds and worked on during November and December of 1897, was in this respect a new departure. A single page of a draft in Cora's hand survives: it was apparently discarded after serving as the basis of a rewritten version, but luckily Cora kept it for scratch paper, crossed out the story, and turned to the other side of the sheet for some writing of her own. Even a single page, it turns out, throws light on Crane's creative process. Whether from the novelty of dictating or from increased con-

[64] Crane to Reynolds, [Oxted, October, 1897], *Letters,* pp. 144–146. Crane's letter to W. H. Crane, London, Oct. 29, [1897], pp. 146–148, helps set an approximate date for the Reynolds agreement since it mentions the troubles with McClure and completion of "The Bride." The letter home talks somewhat feverishly of such projects as going to the Klondike for Bacheller and leaving to cover Kitchener's campaign in Sudan, a kind of extension of his projected newspaper schemes in the letter to Reynolds. It also talks a little more frankly about money problems—$2,000 worth of writing turned out in the last four months, and only $120 of cash income—and even hints vaguely that he may be approaching financial collapse.

sciousness of his literary intention, he was composing at a far remove from his final language. As he suggested to Reynolds in commenting on Cora's newspaper pieces, he thought of himself as able to deal with incidents and ideas without turning on his style. In contrast to Linson's report of his first oral telling of "The Pace of Youth," a testimony to his spontaneous gift of phrase and natural filtering of imagination, he now seemed to develop the literal plot almost to its final form but to experiment tentatively with image, gesture, and tone as if he were waiting for his interpretative vision to become sharper. What Linson heard was a finished story which may also have developed from something closer to a scenario stage. The sense of germination in this case is strong, for Crane was not telling a story, he was composing it. Usually his revisions were matters of polishing or cutting, but in this case he *added* to his first version. The extensive changes between draft and final form supply unique evidence that Crane's conscious art, like his intuitive imagination, led him to put his inward dramas into an increasingly complex outer world.

The draft passage occurs early in the story. Crane, who had gone to Greece not altogether jokingly to check on *The Red Badge*, made his central character a foreign correspondent covering the Greek war and exposed him to *Red Badge* situations. The protagonist Peza comes from Italy but is of Greek emigré extraction, and when he sees war, he finds that ties of blood are stronger than he thought. Carried away by sympathy and patriotism, he decides to join the actual fighting. The declamatory volunteer and the seasoned young officer he turns to in his stress stand in contrast to each other, but Crane in 1897 saw new aspects of these conventional figures. The main novelty in the draft version is the emphasis on the broad planetary context of the action; the main additions in the finished version are psychological nuances both of action and of image:

Draft version	Final text
From the direction ᵃ which they faced came the dulled boom of artillery ᵇ fire. It sounded in regular measures like the ticking of some colossal clock, a clock that was counting the seconds in the	From a land toward which their faces were bent came a continuous boom of artillery fire. It was sounding in regular measures like the beating of a colossal clock—a clock that was counting

lives of the stars it reverbrated solomnly, potentiously over the land as if God faced the dial as was counting the moments before the extinction of a planet.* These two men slowly threading their way along the bank of the river of peasants found themselves silent in the hearing of this bombardment.

Then suddenly the beats became mingled until a * man could hardly seperate one from another and with them was * the slow rattle of musketry. Suddenly the noise was irritated, silly, infantile. It was to childish this uproar. It forces mens nerves to object, to protest against this noise which was as idle as the noise of a panio thumped by a child. The soldier lifted his arm and pointed. He spook impatiently as if his irritation ' followed immediately upon the correspondents words. "There", he said, "If you are looking for war you have a beautiful opportunity."

The young correspondent snapped his jaws in a way that was near to the nashing of teeth.

the seconds in the lives of the stars, and men had time to die between the ticks. Solemn, oracular, inexorable, the great seconds tolled over the hills as if God fronted this dial rimmed by the horizon. The soldier and the correspondent found themselves silent. The latter in particular was sunk in a great mournfulness, as if he had resolved willy-nilly to swing to the bottom of the abyss where dwelt secrets of this kind, and had learned beforehand that all to be met there was cruelty and hopelessness. A strap of his bright new leather leggings came unfastened, and he bowed over it slowly, impressively, as one bending over the grave of a child.

Then suddenly, the reverberations mingled until one could not separate an explosion from another, and into the hubbub came the drawling sound of a leisurely musketry fire. Instantly, for some reason of cadence, the noise was irritating, silly, infantile. This uproar was childish. It forced the nerves to object, to protest against this racket, which was as idle as the din of a lad with a drum.

The lieutenant lifted his finger and pointed. He spoke in vexed tones, as if he held the other man personally responsible for the noise. "Well, there!" he said. "If you wish for war you now have an opportunity magnificent."

The correspondent raised himself upon his toes. He tapped his chest with gloomy pride. "Yes!

"Yes.^g There is war there is the war that I wish to enter. I fling myself in. I was not intending to be so throughly a Greek. I find that I am a Greek. I wish to fight my countrys enemies. You know the way. Lead ^h me."

There is war! There is the war I wish to enter. I fling myself in. I am a Greek, a Greek, you understand. I wish to fight for my country. You know the way. Lead me, I offer myself." Struck with a sudden thought, he brought a case from his pocket, and extracting a card handed it to the officer with a bow. "My name is Peza," he said simply.

The soldier smiled inscrutibly. There was pity in it, there was pride in it—the vanity of experience— There was a slight contempt in it. "Very well" he cried, "If my company is in the thick of the fight I shall be glad for the honor of your companionship. If my company is not in the thick of the fight I will if you like send you on to where ⁶⁵

A strange smile passed over the soldier's face. There was pity and pride—the vanity of experience—and contempt in it. "Very well," he said, returning the bow. "If my company is in the middle of the fight, I shall be glad for the honor of your companionship. If my company is not in the middle of the fight, I will make other arrangements for you."

Perhaps the first thing to catch the eye when the two versions are juxtaposed is what Crane added to the stage action. That Peza should carefully bend over to refasten his bright new leggings or that he should suddenly, in the midst of passionate declamation, think to present his card in formal introduction is superfluous to the literal plot. The gestures are like life, not like

---

[65] MS in Columbia University Libraries. Miss Lillian Gilkes discovered this manuscript on the verso of the second page of Cora Crane's review of the play *Peter the Great* by Lawrence Irving. (A fragment of a draft of "The Blue Hotel" in Cora's hand was used by her for the first page of her review; see note 83 below.) Joseph Katz systematically describes the manuscript in *Stephen Crane Newsletter*, III (Spring, 1969), 1. It is on ruled laid foolscap watermarked "CARISBROOK SUPERFINE," and it is paged 3. The manuscript changes, as noted by Fredson Bowers, are as follows:

a   direction] *preceded by deleted 'dir' and followed by deleted 'in'*
b   artillery] *preceded by deleted 'cannon' and altered from 'artilery'*
c   planet.] *final 't' added after deletion of one or perhaps two illegible letters*
d   a man] *preceded by 'one coul' and the start of a 'd'*
e   was] *preceded by deleted 'came'*
f   irritation] *altered from 'irriation'*
g   Yes.] *a double quote deleted above the period*
h   Lead] *altered from 'lead'*

some rational perspective that common sense might recommend. Nor are they mere stage business. In the first version the vision of artillery fire as mere ticking of a cosmic clock stands by itself as the author's figurative description. In the second version the image is related more closely to the action. If the firing is like the ticking of a colossal clock, still "men had time to die between the ticks." When the human perspective is thus restored, the correspondent gets a glimpse of the world as abyss, feels the lure of it, and is savingly distracted by his own stream of consciousness and a random sensation. Concentrating on the leather strap shuts out the boom of firing just as surely as concentrating on war may shut out the vision of the stars. The need to adjust the legging, though irrational, has a logic of its own. Such revisions and refinements occur also with the crossing rhythms of artillery and musket fire, which are only mixed-up noises in the first version. In the second version they become irritating specifically "for some reason of cadence" in someone's ear, and the lieutenant's vexation, in being displaced toward the correspondent, is another trick of consciousness that is patently absurd. As he reworked his story, Crane bound action and imagery more closely by developing both in relation to the way things appear, the way they may be sensed. Presenting objects and events through the rich medium of his dynamic psychology, he made a stronger unity as he expanded on his early conception. Moreover, the principle on which he made his additions to the text affected his cutting also. In the opening of his tale he had described the peasants streaming down a mountain trail and, picking up the cliché image, turned it into a new and thematically essential figure: the refugees poured down the mountain "as if fear was a river," a "torrent," a "freshet." The image lends itself to elaboration, but the metaphorical landscape is diminished by comparison with the actual: "The sea, the sky, and the hills combined in their grandeur to term this misery inconsequent." The three careful opening paragraphs of the final version must derive from a substantial passage in the original draft, for the draft fragment refers back to it with the men "threading their way along the bank of the river of peasants." But the reference, while it makes a rhetorical connection with the opening passage, has no connection with its immediate context; it is extraneous to the sensibilities of the two characters, and so, in the process of imaginative reworking, it is dropped. Dissatisfied with a merely verbal pattern of images, Crane concentrated on the single intense vision of the world as it might be known to the people in it. Though the controlling image is given in the opening exposition, it exists at that point outside the experience of the characters. Only when someone in the story has apprehended it directly and become qualified, as the author of "The Open Boat" termed it, to be an interpreter, would the meaning of the landscape be realized.

It was harder for Crane to dramatize the initiation of Peza into the nature of the universe than Henry Fleming's passage from innocence to experience in *The Red Badge*. For one thing, his conception of character was no longer summed up in the categories of innocence and experience. The lieutenant, for example, is not simply a stoical veteran. He is that, but he is assigned more qualities than the role requires—"stern, quiet, and confident, respecting fate, fearing only opinion." Even in the draft passage, the pity and pride that he feels as he talks with the excitable correspondent are undercut as "the vanity of experience," a term that the author of *The Red Badge* could not have conceived. And the uninitiated protagonist is older than Henry Fleming in more than years. Though he has hardly more control of the flux of sensation and will, he is conscious to a degree of what is happening in his mind. Appropriately, it is nationalism rather than personal glory which motivates him at first; he recognizes the emotion even though he is surprised at its force. And his compulsion to enter the war is different from Henry Fleming's bloodthirst, the red sickness of battle. Perhaps the most important change between the draft and the final text shifted the emphasis from "I was not intending to be so throughly a Greek" to the resolve, formed in a time of sunken spirits, to "swing to the bottom of the abyss"—from nationalism as the primary motive, to war as the way to the heart of things. The resolve comes willy-nilly, but it serves to connect Peza by conscious intent with the destiny he does not himself enact. Between the resolution and its accomplishment occur complications which also go beyond *The Red Badge*, for Crane was learning to use literary models as well as popular conventions and

personal experience. Peza's name suggests that the character
owes something to Tolstoy's Pierre Bezuhov, who also to his
surprise was caught up by pity and national feeling and a desire
to get to the meaning of war. Like his near namesake, Peza
witnesses the patternless cross-purposes of battle. And Crane
followed Tolstoy in setting the clash of soldiers into its larger
social context and the war itself into an overarching natural
scene that made human catastrophe seem inconsequent. Drama-
tizing his correspondent's education in humility, he seemed to
consult Whitman as well as Tolstoy and yet to modify both in his
vision of a modern multiverse:

Absorbed in listening to the hurricane racket from the front, he still
remembered that these trees were growing, the grass-blades were extending according to their process. He inhaled a deep breath of
moisture and fragrance from the grove, a wet odor which expressed
all the opulent fecundity of unmoved nature, marching on with her
million plans for multiple life, multiple death.

The passing of egotism, which takes place for Peza in the moment when he first obeys a military order, makes possible this
larger vision of war and nature; but the vision still must be made
actual and particular, and this can only occur with his experience of death and the child. The swing to the bottom of the abyss
begins as he takes up arms at last—specifically, as he accepts a
rifle taken from one corpse and a cartridge belt stripped from
another. The look he sees in the eyes of the dying and dead and
the feel of the bandoleer like the embrace of death have a
mounting effect, and Peza finally bolts. In his panic and diso-
rientation, he loses "all the spick of his former appearance" and
is reduced to "general dishevelment." Then, when he has
touched bottom, he enounters the abandoned peasant child; or
rather, the child encounters the panting, sprawled form of the
runaway and asks, "Are you a man?" The question, repeated,
gets through to Peza's consciousness as if it speaks for the same
force as expresses itself in mountains, sky, and sea, and he
understands at last that "the definition of his misery could be
written on a wee grass-blade."
    Crane worked out the main plot of "Death and the Child"
somewhat schematically, it must be admitted. When he had Peza

modestly wonder "if the universe took cognizance of him to an important degree," he made his parable almost as obvious as that of his poem "A man said to the universe." [66] What makes the story work is not only the ambitious literary ambience in which he developed his plot, but even more the specificity with which he could evoke the benign landscape and the horrors of war that so affect his hero. He had seen Greece in its one green season, and the closeness of mountain and plain, sky and sea, was much in his eye. But the artistic usability of eyewitness experience was not automatic. The first time he reported the sound of musketry, he could not conceal the callowness of "It was the most beautiful sound of my experience, barring no symphony," even when he undercut his rhapsody with "This was from one point of view. The other might be taken from the men who died there." Still less promising was the dispatch that seems to be the origin of the symbolic child of the story. At the battle of Velestino, Crane picked up a little puppy which he was to keep and take to England. He named it whimsically after the battle which it so amusingly ignored, just as it ignored "with the insolence of babyhood" the soldiers who stopped under fire to offer it some hardtack. Details of the story, and a clue to its one great weakness, are present in his dispatch "The Dogs of War": "He was simply a Greek pup deserted by his relatives and friends in a most trying hour, who had accepted the assistance of a correspondent of the New York Journal. His home had probably been in one of the stone huts that stood here and there along the road, now all lonely. His owners had probably scuttled out at word of the coming of the Turks. But he didn't care about this, either. He simply lolled on the correspondent's arm and blinked fatly at the passing landscape." Crane's best dispatch of the war, called "A Battle in Greece," showed him gaining control over his materials. In this piece he caught both the landscape and the crossing rhythms of artillery and musketry, and a soldier with his jaw half shot away and blood dripping through his bandages—so like the wounded soldier whose "mystic gaze" Peza runs from—"explained the

[66]   A man said to the universe:
         "Sir, I exist!"
         "However," replied the universe,
         "The fact has not created in me
         A sense of obligation."

meaning of all that racket. Gazing at this soldier, with his awful face, one felt new respect for the din." The defining presence of the wounded soldier, whose "great and reaching dignity" gives meaning to the roar of gunfire, has virtually the same function in the later story. So, appropriately, Crane also noted in this dispatch the encounter of the brisk captain of artillery and the "tall, pale young man in civilian garb," irritating and bombastic, for whom an officer concerned with his business could spare little time. Peza, it would seem, was not simply a personal projection or a literary pastiche, but a character founded on someone actually seen, an immiscible figure for whom Crane was to find a place in the general incoherence of the drama.[67] The objective facts of war were evolving in Crane's journalism into the materials of fiction. When he began to use these materials four months later, experience counted for less in the making of his story than he could theoretically have explained and yet it did make a serious difference. For the facts which the journalist had gathered gave particularity and relevance to the artist's abstract scheme.

Though Crane's being both journalist and artist worked out well enough for the imagination, it became clear while he was writing "Death and the Child" that he could not carry the two roles so easily in his day-to-day living. Specifically, his friend-ships with Harold Frederic and Joseph Conrad exemplified the contrary effects of journalist and artist on his work. He and Conrad had struck it off at once when they met in October, and though neither was much given to critical discussion, they felt a spontaneous artistic sympathy. Crane, reading *The Nigger of the "Narcissus"* in proof, was able to give the novelist strong encour-agement in one of his recurrent moments of self-distrust. Crane received encouragement in turn when, just before the last spate of work on the Greek story, he went to visit the Conrads at Stanford-le-Hope and brought along two of the stories he was about to put into a new collection. Conrad read "A Man and Some Others" and "The Open Boat" with excitement, amaze-

---

[67] "Stephen Crane at Velestino," New York *Journal*, May 11, 1897, in *Uncoll. Writ.*, p. 258; "The Dogs of War," New York *Journal*, May 30, 1897, in *Uncoll. Writ.*, pp. 271–272; "A Battle in Greece," New York *Journal*, June 13, 1897, in *Uncoll. Writ.*, pp. 274–283.

ment, even a touch of envy. He was so full of admiration that he broke for once into critical statement, thus introducing his young American friend to new terms by which to define his artistic purposes: "You shock—and the next moment you give the perfect artistic satisfaction. Your method is fascinating. You are the complete impressionist. The illusions of life come out of your hand without a flaw. It is not life—which nobody wants—it is art—art for which everyone—the abject and the great hanker—mostly without knowing it." [68]

Frederic, on the other hand, was a forty-year-old version of Crane's Newspaper Row cronies of a few years earlier. Heavy, bluff, coarse, he was a prolific part-time novelist, and as *Times* correspondent in London, he had once done Crane a great favor: his dispatch of January, 1896, on the English success of *The Red Badge* had helped Crane win a wider recognition in the United States. In November, 1897, at about the time he was starting "Death and the Child," Crane tried to return the favor by writing a sketch of Frederic and a puff of his work; he praised its craftsmanship, which he left undefined except by reference to Frederic's subject, "the impressive common life of the United States." Frederic not only failed to evoke critical profundity in others, he also decidedly lacked it himself—as he showed in his vociferous low opinion of "The Monster," *The Nigger of the "Narcissus,"* and all the works of Henry James. Yet he could, because of his own unblessed domestic arrangement, supply Crane with tacit understanding of his sometimes awkward domestic situation. The Frederics took in the Cranes after their carriage accident of August, 1897, and cared for them. "The Monster" was written under their auspices, so to speak, first in Surrey and then, when the recuperation turned into a great vacation party, in Ireland. And Frederic provided the fellowship that brought out Crane's readiness to put on cowboy chaps or show off his marksmanship with the revolver. But that fellowship wore thin at the end of November when Crane, just returned from his cordial visit with Conrad, was trying to finish "Death and the Child." On the afternoon of the thirtieth, Frederic with five other men in tow dropped in unannounced for

[68] Conrad to Crane, Stanford-le-Hope, Dec. 1, 1897, ALS in Columbia University Libraries; *Letters*, p. 154, silently improves Conrad's punctuation.

lunch, and the party, complete with target demonstration, lasted through tea. The next day—the day of Conrad's encouraging letter—Crane fled to London in order to work in the peace of a hotel room. In time it dawned on him that "some of these Comanche braves seem to think I am running a free lunch counter," but it did not occur to him to reckon the expense of spirit.[69]

The complications of writing "Death and the Child" were more than matched by the complications of selling it and getting it into print. The split between journalist and artist that was discernible in Crane's writing and his social temperament existed most seriously in his business affairs. When he worked for the newspapers, he got regular income; when he worked for himself, he seemed to get no income at all. He had half a dozen books before the public at the end of 1897, but he received virtually no royalties. Though poems and stories might not pay, *The Red Badge* should have; but the American royalties were tied up in a lawsuit, and Appleton had sold the British rights to Heinemann for a flat payment without thinking to arrange a royalty for the author. When the young American appeared in London, Heinemann showed his gratitude to a best-selling novelist whom he wanted to keep on his house list: he gave him, as bonus rather than royalty, a modest twenty pounds ($100). Only a large book sale could keep Crane from becoming dependent on newspaper earnings or the haphazard income from magazine publication of short stories. So, although McClure's hard practice of holding stories unsold had hurt him badly, even worse was the failure of *The Third Violet*, published in May and generously reviewed, to sell very well. Heinemann guessed early what Professors Bruccoli and Katz have lately proved, that Crane had passed the peak of his popularity in 1897.[70] He would shortly try to improve Crane's attractiveness in the market by demanding a collection half again as long as McClure's so that the London *Open Boat*

---

[69] "Harold Frederic," *Chap-Book*, VIII (March 15, 1898), 358–359, in *Uncoll. Writ.*, pp. 306–309; article sent with covering letter, Crane to Reynolds, Oxted, Nov. 3, [1897], typed copy in Syracuse University Library; Beer, *Crane*, pp. 165–166. Crane's refuge was Brown's Hotel in Albemarle Street, not a very thrifty choice!

[70] Matthew J. Bruccoli and Joseph Katz, "Scholarship and Mere Artifacts: The British and Empire Publications of Stephen Crane," *Studies in Bibliography*, XXII (1969), 277–287.

volume might make up in weight for what it lacked in glamour. What Crane understood at this stage was the simple fact that he had no money coming in, and he began to be panicky. In the letter he sent to his agent Reynolds along with "Death and the Child," he began confidently but could not keep his voice from rising as he went along. He signaled his panic in the readiness with which he thought of falling back on McClure for good money and hard terms even though he had not yet, so far as he knew, worked off his last debt in that quarter and even though his desperate cry about selling "The Monster" only reinforced his memory of what debt to McClure could mean. But the cool first paragraph masks a subtler and less sympathetic sign of his economic hysteria. Forgetting his exclusive agreement with Reynolds, he tried to keep back the British rights to his story for the sake of some quick cash. The letter, sent from Oxted in early December, 1897, reads:

Dear Reynolds: I send you the child story of the Greek business. McClure has a call on it. He should give $300 for it—at least. The English rights are sold.

I have made a proposition to McClure that he advance £200 on the 1st of January for the book rights of my new Greek novel—not yet begun. If he takes the offer he may want to hold back on payment for this story. I wouldn't have done it if I was not broke. For heaven's sake raise me all the money you can and *cable* it, *cable* it sure between Xmas and New Year's. Sell "The Monster"! Don't forget that—cable me some money this month.[71]

Reynolds' reply must be inferred from Crane's side of the correspondence. He may have reminded Crane of his exclusive agency agreement, and he may have let Crane know that "The Bride" had provided final payment on his earlier debt; he certainly made it clear that for the kind of money Crane wanted, the agent would do best to try selling the story to one of the international monthlies. So on December 20 Crane took back what he had said about a prior sale and reassured Reynolds: "Death and The Child is not being sold in England. I am holding it in order to give you a chance with the big fellows. I shall hold it until I hear from you."[72]

[71] [Oxted, December, 1897], *Letters*, pp. 156–157.
[72] Oxted, Dec. 20 [1897], typed copy in Syracuse University Library.

At this point the discussion of "Death and the Child" became intertwined with a multiplicity of other subjects which a short-story writer had to keep track of, most especially with the making of the *Open Boat* volume. The big news Reynolds had sent Crane was that he had tentatively sold "The Monster" to *Harper's Magazine* provided Harper's could also have the book rights and enough other stories to make up a fair-sized collection. Crane hastened to agree to the proposed terms, but he did not fully understand the necessity of granting international rights for both serial and book publication. Acting on his misapprehension of the Harper terms, he told Reynolds in his December 20 letter: "I will send over soon, proofs of a lot of stuff of mine which is to appear in the English edition of The Open Boat, but not in the American edition. These stories added to the Monster would make about 40000 or 45000 words." His mistake reveals that both editions of the *Open Boat* collection were nearing their final form and that Heinemann already had the stories which would permit him to bring out a larger and presumably more salable volume. The misunderstanding also explains how he could have let Reynolds sell "Death and the Child" to *Harper's Weekly* on the assumption that the Harper firm would have book rights, while he had consigned the story in his own mind to the *Open Boat* collection.[73]

A stiffer tone must have characterized Reynolds' next letter, for on January 14, 1898, Crane took pains to explain how he justified his independent dealing with McClure for an advance on his unwritten novel *Active Service*. Robert McClure, younger brother of the publisher and head of the McClure Syndicate's London office, is the person he refers to in his highly impersonal euphemism:

In all the months I have been in England I have never received a cent from America which has not been borrowed. Just read that over twice! The consequences of this have lately been that I have been

[73] The same. While promising to hold "Death and the Child" off the English market, Crane warned Reynolds: "The Five White Mice however is on the market here." Since he hoped for proofs soon for the *Open Boat* volume, he was obviously trying to arrange magazine publication wherever he could before the book would come out. He did not say so, however, and it did not occur to Reynolds that Crane's earlier warning about "Death and the Child"—"McClure has a call on it"—referred to book rights as well as magazine option.

obliged to make arrangements here with English agents of American houses but in all cases your commission will be protected. This is the best I could do. My English expenses have chased me to the wall.

The availability of Robert McClure for transmitting copy to his home office explains how Crane could send copy for the *Open Boat* volume without Reynolds' knowing what was in it; and Crane's renewed assurance—"I have withheld the 'Death and the Child' story from an English sale because I think you can hit one of the three big fellows with it"—explains how the agent could feel confirmed in the assumption that all rights in the story were intact.[74]

The placing of "Death and the Child" in the *Open Boat* volume may not have been irrevocable until late January when Crane wrote out, along with the dedication of the book, the Table of Contents of the Heinemann edition. As he went through the list, he recorded approximate word counts—and where relevant for printer's copy, British magazine appearances—of the first eight stories. The sum of his eight figures came to 50,000, beside which he added the note—"or in actual count about 53,000." That exact figure, which he echoed in—or repeated from—his January 31 letter to Reynolds, helps to date the list and puts it over a month after his offer of early proofs from Heinemann to fill out the Harper volume. At the end of January the selection of

[74] Crane to Reynolds, [Oxted], Jan. 14, [1898], *Letters*, pp. 168–169. This letter also throws light on how Reynolds received copy of the stories Crane had recently sent. If the agent's complaint can be inferred from Crane's reply, Crane was having his manuscripts typed in London and then sending one copy and a bill for half the expense to Reynolds: "Don't kick so conspicuously about the over-charge on the damned manuscripts. If I was a business man, I would not need a business man to conduct my affairs for me. I will try to do better but if I shouldn't, don't harangue me. The point is of minor importance." This interpretation of the letter would suggest, with respect to "Death and the Child," how McClure could have had a later revised version of the text even though the New York *Open Boat* went to press before the *Harper's Weekly* publication of the same story.

Finally, when Crane made his statement in this letter about keeping "Death and the Child" off the English market, he added: " 'The Five White Mice' is sold in England." No English publication has yet been discovered; and in the Table of Contents for the London *Open Boat*, made perhaps as much as two weeks later (discussed in the text below), there was no entry to indicate that magazine proofs might shortly be available for Heinemann copy. This phantom sale, like the earlier alleged sale of "Death and the Child," may indicate actual or intended activity by Crane himself in London publishing circles. But in this case, it may also be a slip: about this time he did sell "The Wise Men," a story often linked in his mind with "The Five White Mice," to the *Ludgate Monthly*.

contents was firm enough so that Crane went through his list and numbered the titles, not consecutively as he wrote them down, but in the order which the Heinemann collection was to follow. The fact that the McClure volume followed neither the listed nor the indicated order is a sign that Crane had relatively little chance to supervise the New York edition. The basic collection, which appeared in both editions, included the two shipwreck stories from the Florida episode, the early Western stories and "The Bride," and "Death and the Child." After these eight, he began numbering again and worked out an order for the nine stories which he had long thought of as his "Midnight Sketches" —mostly New York tales, but also "The Pace of Youth." [75] Though he kept the two sets of stories apart in his own mind and in his numbering, he had not yet determined how he would do so in the actual volume. Later, when he decided to use "Midnight Sketches" as the subtitle of the second group, he obliged himself to think of a subtitle also for the first. The unity was hard to find among these major stories of chance and violence in the West, disasters at sea, and the "great carnival of woe" which is battle, but at least the miscellaneity of the group prevented his stopping short with such easy classification by subject as tales of the West, or the sea, or war. From the artistic view at which he had arrived, the touchstone story of the group was "The Open Boat." Compelled to find a name which would express that point of view, he decided on "Minor Conflicts." A better name for the collection is unthinkable.

Before Crane got to the final stage of giving a title to his tales of adventure, he had to see to it that his general intention about contents would be followed in New York. The transatlantic confusion was not made simpler by Crane's finishing "The Blue Hotel" and including the negotiations over that story in his business tangle as quickly as he could send off the manuscript. The main difficulty was that, as of January 31, 1898, Crane did not know whether Reynolds had sold "Death and the Child" for magazine publication, and Reynolds did not know that the story could not go into a Harper's book. On that date Crane wrote Reynolds that his debt to McClure had been worked off and to spare with the publication of "The Bride" for a price of two

75 MS in Columbia University Libraries.

hundred dollars, and that his literary obligation was just about worked off, too. Poor Reynolds may well have reeled at learning how Crane thought he was filling out the McClure book, especially since in the very next paragraph—announcing virtual completion of "The Blue Hotel"—he showed that he finally understood Harper's stipulation about wanting all rights to a story, the same stipulation which he was ignoring with respect to the Greek story. Crane wrote in his most engaging tone:

I am waiting your letter in regard to the Death and The Child. I expect it on Wednesday steamer.

It turned out that I only owed McClure $71.09 and of course he copped that out of the $200. And at the same time, he already has 53000 words for a book—at least he has as soon as he gets a copy of Death and the Child.

I expect to mail you a story of 10000 words on Saturday. I will keep it open at all ends so that if Harpers want it. They can afterwards put it in the book. Of course I see my mistake about their taking some of the stories that Heineman is to use here.[76]

In the meantime, however, Reynolds had of course sold "Death and the Child" to Harper's. He had managed to sell them "The Monster" for *Harper's Monthly Magazine* even before McClure had fully let go his clutch on the story; and now, having kept McClure from getting hold of "Death and the Child" at all, he sold it for immediate payment and early publication in *Harper's Weekly*. In a letter which crossed Crane's of January 31, he let his client know how well he had done. Congratulating Crane on having two-thirds completed a Harper's book, he no doubt expected congratulations in return. Crane, in his reply of February 7, was at last on the point of sending "The Blue Hotel," "with every solitary right free" and worth $500 from Harper's, and he expressed his thanks for the payments from that quarter which had already come in—his use of the plural indicating that he had been paid for both "The Monster," not to come out until August, and "Death and the Child," which would come out in two installments on March 19 and 26.[77] However, he also made it

---

[76] Oxted, Jan. 31, [1898], typed copy in Syracuse University Library.
[77] Because *Harper's Weekly* did not have simultaneous English publication as *Harper's Monthly Magazine* did, Crane was free to market the story in England. It appeared in *Black and White* on March 5 and 12, 1898.

clear that while he finally understood Harper's terms, he had a rather vague conception of the nature of contract:

As for "Death and The Child" it is to go to the McClure book. So is "The Five White Mice."

Besides it would be absurd to conjoin "Death and The Child" with "The Monster." They don't fit. It would be rotten. Now, "The Blue Hotel" goes in very neatly with "The Monster" and together they make 32,000. Very little more is needed for a respectably sized $1.00 book, and that can readily be submitted within the next six weeks.[78]

At the House of Harper evidently someone got mad. Yet Crane was still the innocent: more than a month went by, and he continued to urge Reynolds to get the fifty-pound advance from Harper's for the *Monster* volume. Once again in a crossing letter, Reynolds must have been explaining what went wrong, for on March 17 Crane wrote back: "Your letter of the 8th with the enclosed one from Mr. Nelson reached me this morning. I regret very much the misunderstanding about the story for Harpers Weekly and apologize to you for my neglect. It will not happen again. I shall write a personal letter to Mr. Nelson." After putting in jeopardy Reynolds' position with the whole publishing world, Crane apologized handsomely enough. But if he seems to have mollified the agent, he did not have equal success with Harper's. The experience left them chary, and when Reynolds reopened the question of the *Monster* volume, the best he could do was, on March 31, to draw *one-half* of the advance which he had earlier arranged.[79]

[78] [Oxted], Feb. 7, [1898], *Letters*, pp. 171–172.
That Crane was acting in good faith, however obtusely, is confirmed by his note to Reynolds of the very next day:
Dear Reynolds: Please say to Harpers that it will be very necessary for me to have early proofs of The Monster as I note now, from the original ms, many crudities in style.
The same applies to The Blue Hotel (Oxted, Feb. 8, [1898], typed copy in Syracuse University Library).
Besides his sanguine assumption that all was well between him and the House of Harper, this letter indicates that the day after sending copy to Reynolds, he had his manuscript back, that is, that he had mailed off a typescript before taking time to revise and so the Reynolds copy did not arrive in the final form which the author intended.

[79] Oxted, March 13 and March 17, 1898, typed copies in Syracuse University Library; receipt, dated March 31, 1898, for $125 as one-half of the advance due on contract for "The Monster" and "another story," Harper and Brothers Contract Book 11, p. 18.

The business history of "Death and the Child" thus came to an appropriate end. The need for money pressed Crane into involvements which affected publication both of the story in hand and other stories, other books. Fulfilling one obligation, he violated another. Making good on a bad contract, he halved the benefit of a good one. Raising money and juggling stories from magazine to book used more and more of his time and energy, and unlike that other costly distraction, his prodigal hospitality, there was no fun to balance the expense of spirit. The difficulty was only partly a matter of temperament, though the easygoing, unbusinesslike Crane had done better in his Bacheller days with an expense account in Mexico and a heavy money belt in Florida. The economics of short-story writing, if a man were to try and live off it, were appalling, and even with the best of agents an artist had to be also an entrepreneur. While Crane was working his way through the tangle around "Death and the Child," the *Open Boat* volume, and his relations with McClure, Heinemann, Harper's, and others, he managed to conceive and write "The Blue Hotel" and send it to market in its turn, meanwhile fending off friends and creditors as best he could. Little wonder that the dream of a successful novel and the temptation of journalistic adventure were so present to him. In December, while he had been intensively at work on his story of a correspondent in Greece, he first proposed to do a popular novel, *Active Service*, also about a correspondent in Greece. Before "Death and the Child" was out in book form, he was on his way to the Spanish-American War. April 18, 1898, the day *The Open Boat* copyright deposit was made in England and the United States, Crane was on the high seas.

There was continuity as well as tangle in Crane's affairs, as the history of "The Blue Hotel" shows. When he visited Conrad on the eve of finishing "Death and the Child," he was in a "strangely hopeless" frame of mind as far as his friend could tell, and he made his way home through a severe late November storm that could hardly have cheered him up. Almost immediately thereafter came his flight to London, where it was possible to be as desolate in affluence as he had ever been in poverty. The circumstantial link, though slight, may have been enough to put Crane

in mind of his Nebraska desolation of almost three years before
and of the howling prairie blizzard even wilder than the present
sea storm.[80] But the esthetic link between the very different
stories is stronger than the circumstantial. Though the grass-
blade image of the fecund Greek spring dominated the earlier
story and the blizzard this, the change of mood was by no means
a change of world. The "great calm thing rolling noiselessly
toward the end of the mystery" and the "whirling, fire-smote,
ice-locked, disease-stricken, space-lost bulb" equally imply that
the world is vast, incomprehensible, and indifferent to the minor
conflicts of humankind. The opening sentences of "The Blue
Hotel" give the theme of human littleness in its chillier form:

> The Palace Hotel at Fort Romper was painted a light blue, a shade
> that is on the legs of a kind of heron, causing the bird to declare its
> position against any background. The Palace Hotel, then, was always
> screaming and howling in a way that made the dazzling winter land-
> scape of Nebraska seem only a gray swampish hush. It stood alone
> on the prairie, and when the snow was falling the town two hundred
> yards away was not visible.[81]

Though visibility can be snuffed out by a change of weather, the
vaunt of color commands the attention of every traveler,
whether entering Fort Romper or merely passing through on the
train. The proprietor who picked that color "had performed a
feat" which the reader may consider from the admiring Western
or the condescending Eastern point of view or which he may
judge a mere coxcomb show against the engulfing blizzard. This
interpretative choice, it turns out, is what principally differen-

[80] Conrad to Edward Garnett, [Stanford-le-Hope], Dec. 5, 1897: "I had Crane
here last Sunday. We talked and smoked half the night. He is strangely hopeless
about himself. I like him" (*Letters*, p. 155).

Conrad to Crane, [Stanford-le-Hope], Dec. 1, 1897: "Glad to hear you haven't
had your head taken off. We had here on Monday a high tide that smashed the
sea-wall, flooded the marshes and washed away the Rwy line. Great excitement"
(*Letters*, p. 154).

For the Nebraska experience of analogous weather, inward and terrestrial, see
pp. xviii and xxxiv above.

[81] Clell T. Peterson gets the last word in an ornithological controversy by
pointing out that the Little Blue Heron, in proper light, has "legs of precisely the
shade of light blue that I have always supposed the Blue Hotel to be painted," in
contrast to the Great Blue Herons that do not thus declare themselves. For a
"convincingly unambiguous color photo," he refers readers to E. Thomas
Gilliard, *Living Birds of the World* (Garden City, N.Y., 1958), Color Plate 21
("Reply: Crane on Herons," *Notes and Queries*, ccviii [1963], 29).

tiates this story from the one which Crane wrote immediately before it. In "Death and the Child" the reader follows the protagonist through his initiation in chaos to his apprehension of the vast enveloping universe. In "The Blue Hotel" no character by himself gives the clue to the action, and even the narrator's general view, in which the central action appears diminished, is open to question. If the conceit of man is taken to be the engine of life, it is hard to say whether the folly is more to be emphasized than the vitality; for the protagonist, the conceit of man turns out also to be an engine of death. Instead of a straightforward plot of discovery, Crane presented a narrative in which characters and narrator attain to partial truths about an event, but only the reader is able to comprehend its multiplicity.

The anecdote of the story goes back to the barroom fight in Lincoln (pp. xxxiii–xxxiv above) that Crane had naïvely tried to break up. Departing from his well-meant interference with what turned out to be local custom, he now invented a case of noninterference and explored its possible ironies. And he devised a central character whose mistakes about the custom of the country stem from illusion rather than naïveté. The Swede who comes to Fort Romper with his head full of Wild West stories offends the hotelkeeper Scully and the assembled company, for he is almost hysterically sure that many men have been killed on this spot and that he will soon be next. Scully's attempt to cheer him with drink only changes his wild fear to wilder courage that no one sees in time. He joins a friendly game of cards and surprises the company after a bit by turning on the host's son with the "three terrible words: 'You are cheatin'!'" The Swede is glad to fight the indignant boy and roundly beats him, then leaves the hotel. When he takes refuge from the snowstorm in a Fort Romper saloon, he tries to bully the company there into drinking with him. Enraged by the soft refusal of the slim little gambler at one of the tables, he tries to drag him to the bar: "There was a great tumult, and then was seen a long blade in the hand of the gambler. It shot forward, and a human body, this citadel of virtue, wisdom, power, was pierced as easily as if it had been a melon. The Swede fell with a cry of supreme astonishment." The Swede is astonished to discover, like the tenderfoot of "A Man and Some Others," that it is easy to kill a man.

But it is really nondiscovery, and ironic nondiscovery is even more clearly the case when the dead man's open eyes gaze sightlessly at the imprint on the cash register: "This registers the amount of your purchase." The motto suggests that the Swede is responsible for his fate, though that lesson comes ironically when the Swede is past all teaching. Moreover, the easy moral explanation may be wrong; maybe no one is an agent. In the actual killing no villain thrusts a knife, but a blade is passively seen and shoots forward as if by a law of its own. The story gives a set of facts and a number of implicit ways of taking them. The logic of the narrative is that no particular moral view is exclusively sanctioned by the nature of things, and everything which makes the action convincing helps to enforce that argument.

Up to the last section of the story, "The Blue Hotel" is a kind of literary experiment in which Wild West conventions operate in the mind of a real person who is caught in a real situation. The Swede's illusions have psychological and social effects which, in contrast to the usual working out of Wild West situations, can be understood in everyday terms. But the play of convention and reality, which in "The Bride Comes to Yellow Sky" had been comic, has turned grim, not for the gulled character only, but for the society of which he is part. The final section of the story brings together the other guests of that fateful evening at Scully's hotel, an Easterner "who didn't look it, and didn't announce it," and a cowboy. Though the cowboy does not want to hear it, the Easterner discloses that Johnnie really had been cheating. Oppressed by his own silence when he might have stood up and broken the chain of circumstance, he is ready to claim that every sin is a collaboration. The story ends with a line which perfectly balances the motto on the cash register, the cowboy's "Well, I didn't do anythin', did I?" The one bond which unites men is their dark complicity, and even so they remain apart. Thus each of the three lines of thought in the story leads to equivocal argument. From one point of view, events are fortuitous except for an occasional feat—like painting the hotel an arresting blue—whereby the assertion of identity seems to bring identity into being. From another point of view, man makes his own destiny, if it is a proof of human agency that Wild West illusions about Nebraska make the Wild West fantasy come true.

And, finally, all men share responsibility even doing nothing—or at least they do so if they think they do. Given the facts as presented, the story constructs a universe which defies every quest for certain meaning.

In order to support so many interpretative possibilities, Crane had to take the greatest pains to make the facts as presented appear utterly logical and credible. His slow writing of the story, from the evidence, shows the kind of care he gave to his task. He began in early December, 1897, shortly after sending "Death and the Child" to Reynolds. But his main intention then was to turn from his Greek story to his proposed Greek novel *Active Service*, of which he set down some twelve thousand words in the next two weeks. But when he reported this progress to Reynolds on December 20, he added, "The Blue Hotel will come to you in about two weeks. It may be 10000 words." Since he could refer to the story by title, estimate its eventual length, and predict he would have it ready so soon, he clearly was well along in a first draft. After that there is no mention of either the novel or the story until Crane wrote Reynolds on January 31, 1898, announcing that he expected to mail off "The Blue Hotel" at the end of the week and would keep all rights for Harper's in case they should take it for both magazine and book. He went on to say, "I am going to write about a thousand or twelve hundred more dollars in short stuff and work only on my big book," as if his short stories were potboilers and the big book represented his artistic calling. If he thought so, he misjudged himself. He had just turned aside from the novel for which he expected a fat advance, and he had given six weeks, instead of two, to a concentrated effort that he could explain only as a run for quick pay. In fact, he held the story still another three days before posting it to Reynolds at last on February 7, and on February 8 he was already asking for early proofs so that he could further polish its style.[82]

What he meant by polishing style can be illustrated from the fragment of manuscript which survives, once again, because Cora Crane used the clean side of the sheet for her own writing. The draft, in Cora's hand, is closer to the final text than the

[82] Oxted, Dec. 20, [1897], Jan. 31, [1898], and Feb. 8, [1898], typed copies in Syracuse University Library.

fragment of "Death and the Child." Evidently Crane was becoming more skilled at dictation without really adapting to the new process; that is, unlike Henry James he did not shift toward a more open, colloquial, or cadenced style when he changed from composing by pen to composing by voice. He had worked out his plot and method of presentation almost to their final form, sentence by sentence, but he was right to think that the sentences needed to be tightened and polished. Between the draft and the text he did not add action, gesture, or characterization, but rather he got rid of triteness, imprecision, wavering of tone. In dictating, he spoke more or less as he wrote but without stopping to improve separate phrases as he went along. The fragment is the eighth page of the dictated version, the last ten short paragraphs of the second section of the story. The fear-ridden Swede, scarcely arrived, is about to leave the hotel without staying the night, and when the proprietor comes in upon the scene, he cannot believe that someone has not been troubling his agitated guest:

Draft version	Final text
"You will not go away" said Renigan "until I hear the reason of this business who has threatened you? If any man has troubled you I will take care of him.' This is my house, and I wont allow any peacable man to be troubled here." He cast a terrible look upon Jimmie, the cowboy and the Easterner.ᵇ	"You will not go 'way," said Scully. "You will not go 'way until I hear the reason of this business. If anybody has troubled you I will take care of him. This is my house. You are under my roof, and I will not allow any peaceable man to be troubled here." He cast a terrible eye upon Johnnie, the cowboy, and the Easterner.
"Never mind Mr. Renigan never mind. I will go away. I do not wish to be killed." He moved toward the door which led upstairs as if his intention was to at once get his baggage.	"Never mind, Mr. Scully, never mind. I will go 'way. I do not wish to be killed." The Swede moved toward the door, which opened upon the stairs. It was evidently his intention to go at once for his baggage.
"No, No" shouted Renigan peremtorially but the white faced Sweed slid by him and disappeared. "Now" said Renigan to the others in a very cold and	"No, no," shouted Scully peremptorily; but the white-faced man slid by him and disappeared. "Now," said Scully severely, "what does this mane?"

deadly tone "what does this mane?"

Jimmie & the cowboy dueted: [c] "Why we didnt do nuthin' to him." Renigan was dangerously suspicious "No?" said he. "You didnt?"

Jimmie swore a deep oath. "Why this is the craziest lone I ever see. We didnt do nuthin' to him at all. We were just sittin' here playin' cards and he—"

Renigan interrupted with a question to the Easterner. "Mr Blank" he asked "What has these boys been doin'?"

After a deliberation the Easterner answered quietly [d] "I didn't see the slightest thing wrong."

"But what does it mane?" howled Renigan. He stared ferociously [e] at his son. "I have a mind to lather you for this my boy".[f]

Jimmie made a gesture that denoted he was frantic "Well what have I done?" he bawled at his father.[83]

Johnnie and the cowboy cried together: "Why, we didn't do nothin' to 'im!"

Scully's eyes were cold. "No," he said, "you didn't?"

Johnnie swore a deep oath. "Why, this is the wildest loon I ever see. We didn't do nothin' at all. We were jest sittin' here playin' cards and he——"

The father suddenly spoke to the Easterner. "Mr. Blanc," he asked, "what has these boys been doin'?"

The Easterner reflected again. "I didn't see anything wrong at all," he said at last slowly.

Scully began to howl. "But what does it mane?" He stared ferociously at his son. "I have a mind to lather you for this, me boy."

Johnnie was frantic. "Well, what have I done?" he bawled at his father.

[83] MS in Columbia University Libraries. Miss Lillian Gilkes discovered this manuscript on the verso of the first page of Cora Crane's review of the play *Peter the Great* by Lawrence Irving. Joseph Katz systematically describes the manuscript in *Stephen Crane Newsletter*, III (Fall, 1968), 1–2. The ruled foolscap laid paper with Britannia watermark is also found in some of the Whilomville stories. The manuscript changes, as noted by Fredson Bowers, are as follows:

a   him] 'hi' *written over two doubtful letters, the second of which may be 'e' before the final 'm' added*

b   Easterner.] *a deleted double quote mark appears above the period*

c   dueted:] *the colon is written over an original comma and a following 'to' is deleted*

d   quietly] *Cora's 't' is often crossed far to the right: here the word looks like 'quielty' but the formation of the 'l' indicates that the spelling was actually correct*

e   ferociously] *the 'e' is altered from an 'o' and before this word appears to be deleted trial 'foro'*

f   boy".] *curiously, the original double quote mark after the period is deleted and the quote moved just inside the period*

Of Crane's revisions, the most obvious are the changes of names. Though the significance of each change is slight, it is enough to suggest that care for detail could have a great cumulative effect. The change of the proprietor's name from Renigan to the more common Scully seems to make him less of a stage Irishman. Crane kept up and even improved his Irish accent, for like the others in the story he belongs first of all to a genus—Irishman, Swede, Easterner, cowboy—but the man who painted his hotel blue is the only one in the story with a full-fledged name, and his individuality apart from generic qualities is better designated by a more neutral, less obviously generic name. Compared to him, Johnnie and Mr. Blanc do not bear really distinguishing names; like the cook or the correspondent compared to the oiler Billie Higgins, they fall short of ultimate individuation. The son's original name, Jimmie, recurs often in Crane's work from Jimmie Johnson in *Maggie* to Jimmie Trescott of the late *Whilomville Stories*, and Jimmie Trescott had only recently been invented in "The Monster." In changing it to Johnnie, Crane dissociated himself from sympathetic involvement with this boy and at the same time made him more nearly anonymous. Mr. Blank's name was obviously devoid of individual significance, but the change of spelling to Blanc added one more negative quality—the no-color, as Melville called it, against which the blue of the hotel is Scully's brilliant counter gesture. Crane's improvement of a number of phrases was more strictly a matter of polish. "As if his intention was," "a very cold and deadly tone," "dangerously suspicious," and "made a gesture that denoted" all gave the narrator away as knowing more than met the reader's eye. The multiplication of such nice improvements produced the ultimate Crane style which led Edward Garnett to say of him that "he keeps closer to the surface than any living writer, and, like the great portrait-painters, to a great extent makes the surface betray the depths." [84] To increase the surface tension, he got rid of the signs of omniscience and theatrical manipulation, so that appearances alone might convey all the significant details. Even in the draft he seemed fully to have thought out the logic of the story: the cross-purposes of the Swede, the hotelkeeper, and the bystanders, the natural collusion of the hotelkeeper's son and the cowboy, the Easterner's deliberate commitment to seeing

84 "Stephen Crane: An Appreciation," *Academy*, LV (1898), 484.

nothing. He had also gone a long way toward working out the surface effects. The last words of this section, Johnnie's "Well, what have I done?" would echo in Crane's ear when he made the cowboy's "injured and rebellious" cry against responsibility the last words of the story. Though the draft version had lines which could stand up to Crane's intensest scrutiny, he did make one substantive change for just about every line of the draft fragment, and his immediate afterthought on sending off the story was a need to scour out the "crudities" that still caught his eye.

Crane's eagerness to revise and perfect was to be chilled by the tedious and frustrating history of "The Blue Hotel" as a literary commodity. He assumed when he sent the story to New York on February 7, 1898, that *Harper's* would take it, and the next day when he asked Reynolds to get him early proofs for revision, he thought he was sending the agent to Harper's. There, however, reaction to the story was bound up with questions of how to constitute the *Monster* volume and how to deal with the mix-up over "Death and the Child," and after a good two weeks of deliberation, they turned it down. *Century* took less time. When Reynolds submitted the story on March 1, he asked the editor to read it "please at once," and by a week later, as we know from Crane's acknowledgment of the news, the manuscript had gone on to *Scribner's*.[85] Then came the turn of the *Atlantic*, and it became clear that the publishing-house connections of the great monthly magazines were not necessarily so good for the writer as the Harper connection had led Crane to think. On March 30 the editor of the *Atlantic*, Walter Hines Page, coyly expressed interest in "The Blue Hotel" provided he could have for the firm of Houghton Mifflin a novel or at least a complete volume of Western tales. When Reynolds told him that "The Bride," which Page particularly wanted, was about to come out in the McClure volume and that "The Blue Hotel" was earmarked for Harper's, Page returned the manuscript with the petulant observation that "one stray story is hardly worth our while." Reynolds' quick reply

[85] Crane to Reynolds, [Oxted], Feb. 7, [1898], *Letters*, pp. 171–172; same, Feb. 8, [1898], typed copy in Syracuse University Library; Reynolds to Robert Underwood Johnson, New York, March 1, 1898, TLS in New York Public Library; Crane to Reynolds, Oxted, March 13, 1898, typed copy in Syracuse University Library.

elicited a letter that was different in tone but not in substance: the *Atlantic* and Houghton Mifflin would welcome a novel or unified book of stories by Crane, but "a single short story is of hardly sufficient importance for the Atlantic to buy—it ought to give its space and attention to enterprises of more importance." [36] So Reynolds turned to *Collier's Weekly*. Robert

[36] Page to Reynolds, Boston, March 30, 1898, TLS in University of Virginia Library:

I thank you very much for sending me Mr. Crane's story "The Blue Hotel", which I think a pretty good story, but by no means (let me say confidentially to you) as good a western story as the one that appeared a month or two ago in McClure's Magazine. I look favorably therefore upon the possibility of accepting it for the Atlantic, but not enthusiastically.

But the acceptance of a single story by any writer is a matter of little consequence, and I wish to write you in frankness and in confidence several things that have a bearing upon such a problem as you were kind enough to present by giving me an opportunity to read this story. I prefer, of course—very greatly prefer—to use in the Atlantic only those stories that may be afterwards published in book form by Messrs. Houghton, Mifflin & Co., or stories from authors whose books come to us.

I had some very pleasant correspondence with Mr. Crane soon after his "Red Badge of Courage" was published, and I hoped that we might then use him in the Atlantic, and subsequently publish something from him for the book market; but he went then into newspaper work and made a trip to Cuba, and did not finish, so far as I know, any complete work other than the books which he had already promised to other publishers.

Following this thought, may I ask you whether you have it in your power to induce Mr. Crane to submit to us preferably a complete novel, or if not a complete novel, would it be possible for him to submit to Messrs. H., M. & Co. the project of publishing a book of short stories, all of western life, so that the book would have a definite unity? If, for instance, we were to accept this story for the Atlantic, would he let us publish the story from McClure's Magazine, and perhaps others which he has already published, and a few more that he may yet write, in a volume for him?

If you will pardon me for keeping this manuscript for a day or two more until I can hear from you, and if you will be kind enough to inform me frankly how far you think you can make it easier in these points for me to use in the Atlantic the "Blue Hotel," I shall be greatly obliged.

Same, April 6, 1898, in Allen, *Reynolds*, pp. 58–59:

It seems to me better that I should return Mr. Crane's story to you, because one stray story is hardly worth our while. You told me, I believe, you had the sale of Mr. Crane's whole output in the United States. When you had one or two longer stories which have a book value as well as a serial value, you took them to the Harpers, with which of course I have no complaint to make nor any disposition to complain. But after you have taken the really valuable part of Mr. Crane's work to another magazine and another publisher, it hardly seems to me worth while for the Atlantic to step in and buy the remnant.

When you have something from Mr. Crane that is of serial as well as book value in hand, you may be sure that it will be a great pleasure to consider it.

Same, April 9, 1898, TLS in University of Virginia Library:

Collier, the son of the founder, had come to the editorship fresh from Harvard and was revitalizing the magazine. With his taste for high literature—he began his career by buying a Henry James serial—and his instinct for journalism—he hired Jimmy Hare, who became the star photographer of the Spanish-American War—he was obviously the right man to publish Crane. But his editorial view of the art of the short story was primarily economic. In his first letter to Reynolds on "The Blue Hotel," he went directly to the point: "Four Hundred Dollars is a big price for the Stephen Crane story. Could you not get it for us for less?" Reynolds acted fast to keep this fish on the hook, but he had to settle for Collier's odd idea of how to be fair to the writer, namely, three-quarters of the story for three-quarters of the price! On April 26 he confirmed in writing that he would take Crane's story, "shortened to seven thousand five hundred (7,500) or eight thousand (8,000) words for Three Hundred Dollars." [87]

Crane gave his personal assent to the Collier proposal, for by the time of the crucial negotiation he was in New York. Convinced that war would soon break out, he wanted to enlist in the Navy. Like Peza in "Death and the Child," he found himself more of a patriot than he expected. He had taken no part in the noisy reaction to the sinking of the *Maine*, but casually expressed British contempt for American power got under his skin

---

I was very much pleased with your spirited letter about Mr. Crane, or really about the Harpers. Of course I care nothing about the Harpers, or about what they publish or do not publish. I spoke of them only because you remarked that you had sold two long stories to them. My only point is that a single short story is of hardly sufficient importance for the Atlantic to buy—it ought to give its space and attention to enterprises of more importance. If at any time you have a longer story by Mr. Crane which might make a book, or if you know that he is of a mind to write a sufficient number of short stories of the same general kind with their scenes pitched in the same general part of the earth, then there would be some inducement to publish a part of them in the Atlantic. You know, however, that a book of short stories is always less valuable for book publication than a book which contains a long story.

I am sure that you understand my meaning, and I repeat that we shall have a hearty welcome for Mr. Crane if he come in sufficient volume to make it worth our while to take him up.

[87] Robert J. Collier to Reynolds, New York, April 20, 1898, TLS in University of Virginia Library. This letter includes a warning about the story: "We should probably, at any event, not be able to use it for four or five months."

Same, April 26, 1898, TLS in University of Virginia Library. With this letter, effectively a contract, Collier returned Crane's story to Reynolds for shortening.

as journalistic atrocities could not. Proud of his Revolutionary ancestors, including a general and a commodore, he knew that an American war was different for him and he wanted to commit himself to more than being a correspondent. His patriotic intention coincided, as it happened, with a chance to get away from his always worsening debts to the greengrocer, the wine merchant, the carriage maker. Frantically raising money to buy his passage, he told poor Conrad he had to help. Conrad, with a new baby at home and no savings, could do nothing himself, but he helped Crane get a sixty-pound loan from *Blackwood's*, to be paid off by cash or stories. Crane embarked April 14 and reached New York April 21, tried to enlist but did not make it for physical reasons, signed on with Pulitzer to report the war for the *World*, and left as soon as he could get a passport.[88] In the three or four days that all this took, he had little time for literary business, but he may have signed a few copies of *The Lanthorn Book* for Bacheller, and he did see Reynolds long enough to agree to the contract for "The Blue Hotel" and to the drastic cutting it entailed. But he was in Key West before Reynolds knew it and even before Collier sent the story back to Reynolds. The story was briefly lost, but Crane wrote his agent to try looking for it at his New York hotel. The manuscript was found, sent to Florida, and returned on May 8

[88] Beer, *Crane*, pp. 173–178, gives the basic story of Crane's slowly roused patriotism and his attempt to enlist. Joseph Conrad, "Introduction" to Beer, *Crane*, pp. 31–33, tells of "rushing all over London together" trying to raise passage money "before the sun set, before dinner, before the 'six forty' train to Oxted, at once, that instant—lest peace should be declared and the opportunity of seeing a war be missed." Stallman, *Crane*, p. 350, gives dates for Crane's passage on the *Germanic* but, p. 347, gives a wrong date for the Conrad incident, which occurred *before* American recognition of Cuban independence made war an official certainty. A receipt, not in Crane's hand, for £60 from *Blackwood's* acknowledges the money as an advance on articles "from the seat of war in the event of a war breaking out" and is dated April 7, 1898 (MS in Columbia University Libraries). The bottom of the receipt is torn off, and so it is impossible to tell whether this is a copy, a draft proposal, or a returned note with signature and validating stamp removed. However, the William Blackwood and Sons cash ledgers disclose an advance to Crane of £40 on April 7 and to Cora Crane of £20 on April 16. A note in brackets after the second entry, "In full, two articles," evidently records the terms of the advance as understood by the publisher rather than fulfillment of the obligation, for only one piece by Crane, "The Price of the Harness," came out in the magazine (William Blackburn, ed., *Joseph Conrad: Letters to William Blackwood* [Durham, N.C., 1958], pp. 21, 29).

with the note: "Cant cut this. Let Colliers do it themselves. Hold money & telegraph me when payment is made." [89]

May of 1898 proved to be a good month for Crane. He wore newspaper harness easily, sent off regular dispatches, and completed a short story which he sent to Reynolds on the thirtieth. The story of a little boy who runs away from home into a driving snowstorm, "His New Mittens" with its happy ending suggests that the author of "The Blue Hotel" had full control of his literary and, one guesses, his personal symbols. As he forwarded this story, it occurred to him to tell Reynolds, "You might send a copy of The Blue Hotel to Blackwood's Magazine London with information as to when Collier's Weekly will publish it." (He did not mention his having a debt to work off in that quarter.) The agent sent the story to *Blackwood's* in Edinburgh, and William Blackwood eventually passed it on for comment to the head of his London office, David Meldrum. Meldrum had met Crane through Conrad and thought highly of him, so he might have been glad to see his early support justified by the work it brought in. [90] Instead, he gave a demonstration—more notable than Gilder's earlier—of the supposed censoriousness of the middle-class audience and the way timid editors enforced it. His report to Blackwood was a model of crassness:

I have now read Stephen Crane's story, "The Blue Hotel", and I cannot say that I find it very easy to give an opinion about it. It runs to about 25 pp. of *Maga* [House nickname for *Blackwood's Magazine*], I estimate, which is long, and yet makes it dear at £50. But these are not the considerations with which I have to do, and I only linger over them because I "funk" the others. Well, the story is extraordinarily strong: the situations are realized in a really wonderful manner. The characters are pictured so that you would know them if you met them: only the Swede, the central character, you couldn't meet, for he is killed in the end. The transformation of this Swede, by drink, from the coward to the reckless blusterer,—his exhibition of so-called

[89] Crane to Reynolds, Key West, Fla., [n.d.], typed copy in Syracuse University Library: "My dear Reynolds: I did not get The Blue Hotel. Look it up and send it on down here. I suppose it is at the Everett." Same, May 8, [1898], typed copy in Syracuse University Library.

[90] Crane to Reynolds, "Off Havana," May 30, [1898], typed copy in Syracuse University Library.

On Meldrum's attitude toward Crane after their March meeting and some reading of his work, but presumably before the arrival of "The Blue Hotel," Conrad wrote to Cora Crane: "Meldrum was here (I suppose you've heard of him? Blackwood's man in London) the other day and spoke of Stephen with real enthusiasm" (Stanford-le-Hope, June 27, 1898, *Letters*, p. 182).

Dutch courage,—is conceived in the best vein of ironic humor; it is very strong stuff, and would make a mark. On the other hand, it is not *Maga's* line; altogether, it seems to me, too strong and brutal for Maga's readers. I am sorry, for I admire the story greatly and precisely for its strength, but I couldn't take the responsibility of advising its publication. It seems to me to be one of those cases where, greatly against our will, rejection is the wise course.[91]

Blackwood, shrewd enough to guess that timidity might not be the best policy, was also more broad-minded than his adviser: "I don't mind the brutality if it is not immoral and it is only human nature in low form." So he passed the manuscript around in the family and especially to that maiden sister whose judgment on "too strong food for the Magas readers" he was ready to abide by. When, apparently, nephew George and sister Bee proved to be of Meldrum's mind, Blackwood obeyed their conscience and turned the story down. (There is no evidence that he read it himself.)[92] The comedy which Crane had set in motion in May took on a dismal slackness during the summer. The English typescript of "The Blue Hotel" disappeared into the office of the London agent who acted for Reynolds, where for more than six months no more was heard of it. Coincidentally, on the other side of the Atlantic, Robert Collier misplaced his copy of the story and, in no hurry to publish, did not yet miss it. "The Blue Hotel" became for a while a dead letter.[93]

[91] David S. Meldrum to William Blackwood, London, July 23, 1898, in *Joseph Conrad: Letters to William Blackwood*, pp. 201–202.

[92] His notes on this letter, as given in Mr. Blackburn's edition cited above, read:

[*Penciled in William Blackwood's hand*] M. S. handed to Mr. George. *Across the face of the first page*: George read this story and then ask your aunt Bee to read it and if she thinks it too strong for Magas readers then we must I fear decline it but Meldrums account of it tempts me rather to use it as we require some stronger stories to wake up people's attention. Shew your Aunt this letter when you take out the M. S. to her.—W. B. *On the final page in pencil*: I don't mind the brutality if it is not immoral and it is only human nature in low form W. B.

[93] For Reynolds' use of an English agent and the misinterpretations to which it has led, see pp. cxiii–cxiv below and footnote 103.

Robert J. Collier to Reynolds, New York, Sept. 20, 1898, *Letters*, pp. 184–185: "With regard to the 'Blue Hotel,' I had intended publishing it before Christmas, or the week immediately after, but I cannot lay my hands on it at present. Do you remember the date on which you left the shortened version here? It was in manuscript, not typewriting; was it not? Kindly let me hear from you with regard to this." The manuscript which Collier recollected must have been the original since Crane never made a shortened version and *Collier's* published the story entire. The manuscript may have been mislaid at Reynolds' office, if the typescript which the agent sent to Blackwood was newly made. The absence of

Crane's personal fortunes also took a bad turn. In June, with
the American forces in Cuba, he contracted a fever that kept him
on the verge of delirium, and sometimes over the verge. At
Guantanamo, the Marine surgeon who had taken care of him got
caught in cross fire and died agonizingly through the long dark
night just a few feet from where Crane was lying. Ten days later
at Las Guásimas, his friend Ed Marshall, who had opened the
New York *Press* to him at the beginning of his career and who
had, after the *Commodore* affair, taken him on the *Journal* payroll, was hit badly near the spine. Crane managed to get help for
his friend and then, running some nine miles through the tropic
heat, filed his story for him. After these incidents, he could not
shake an obsessive imagining of what it must be like to be hit at
this or that point of the body. Twice in this period of intense
action, he reportedly stood up in enemy fire as if in a dream. He
took his chances among the bullets, not like a reckless gambler
testing his nerve, but in John Berryman's words, like "a young
man very willing to be killed." Once more the usually neat Crane
was notably unkempt. One reason was that he had lost all but
the clothes he had on, but fever, exhaustion, and prolonged
immersion in the nightmare chaos also had their effect. On July
8 he was sent back on an army transport to Old Point Comfort,
Virginia, suspected of having yellow fever and probably a victim
in fact of malaria. When he had recovered somewhat, he bought
himself a new outfit and took the train to New York.[94] Reporting
in at the Pulitzer Building, he found that they remembered the
dispatch he had filed for Marshall much better than they did any
of his own. He listened briefly to the sardonic financial manager,
said a quiet, courteous good-bye, and left to sign with Hearst instead.[95]

further correspondence on the loss and the lack of an attempt to recover the
copy in England suggest that wherever the story was mislaid, it was not missing
very long once the loss was noticed. At any rate, Collier's letters to Reynolds of
Nov. 4 and 6, setting dates for publication, then hedging, and finally in a
postscript confirming them, are routine in tone (New York, Nov. 4, 1898, TLS,
and Nov. 6, 1898, ALS, in University of Virginia Library).
[94] The clearest accounts are Ames W. Williams, "Stephen Crane, War Correspondent," *New Colophon*, I (April, 1948), 113–123, and Berryman, *Crane*, pp.
217–228. The quoted phrase from Berryman is from p. 224.
[95] A great mystery concerning Crane's finances arises from the statement of
Don C. Seitz, who was business manager of the *World*, that Crane received a
three-thousand-dollar fee from Pulitzer ("Stephen Crane: War Correspondent,"

Back in the war zone at the end of July, he saw little more hard fighting. At the end of hostilities, he slipped into Havana—despite the ban on American correspondents—and sent some of the early dispatches from there. He set himself up at the elegant Hotel Pasaje, obviously a different man from the sick and ragged Crane of a month before, and he began a stiff regimen of writing in order systematically to free himself from debt. His understanding of where he stood with Hearst, however, was all wrong. He thought that he was living on an expense account and that payment for his articles would go to Cora in England. In Hearst's eyes, it turned out, he was drawing inordinate advances on future articles, for which the pay was going to be twenty dollars per article and no more. Instead of making headway with old debts, he was compounding new ones at a staggering rate. He discovered his mistake with a shock when Hearst cut off the

---

Bookman, LXXVI [February, 1933], 137). This should have cleared his English debts easily, for Crane's letter to Reynolds, [Oxted], Feb. 7, [1898], mentions that the Harper payments for "The Monster" and "Death and the Child" had enabled him to reduce his debts from $2,000 to about $1,200 (*Letters*, p. 172). Although Crane was broke and had no credit at the time he wanted to get to America in April, there is no reason to think that the two months since February had got him deeper into debt at an abnormal pace. So even if he got only half the fee, as Stallman (*Crane*, pp. 350–351) conjectures, he should have been able to send most of it home and still have money for travel and expenses—especially since the *World*-chartered dispatch steamer on which he lived was presumably free to *World* correspondents. By the end of May, however, he was begging Reynolds: "Let me know by wire as soon as any sale whatever is effected. I need money. Address Key West Hotel" ("Off Havana," May 30, [1898], typed copy in Syracuse University Library).

Where did the money go? Crane's bonanza temperament might account for a little: Thomas Beer reports that he visited a Key West gambling house, where he *won* three hundred dollars; and that he found a hardship case like the Asbury Park cowboy and the stranded runaway in San Antonio and "gave a lad from Wisconsin, discharged for heart trouble without any means of leaving Tampa, the necessary fifty dollars for his fare" (Beer, *Crane*, pp. 180, 182). Once he left Florida, he seemed to have no money as well as no opportunity to spend. Also, he seemed to be sending money to Cora by way of his friend John Scott-Stokes. On June 8 he wrote Reynolds: "If you have collected any money write me both at the Key West Hotel and at Hotel Litchfield, Port Antonio Jamaica. I will then cable you what to do with it. Probably I will ask you to cable it to Scott Stokes, Savage Club, London, as usual" ([n.p.], June 8, [1898], typed copy in Syracuse University Library). Sending money to Cora by way of Scott-Stokes seems to have been a device for keeping his marital arrangement unpublicized in America.

After his illness in June came new costs and then, in Havana, new spending; Cora seems to have got no more money. Moreover, after his letter to Cora of Aug. 16 Crane lapsed into silence (Cora Crane to Reynolds, [Oxted], Sept. 25, 1898, *Letters*, p. 186)

money. In early September he left his hotel with a big bill unpaid and moved into a cheap boardinghouse instead.[96]

His reversals of fortune were occurring more and more rapidly, and though the change in his prospects and the more tangible change in his environment did not have the same effect as fever and war, Crane was hit hard. He could face his debts to Hearst—and the Hotel Pasaje—because steady work gave him hopes of paying off. He wrote six hundred words a day and seems to have spent much of the rest of his time with newspaper friends in the cafés of Havana. In some respects it was like a throwback to the boyish freedom of Mexico City just three and a half years earlier. But he could stabilize his life only within this narrow range. With respect to the world beyond, he had gone into an almost complete withdrawal. From Cora Crane's point of view he had simply disappeared. For her, his letters and Hearst's payments both failed at once. After a letter of August 16, she heard nothing, and when she got a news report that he was missing, her fears began to mount. She did not even hear that he was alive until the end of September, and she seems not to have had word directly from him for more than a month after that. Even Reynolds was so out of touch that, in mid-September, he wrote to England for news, but Crane's letters to him began coming again as if there had never been a break. Part of the difficulty was in the mails: an August letter which Cora forwarded seems to have reached Crane only in November, and a series of his letters home was supposedly never mailed by a faithless and thieving servant in Mary Horan's boardinghouse. Nevertheless, Cora was right in her intuition that Crane did not want to leave Havana and return home. Hearst's stopped pay-

[96] The cutting off of the expense account and reversion from the agreement as Crane understood it to the twenty-dollars-a-column rate are discussed in two letters from Crane to Reynolds (Havana, Oct. 21, [1898], and Oct. 24, [1898], typed copies in Syracuse University Library). About Hearst's putative agreement to pay at least some of Crane's money to Cora in England, further research is needed. But it can be inferred from Cora Crane to Reynolds, [Oxted], Sept. 25, 1898, *Letters*, p. 186: "I am in great distress of mind as I can get no news through the Journal office here. . . . The Journal is behaving very shabily. I have been served with two summonds so you can see how bad matters really are." There are other evidences of Cora Crane's direct acquaintance with James Creelman, who headed Hearst's London office. And there is also Crane's statement to Reynolds: "I am afraid these Journal people have ruined me in England" (Havana, Nov. 1, [1898], typed copy in Syracuse University Library).

ments, he well knew, were ruining him in England, and within
the shelter of his routine he tried to ignore what he could not
handle. If he had been evasive with Port Jervis and his family,
he was now dodging his most serious personal obligation.[97] Even

[97] Crane's letter of Aug. 16 is mentioned in the Cora Crane letter to Reynolds
just cited. The postal blackout delayed for months Crane's receipt of a most
encouraging overture from the best young literary agent in England (James B.
Pinker to Crane, London, Aug. 22, 1898), discussed on p. cxvi below.
The demoralization implied by Crane's Havana withdrawal is most clearly
seen in his virtual desertion of Cora. Despite extenuating possibilities, he seems
to have acted worse than on any other occasion of his life. Two items of specific
evidence raise damaging questions about his conscious intent. First, when his
disappearance was confirmed by Reynolds' inquiry, the frantic Cora cabled the
Secretary of War to see whether the American authorities in Havana could trace
the missing man. The cable was held up in Washington until October, by which
time Cora had word of Crane's safety from Reynolds, and then was finally sent
on to Cuba on Oct. 9 (Cora Crane to the Secretary of War, Oxted, Sept. 25, 1898,
Letters, p. 187 and note). Otto Carmichael, a fellow newspaperman in Havana,
witnessed Crane's reaction to the news that he was being looked for:

The first time I ever met Crane was when General Wade, then chairman of
the American Evacuation commission in Havana, asked me to carry word to him
that he had a London cablegram for him. I told him in a cafe. He said,
"Thanks," and it passed out of his mind. The next day General Wade told me he
had another cablegram asking if the first had been delivered and would I kindly
tell Mr. Crane that the cablegram seemed important and that he should call at
the offices of the commission and get it. I delivered the second message at the
same place. Crane said:
"Say, didn't you tell me something about a cablegram yesterday?"
"Yes, I told you about one, and this second is an inquiry as to whether the
first was delivered."
"Yes, I see. Using the government to find me. Anyway, I'm much obliged."
And again he forgot all about it. Or at least he never paid any attention to my
notices. Some time later, after I had become acquainted, I told him that the
message was still in Wade's hands.
"Oh, it's some tradesman I owe a bill to, I suppose," and that is the last I ever
heard of it, although I saw a great deal of him afterwards. It is not likely that a
London tradesman would spend 60 cents a word to find out about a tailor bill,
even if Crane did owe one. He was not extravagant, or in the habit of owing
large sums. It simply struck him as nothing worth bothering with and he let it
go at that [Omaha Daily Bee, June 17, 1900, discovered by Virginia K. Knoll and
reprinted in "Stephen Crane in Havana," Prairie Schooner, XLIII, (Summer,
1969), 200–204].

It was Oct. 27 when General Wade finally reported back: "After these
inquiries Mr. Crane called and expressed regret at having caused so much
trouble. I do not know his business or why he has not communicated with his
family" (Letters, p. 187 note).
Meanwhile, Crane in Havana had thought of recouping his position somewhat
by having Reynolds sell his twenty-dollar New York Journal articles to out-of-
town papers. He wrote to the agent on Oct. 24, presumably about the time he
called on General Wade and acknowledged the cabled inquiries: "I may stay
here all winter if we can get that syndicate going" (Havana, Oct. 24, [1898],
typed copy in Syracuse University Library). His contemplation of an indefinite
stay is not easily reconciled with his obligations elsewhere.

when he did leave Cuba, he stopped in New York for a few weeks. While he was there, *Collier's* finally brought out "The Blue Hotel" in two parts, November 26 and December 3. The dead letter had been recovered and, with a little prodding, brought to light. Crane's correspondence with Cora also resumed. On November 28 he wrote to a friend: "How do you persuade anybody to do anything by cables and letters? I am very anxious to have Mrs. Crane come to this country. Mrs. Crane is very anxious to have me come back to England. We are carrying on a duel at long range, with ink." At year's end he finally embarked for England, where early in January he began picking up the threads of his life.[98]

Since his departure, Harold Frederic had died, and the ranks of the free-lunch crowd had generally thinned. But the press of creditors, after the recent months of no payments at all and the rumors that Crane might not come back, was more urgent than ever. Still, after the hard work at Havana, he had more stories to deploy and more projects to raise his confidence that 1899 would see him financially safe if only he could slide by the immediate threat of bankruptcy. Among the many details he took up with Reynolds as he prepared to battle for solvency, "The Blue Hotel" figured on two counts. First, there was the additional $125 due from Harper's as an advance for the *Monster* volume as soon as the contents were settled; and secondly, there was the prospect of English magazine sale by an agent who was anxious to take on his hitherto haphazard English business. On January 19 he wrote Reynolds:

I must have every pennie that you can wrest from the enemy. Go to Harpers and beg them for that £25. It is only fair that they shoud pay it because it was *they* who proposed buying the book rights to the "Monster", for a £50.—advance. We didn't Make any such suggestion. Indeed we were rather reluctant. Then they discover that they don't think the book is long enough and hold out £25.—. Who on our side

[98] Reynolds' prodding of Collier to get "The Blue Hotel" into print is inferred from Collier's answers of Nov. 4 and 6, cited in note 93 above.

Crane to Mrs. William Sonntag, [New York], Nov. 28, 1898, *Letters*, pp. 196–197. This letter is apparently Crane's first mention in America of a "Mrs. Crane." Cora had communicated to William Crane in her distress and so he knew of a "Mrs. Crane," but Stephen did not know he knew. Though only a few miles away, and after an absence of more than two years, he did not renew his ties with his brothers at this time; he stayed away from them.

said anything about the length of the "Monster"? Ask them why they don't print "The Blue Hotel" and "His New Mittens" in one volumn with the "Monster" and then pay up like little men. That would make 36000 words. . . . Has the "Blue Hotel" been sold here yet and where is the original ms. Please send it to me immediately. I find my English business in great form as far as go notices and the proper rivalry between publishers, magazines and weeklies. I can make lots of money this year if I can only get started fair. If I can't raise some money at once I'm going bankrupt. You know what that means. It won't do.[99]

Crane's suggestion for placing "The Blue Hotel," like so many of his money-raising schemes, got no immediate response, and so he hardly thought of it as final. As he then began to write the childhood sketches that were set in the same town as "The Monster" and "His New Mittens"—the Port Jervis of his boyhood —he kept track of his work by listing all of these together as "THE HARPER'S BOOK," while he put down "The Blue Hotel" and his recent work from Cuba as "War Stories, etc" and, in a later list, as his "New Collection." [100] A new set of cross-purposes developed, for Reynolds in New York guessed from the first two childhood sketches that they might evolve into a series and that Crane would at last have that unified set of stories which Walter Hines Page had commended as ideal for one of the big monthlies. Once he came to an understanding with Harper's that they could have first option on all the Whilomville stories for their magazine, it was not long before they agreed to the January suggestion about the Monster, paid the remaining $125 on the advance, and drew up a formal contract which Reynolds forwarded to England on March 15. When Crane returned it on March 31, he almost upset everything with a proposal based on the way he had recently been thinking about his new stories:

[99] Oxted, Jan. 19, 1899, typed copy in Syracuse University Library.

[100] On internal evidence the order of the three lists made in March, 1899, when the first tales of Whilomville had been written but were not yet being discussed with Harper's as a separate book, is as follows: one headed "Harper's Book," a list including "The Monster," "His New Mittens," three completed and two proposed tales of the new Whilomville series; one with two headings, "Harper's Book," followed by a list including four tales completed in the new series, and "War Stories, etc.," including "The Blue Hotel"; and "New Collection," a neater copy of the previous sublist including "The Blue Hotel" and four completed war stories and omitting half-formulated projects (MSS in Columbia University Libraries).

I recognize the kindness of Harper and Bro's. in accepting our proposal to print "The Monster" "The Blue Hotel" and "His New Mittens" in one volume. But please point out to them that this proposal was made before any other stories of Jimmie Trescott had been written and that at present my idea would be to remove "The Blue Hotel" entirely. It's introduction was in the nature of an expedient to fill up space. . . . However I recognize the right of Harper and Bro's. to have the phrase read as it now reads in the contract if they chose because it was originally our proposal.[101]

Fortunately he was willing to yield the point of artistic principle, or he might once more have alienated Harper's. As it was, he got a separate advance for the book version of the new Whilomville stories and the *Monster* volume finally reached the printer. Copyright application was made on November 2 and deposit made on December 2, and "The Blue Hotel," supposedly more companionable with "The Monster" than "Death and the Child" would have been, was finally published in book form.[102]

Crane's hope for English serial publication did not work out so well. In answer to his January inquiry, Reynolds let him know that his English agent was William Morris Colles of the Authors' Syndicate.[103] Crane wrote for authorization to retrieve Colles'

---

[101] Crane to Reynolds, Brede, March 31, 1899, typed copy in Syracuse University Library.

[102] Agreement that *Harper's* was to publish the new Whilomville series and that the stories were to be withdrawn from the English market was confirmed in a letter of Crane to Reynolds (Brede, March 2, 1899, typed copy in Syracuse University Library). The $125 advance was paid to Reynolds on March 6, and the contract for the *Monster* volume including "The Blue Hotel" was drawn March 8, 1899 (Harper's Contract Book 11, p. 18, and Harper's Contract Book 10, pp. 321–322). This corrects *Works*, Vol. VII, TALES OF WHILOMVILLE, p. xlix, where the advance is said to be of the same date as the contract. Though Reynolds presumably cabled the money at once, he did not forward the contract until March 15 (Reynolds to Crane, New York, March 15, 1898, ALS in Columbia University Libraries).

[103] Apart from their bibliographical and literary significance, Crane's relations with agents must be clarified for important biographical reasons. Hitherto, gaps in the correspondence and casual attribution of speculative dates to the letters have lent themselves to an impression that Crane was dealing simultaneously with several agents when he was under obligation to deal exclusively with one. But Reynolds' exclusive agreement to sell Crane's work in America, while it implied the possibility of his selling elsewhere, had not led him into the English market until his client was in Cuba. Crane in England had the guidance of his publisher, William Heinemann, who notoriously hated agents and tried to keep his writers from using them; of Robert McClure, whose London office had probably sold the English rights for such early Crane work as was published in *McClure's* and in England; and of friends like Joseph Conrad, who introduced

copy but quickly learned that Reynolds had already directed Colles to him. On February 18, 1899, Crane replied to Colles:

> Thank you very much for your kind note of the 15th—. Was the "Blue Hotel" sold at all in England? If it was not I suppose you still have that typed copy? and I would be very glad if you would send it to me. Since it has already been published in America I suppose there is very little use of keeping it going here. However you might let me know to what papers and magazines you have sent it to [104]

Crane was evidently satisfied that Colles had done the best he could, and he was grateful for the effort. He suggested the *Westminster Gazette* for a last try, but even that failed.[105] On his lists of stories the record of publication for "The Blue Hotel" was to remain "Collier's and" followed by a blank space. And the proper rivalry among publishers which he had hopefully described as his English situation worked out no better for book

---

him to David Meldrum of *Blackwood's*. In the letter of Jan. 19, 1899, Crane not only inquired after the manuscript of "The Blue Hotel" but also asked Reynolds how *Cornhill* and *Westminster Gazette* had got recent stories of his (Oxted, typed copy in Syracuse University Library).

The following month Crane renewed his questions in a way which reflected his having heard from Reynolds in the interval: " 'The Loan Charge of William B. Perkins' appeared here in the Westminster Gazett but where did the money go? If the Author's Syndicate has not yet paid you you had better send me authority to collect the money for this 'Perkins' yarn and also to claim that copy of the 'Blue Hotel' " (Crane to Reynolds, Brede, Feb. 13, 1899, typed copy in Syracuse University Library). This letter refutes the interpretation of Crane's relation with Colles (misspelled Collis) and with the agent James B. Pinker which appears in *Letters*, p. 211 n. ("By what method of rationalization did Crane convince himself of the propriety of his dealing with Collis at the very time he was sending urgent appeals to Pinker to save him from bankruptcy?") and in Stallman, *Crane*, p. 453 ("He was two-timing Pinker by dealing simultaneously with a Mr. Collis of another literary agency, The Author's Syndicate"). The charges of duplicity in his dealing with Colles are groundless.

James Hepburn, *The Author's Empty Purse and the Rise of the Literary Agent* (London, 1968), puts Reynolds, Pinker, and Colles in their historical context and provides a most useful guide to the evolving business of authorship.

[104] Crane to W. M. Colles, Brede, Feb. 18, 1899, *Letters*, pp. 211–212. The original of this letter, in the University of Virginia Library, is a very early example of typing done at Brede Place. The Crane typewriter was still new enough to be mentioned by Crane two weeks later in a letter to his brother: "Since we have had this machine I have lost some of my habits of being an ill correspondent" (to W. H. Crane, Brede, March 2, 1899, TLS at University of Virginia Library). Like dictation, home typing was a sign of Crane's economically prompted movement toward lower costs and more rapid production. He did not produce his best work under the discipline of the machine.

[105] Crane to Colles, [Brede], March 2, 1899, *Letters*, pp. 214–215. The proposed price of £15 came to three-quarters of a cent a word.

than for magazine sales. When Heinemann proposed to bring out a London *Monster*, Crane had to fill out the volume with more stories as he had done in the case of *The Open Boat*. Selecting the additional stories, he made yet another list.[106] But he did not live to see the volume, for which copyright deposit was made on February 25, 1901, more than eight months after his death.

Crane had reasons for thinking well of his English prospects at the beginning of 1899. Almost the first thing he saw when he landed was the *Academy* of December 17 with Edward Garnett's brilliant essay on his work.[107] Garnett admired his way of giving "an amazing insight into what the individual life is. And he does it all straight from the surface; a few oaths, a genius for slang, an exquisite and unique faculty of exposing an individual scene by an odd simile, a power of interpreting a face or an action, a keen realising of the primitive emotions—that is Mr. Crane's talent." Garnett's one reservation, his doubt about what might happen when "the picturesque phases of the environment that nurtured him" gave out, was a kind of witch's warning that Crane did well to ignore: his art did not depend simply on picturesque experience, and the thought that life itself, wasted by tuberculosis and the harassment of circumstance, might give out, could only have made him falter. Besides, his business for the moment had the same deceptive glow as his health. In November, 1898, when some of Cora's mail from England reached him, it included a three-month-old letter from the English literary agent James M. Pinker. Pinker asked for a story and volunteered to try for six guineas per thousand words (slightly over three cents a word). Crane immediately wrote Reynolds that if Blackwood did not accept his current offering, "The Price of the Harness," the story should be turned over to Pinker for the sure money it would bring. He for his part was keeping his New York agent informed of English possibilities. But Blackwood's acceptance of the story did not put an end to the matter; Cora, quite possibly acting on her own, sent Pinker some of Crane's old manuscripts, and so kept the relation alive. The eager London

[106] MSS in Columbia University Libraries.
[107] "Stephen Crane: An Appreciation," *Academy*, LV (1898), 484.

agent seems actually to have paid for the three stories he got before he sold them—as he would one day do quite regularly. Even more important, he opened negotiations with Methuen for a book that would bring a handsome advance and the best royalties that Crane had ever seen.[108]

When Crane returned to England in January, 1899, it was

[108] Pinker to Crane, London, Aug. 22, 1898, ALS in Columbia University Libraries; Crane to Reynolds, Havana, Nov. 3, [1898], *Letters*, p. 193.

Cora Crane may have acted on her own with respect to selling stories that Crane had left in England, but presumably she heard from him before sounding Pinker out concerning an as yet unwritten book-length work. On Nov. 25, 1898, Pinker was responding to her suggestion when he wrote: "I have just received your letter of yesterday. If you will put me in possession of all the facts, I will at once see what I can do; but I ought to be in a position to make a more definite proposal to a publisher than I could do on your suggestion. A publisher would be more ready to advance the amount on a long book than on the short stories, but can you tell me what Mr. Crane's engagements with other publishers are, so that I can offer a definite book on a particular date? I will gladly do all that is possible if you will tell me exactly how matters stand with regard to Mr. Crane's future work" (ALS in Columbia University Libraries).

Cora pressed the negotiation, for she desperately wanted to make his return to England as attractive as it was urgent. If Crane was right to call their exchanges of cables and letters "a duel at long range, with ink" (to Mrs. William Sonntag, [New York], Nov. 28, 1898, *Letters*, pp. 196–197), then Cora was enlisting Pinker as a second. On Nov. 30 the agent wrote: "I have seen about the book to-day, and I hope by the end of the week to have a definite offer to cable to Mr. Crane" (ALS in Columbia University Libraries).

With Pinker's help, Crane's relations with publishers in England became as complicated as in the United States. The agent was switching Crane from his regular publisher, Heinemann (that hater of agents), to another who would offer much better terms. The Pawling referred to in Pinker's letter of Dec. 2, 1898, is Sidney Pawling, Heinemann's partner:

Mr. Pawling sent round to me this morning and presented your note instructing me to pay to Heinemann & Co. the money received for the three stories I at present hold. I did not, of course, mention any other business.

I have received, today, the following offer for the book of which we spoke. Methuens are willing to advance £50, or—if absolutely necessary—£75, at once, as an instalment of an advance of £125 on a novel of not less than 70,000 words: the Ms. to be delivered in July for publication in September or October next. The advance is to be on account of the following royalties: 16⅔ per cent on the first 3000 copies, 20% on the next 3000 and 25% after, with 3½ d. per copy on the Colonial edition. The advance is, of course, not what you anticipated, but I daresay I can persuade them to increase it. But, before negotiating further, can you let me have an assurance from Mr. Crane that he will be able to deliver the Ms. of the book by the time specified (ALS in Columbia University Libraries)?

Pawling was putting together a sum which was to pay Crane's way home, and he objected a few weeks later to being asked for more without any report of Crane (to Cora Crane, London, Jan. 2, 1899, ALS in Columbia University Libraries). His care to keep his help for Crane on a tough businesslike basis makes clear how far Crane had come since working for Bacheller and how great was his need for a skilled agent.

natural that he should regard Pinker as a financial savior of
sorts. He gave him charge of his stories for the British market,
got him to stand surety for his most pressing debts, and chan-
neled his American fees from Reynolds directly to the London
agent for redistribution to the most ardent creditors. He saw
that, quite apart from natural kindness, the agent's patent motive was plain business confidence in his own future career.
When Crane met this dazzling young man, the confidence
rubbed off and he came home with a rather inflated idea of what
was possible.[109] Writing to Reynolds, he advised taking a hard
line with Harper's or even ignoring them with respect to his new
Whilomville story because "my English magazine rights are now
going for sure nine guineas a thousand words, and so it does not
behoove me to sell many stories to the three all-over-the-places."
In February his estimates sank only very slowly in the direction
of reality. He still wanted Reynolds to avoid Harper's with the
new stories, for "with you in the U. S. getting quite ten pounds a
thousand for the American serial rights alone and Pinker over
here getting quite seven pounds a thousand for English serial
rights alone, it seems that the International Magazines are
mainly a source of pain and they will jolly well have to wait until
my present difficulties are over." [110] Crane's playing hard to get
and Reynolds' accurate estimate of what was possible led to the
March arrangements with Harper's. Crane's discovery that
Pinker had been talking about dollars rather than pounds and

[109] Well he might! By Jan. 24, 1899, Pinker had worked the Methuen offer up
to £100 on signature of the contract and another £100 on publication (ALS in
Columbia University Libraries). This was for a novel of the American Revolution which Crane projected, but of which he seems never to have written a word.
    Ford Madox Ford recalled a visit of Crane's to Pinker from which he came
back to Oxted "with hampers of *foie gras* and caviar and champagne," to
celebrate the agent's having promised him "twenty pounds for every thousand
words he chose to write." Ford assigned the incident to the fall of 1897, but if
anything like it occurred, it must have been when Crane got back to England
early in 1899. The memory of twenty pounds per thousand words was the sort of
exaggeration that, when duly spread around, brought the free-lunch friends
from great distances. But the rate is exactly twice the maximum Crane got when
he was able to sell to the international monthlies, and it is more than twice
Crane's fondest illusion of what Pinker might be able to do. Yet the foie gras
and caviar and champagne are realistic details that invite one to find the
credibility within the exaggeration, which in this case seems to be that (a) the
book advance was freshly settled and (b) Pinker apparently promised equal
success when he would be selling English serial rights at the best possible prices
(Ford, *Portraits from Life* [Boston and New York, 1937], p. 25).
[110] Crane to Reynolds, Oxted, Jan. 31, 1899, and Brede, Feb. 13, 1899, typed
copies in Syracuse University Library.

was, it turned out, unable to sell the Whilomville stories in England at all, led to his coming round to Harper's terms.[111] While things went well he scarcely noticed that his high hopes for an English career were not quite coming to pass. Instead, he cheered Reynolds for his brilliant work: "I only wish I could get my English Agent to imitate your success." Business was for the moment like a game, and he laughed as he watched the sharpening rivalry between agents. When he now took the stories consigned to Harper's off the English market, he jokingly told Reynolds: "I may say for your edification that you have one bitter enemy in England, Pinker by name."[112]

At the end of March, Pinker may have been smarting at the way Crane used him as a paymaster to his creditors but kept withdrawing stories from him as an agent. By summer, however, there was a reversal of fortune whereby Reynolds was dropped and Pinker became exclusive agent. In August, Crane was advising his London agent about his American market and bringing him up to date on his current work:

My stories are developing in three series. I. The Whilomville stories. (always to Harpers.) / II. The war tales. / III. Tales of western American life similar to "Twelve O'Clock."

It might be well to remember this. For instance if you could provisionally establish the war tales with one magazine and the western tales with another as the Whilomville yarns are fixed with Harper's, it would be very nice.[113]

[111] "Your last two sales with the Harpers [the Whilomville tales] pleased me immensely and I was delighted to withdraw them without sacrifice from Pinker who was ass enough to think them not good enough" (same, Brede, March 2, 1899, typed copy in Syracuse University Library).

[112] Same, Brede, March 25 and March 31, 1899, typed copies in Syracuse University Library.

[113] Crane to Pinker, Brede, [August, 1899], Letters, p. 214 (my dating). This letter, misdated by editorial conjecture in Letters, belongs very close in time with the letter to Pinker which Crane dated Aug. 4, 1899 (Letters, p. 223). The former promises, "Today I will dictate for you some information as to my U.S. market." The latter says, "I enclose a statement concerning my best American buyers. I shall write to some of the editors who lately have been asking me for stories." The first evidence of a sale of American serial rights by the London agent is in a letter of Pinker to Crane (London, Sept. 10, 1899, ALS in Columbia University Libraries).

As for the break with Reynolds, Pinker—when this new relation was in turn being strained—indignantly quoted back to the Cranes a Crane letter of Jan. 5, 1900: "I must have the money. I cannot get on without it. If you cannot send £50 by the next mail, I will have to find a man who can. I know this is abrupt and unfair, but self-preservation forces my game with you precisely as it did with Reynolds" (Pinker to Cora Crane, London, Jan. 9, 1900, Letters, p. 260).

Having at last got the idea of American marketing techniques, Crane did not let the thought cross his mind that it took a man like Reynolds to make them work. The wonder is that even without the opportunities of New York, Pinker did very well indeed. Luckily Crane had found a man who was not only young, sympathetic, and generous but also the ablest of English agents.

The 1899 stories which Crane described to Pinker lacked the charged intensity of his early work and, even more, the quiet but fully realized depth of the year's work that began with "The Open Boat." His war tales shifted focus from the inner experience of the soldier, or the relation of war to society and nature, to the stoical conduct of men inured to combat. His Whilomville tales concentrated more on the notation of childhood experience and less on the child in society or the small town in the world. The range of the Western tales was also narrower and bleaker but, because the stylized Western conventions constantly evoked for Crane the supposed realities of his middle-class reading public, his old sense of irony was freshened. The Wild West generally, like the boyhood town, was a place of imaginative escape where the mind could play and moments of comedy erupt. But the élan was gone, with which the two Kids in Mexico City had represented the spirit of youth, and the sustained effect of the later Western stories was not gay or even comic, but grim. Writing feverishly against the vague deadlines of bankruptcy and, as he may have guessed by now, of mortality, he showed how he could create variations on themes that he had earlier made his own.

The August letter to Pinker, in which he spoke of Western tales in the plural, indicates that he had finished "Twelve O'Clock" and turned it over to the agent, while he had at least conceived "Moonlight on the Snow." "Twelve O'Clock," which came out in the *Pall Mall Magazine* in December, 1899, is set in the historical moment when the Wild West was coming to an end; the time just verges on the post–Wild West phase which prevails in Yellow Sky and Fort Romper. When the shopkeepers prepare for the cowboys' payday visit to town, they feel a judicious fear for their own skins and a prudent concern for the effect gunplay might have on hypothetical Eastern investors. When the cowboys arrive, one of them, in the lobby of Placer's Hotel, sees a cuckoo clock for the first time in his life and, running to tell his friends, sets himself up as the butt of a practical joke. Another cowboy, "whose mother had a cuckoo-clock in her house in Philadelphia," throws in with the forces of disbelief and directs the teasing. The victim of the joke brings his tormentors to the hotel where, a little before the hour, he can point to the clock but no bird. When the teasing turns to quarreling and two cowboys reach for their six-shooters, the hotelkeeper speaks up from behind his counter "with an aimed revolver in each hand." But the look of authority does not work according to literary rules: "Big Watson laughed, and, speeding up his six-shooter like a flash of blue light, he shot Placer through the throat —shot the man as he stood behind his absurd pink counter with his two aimed revolvers in his incompetent hands." The complicity of the Easterner, the absurdity of the pink counter, the portentousness of the wooden bird cuckooing over the corpse at the end, convey, like the comparable elements of "The Blue Hotel," Crane's belief that life is mysterious, fragile, and of little import to the universe. And yet it seems as if not character but incompetence is fate; there is no shadowing doubt about the Philadelphia cowboy's involvement; the absurdity of the pink counter lacks the vital assertiveness of Scully's feat with blue paint on the prairie. The well-made plot ends with the finality of Q.E.D. The unanswered questions that art and life tend to raise are missing. There is no need for interpreters.

"Moonlight on the Snow," presumably one of the "tales of western American life" which Crane had in mind in August, 1899, began as an ironic anecdote of the same order as "Twelve O'Clock," but despite the pressures of his harassed final year, Crane let this story mature in his imagination until it became something more complex. His first note for the story reads simply: "The town was troubled over it. Nobody had been hung in Crazy Cross for months and it seemed unnecessarily harsh that the first victim of the new law should be such a valuable citizen as Snub Parsons." [114] Nothing at all came of this at first because

[114] MS in Columbia University Libraries. This fragment, discovered by Fredson Bowers, is published here for the first time. It is on wove paper, unlined, without watermarks, vertical measurement 203 mm., horizontal measurement 150 to 167 mm., with the left margin torn irregularly (description courtesy of Kenneth A. Lohf, Librarian for Rare Books and Manuscripts, Columbia University). The

Crane had his hands full with the other projects he had described to Pinker: he wrote war stories with an eye on the stipulated word count that would bring him the advance for his Cuban volume, and he resumed the Whilomville series, which brought quick and certain payment. Sometime in late September he returned to his story of the town that was reluctantly outgrowing its Wild West phase. This time he had the name of the town right and obviously had greater command of the details. He had even found his social theme: the town's desire to join the real estate boom and the universal itch to get something for nothing were the forces behind the drive toward law and order. Yet the surviving page of manuscript, neatly written and conscientiously corrected as if it were to go from Crane's hand directly to a typist, must be called a false start rather than a draft of the final version. It reads:

The citizens of War Post were annoyed and dubious. They had not expected that the first man to fall under the shadow of the new rule against promiscuous shooting would [*] be Ignatius Burke, the talented young bar-keeper, the man who had [b] chiefly concerned himself with the passing of the law. It seems that War Post had been getting a bad name. The word had gone among the mountain trails that when the stranger went to War Post there was hardly a known line of conduct which would please that critical town and the stranger usually came away bewildered and bandaged. Three-ace Frederickson, a well-known brawler from Fargo City once sojourned in War Post and afterward he often cared to tell his impressions. "They aint no use in being polite with 'em. They don't give a dam whether you're polite or not.[c] Now, look at me. I went over there thinking I'd be nice to 'em an' I was polite as hell. Well, what [d] did they do pretty soon? [e] Get mad! Get mad so bad that after about three fights, I hit the trail. I see there was no good a-stoppin' to reason with 'em when they got mad just b'cause I was polite".

For a long time War Post had taken a high pride in her sinister fame. When abroad, her swaggering citizens said: "I'm f'm War Post" much as they would have said: "I'm the devil himself." They thought

handwriting, larger and rounder than Crane's finished copyscript of the fragment discussed below, may indicate the informal nature of the note (there are six uncrossed t's in two sentences) or, possibly, an earlier date of composition than 1899. There are no deletions or corrections.

it very nice to be known [f] as one of such a justly celebrated collection of desperados.

All went well until certain real estate booms began to strike here and there among the hills. New towns leaped into being [115]

Breaking off in the middle of a sentence and the middle of a line, Crane evidently recognized that he did not yet have the key to his story. However long he set the work aside—he probably wrote the story in late September or early October, and at any rate he had it in Pinker's hands unsold in the latter part of October [116]— he conceived a new central character before he took it up for the last time. Instead of the simple irony whereby the bartender-lawgiver would be the victim of his own law, he now emphasized

[115] MS in Columbia University Libraries. This fragment, discovered by Fredson Bowers, is published here for the first time. It is on wove paper, unlined, without watermarks, measuring 228 × 138 mm., and it is written on the verso of a sheet of "Royal Pavilion Hotel, Folkestone" stationery (description courtesy of Kenneth A. Lohf). The following manuscript changes occur:

a would] 'w' *written over* 'sh'; *note that the grammatical structure of the earlier fragment required* 'should'
b had] *a following* 'been' *is deleted*
c not.] *a following* 'Do' *is deleted*
d what] *inserted with a caret*
e soon?] *written above an original* 'ma' *deleted*
f known] *final* 'ed' *of an original* 'knowned' *deleted*

The use of Royal Pavilion Hotel stationery suggests a rough date for the fragment. The suggestion is not entirely unequivocal since there were a number of occasions on which Crane might have picked up the paper. He and Conrad sometimes moored their jointly owned boat at Folkestone (Stallman, *Crane*, p. 466), but if there were not time to get home after boating, Crane would have stayed with the Conrads, who had moved to Stanford, near Hythe, only a few miles down the coast. In early September, 1899, when he was to take his niece to her school in Switzerland, he decided that Cora and their guest-in-residence Edith Richie should come part of the way and spend a few days in Paris. On the way out, according to Edith Richie, they spent the night before taking the Folkestone steamer at the H. G. Wellses' house, just outside the channel port. The way back was another matter, as she further remembered: Paris was gay, Crane was doing a lot of writing, "but suddenly we all got homesick for Brede and the dogs and decided to go home" (Edith R. Jones, "Stephen Crane at Brede," *Atlantic Monthly*, cxciv [July, 1954], 59–60). An unexpected return would have left them without the chance of staying with friends or of being met at Folkestone by a carriage from Brede, and a Baedeker-starred hotel in that fashionable town was just the sort of place in which the Cranes would stay. On Sept. 4 Crane had not yet left Brede. On Sept. 22 he was very recently returned, back at his desk, and free to turn his mind to other tasks than his war stories. On "September 31" (!) he sent Pinker the first of his Wyoming Valley stories. On the first two occasions when "Moonlight on the Snow" is mentioned in the surviving documents, it and the Wyoming Valley stories are mentioned together and in that order (*Letters*, pp. 229, 231, 232–233, 235, 260).

[116] Crane to Pinker, Brede, [Oct. 21?, 1899], *Letters*, p. 235.

the reflective irony of a victim who understood his destiny. Among fellow townspeople who are carried along by events they do not understand, he alone can explain the historic laws of progress to which the town has instinctively committed itself: "'The value of human life has to be established before there can be theatres, water-works, street cars, women and babies.'" The Wild West must pass, and at least one witness to the event is capable of being an interpreter.

With this change, the elements of his composition fell into place for Crane. He discarded the old beginning and now wrote instead his epical description of the ferocity of War Post and the "serene-browed angel of peace" that subdued it. In the brilliant opening pages of the story, only one sentence of the early version survives, and even that is improved by the rounder cadence: "When a citizen went abroad in the land he said, 'I'm f'm War Post.' And it was as if he had said, 'I am the devil himself.'" The humor of the story becomes at once both broader and grimmer, for given an interpreter within the tale, the narrative voice may freely develop its stylized hyperbole. In a sense the story becomes more impersonal with the change of victim. The new character and "chief factor in the life of the town" is Tom Larpent. He is the ironical descendant of the gambler in "The Blue Hotel," but there are evidently other sources also. He bears unobtrusive signs of education (in private, he reads). And "his slow speech had a certain mordant quality which was apt to puzzle War Post, and men heeded him for the reason that they were not always certain as to what he was saying." He speaks, in short, like a cross between Stephen Crane and Mark Twain's Colonel Sherburn. On the day after War Post has opted for law and order, the gambler kills a man for saying that he cheated, and accepting the town's new righteousness as irrevocable, he quietly awaits the consequences. His coolness, founded in an inexplicable readiness to be hanged, permits him to comment derisively on the textbook-conventional events which follow, as if he were the detached observer and not the appointed victim. His fellow townsmen and would-be lynchers seem not to know the usual script, and so they feel more and more as if they were helplessly caught in an ungovernable drama. Then, out of another fictive world, Jack Potter and Scratchy Wilson, sheriff and deputy now, arrive on the scene to arrest Larpent on a charge of grand larceny. The wicked citizenry of War Post, happy to be relieved of their lynching, relapse to what they think is lawlessness and resolve to stand by their leading citizen: "All he's up against is a case of grand larceny; and—even supposin' he done it—what in hell does grand larceny amount to?" But the ironic interplay of law and anarchy, virtue and commercial value, is not so jolly as that last question makes it sound. What lies beneath the surface is suggested by the title, which is deceptively romantic in tone but not in meaning. "Moonlight on the Snow" has nothing to do with the literal plot, which takes place in no particular season. The phrase is adapted from a description of Tom Larpent and suggests the origin of his ironic powers: standing with a noose around his neck, he looks "handsome and distinguished and—a devil. A devil as cold as moonlight upon the ice." His slow mordant speech evidently expressed a chill that matched such blizzards as Crane had known and imagined.[117]

As a literary property, "Moonlight on the Snow" did not do well. In October, Crane tried to get Pinker to advance out of his own pocket what the story *might* eventually bring. As Pinker began making payments on future values, Crane minimized the speculative risk by assuring the agent of his own steady industry. Unfortunately, his demands on the agent exceeded his capacity to reassure. By January, 1900, when the story was still unsold, he became so importunate that there was almost a break with the English agent like the earlier break with Reynolds. But with the unmistakable onset of tuberculosis, prudence went into the balance, and he declared his harshest words unsaid. Pinker's compassion entered the balance, too, and he continued to work

[117] It is widely held (Beer, *Crane*, p. 178; Berryman, *Crane*, p. 219; Stallman, *Crane*, p. 355) that Tom Larpent is modeled on the roulette man whom Crane observed in a Key West gambling house during the Spanish War. Beer cites a letter from Crane to Robert Barr, May 23, 1898: "You should see the jay who runs the table here. He is straight out of a dime novel, moustache and all, with bunches of diamonds like cheap chandeliers on each hand." Beer also goes on to paraphrase Crane's report that this gambler knew at least nine hundred different oaths, told wildly bawdy stories, and was highly theatrical in his sarcasm. But Larpent scarcely swears—not at all in polite company—and he does not tell dirty stories. He does qualify as sarcastic, but he is not in any ordinary sense theatrical. A few of those rings like chandeliers would have brightened him up considerably.

for Crane as before. He placed this story with *Frank Leslie's Popular Monthly*. His knack with the American market was improving. Toward the end of February he conceived a whole new series and had *Harper's Bazaar* ready to take it on the basis of his proposal only. By then, however, there were to be no more stories at all. And by the time "Moonlight on the Snow" came out in April, Crane was a dying man.[118]

After Crane died, on June 5, 1900, Cora took the body home for burial and stayed on for a few weeks of sad, warmhearted family visit with the Port Jervis Cranes. When she returned to England, she began as efficiently as she could to settle Crane's affairs. First of all, she gave up their elaborate and costly establishment at Brede Place and moved to a London flat. Then she went through Crane's manuscripts and records to find what was unsold, or published in magazines only, or published in one country only—to find, as she thought, what he had left her to live on. "Moonlight on the Snow" came up in her questions more than once. In asking Pinker whether it had been published in England, she made clear her hopes for selling serial rights. In asking about book contracts, she brought it up again. She claimed that, concerning the "list of stories you say Mr. Crane promised Harpers I can only find note of 'Moonlight on the Snow —& one or two possible others.'" Wishfully suggesting so small an obligation, she revealed her obvious reluctance to use up much of her capital to enlarge the London *Monster* beyond the New York edition.[119] Her need was great. She had no money to

[118] Crane to Pinker, Brede, [Oct. 21?, 1899], *Letters*, p. 235.
"I am sorry that the collections are so slow. I can do nothing save to continue to turn out the best work in my power and turn it out as fast as possible" (same, Brede, Nov. 4, 1899, *Letters*, p. 239).
Cora Crane to Pinker, [Brede, Jan. 8, 1900], *Letters*, pp. 259–260 (my dating); Pinker to Cora Crane, London, Jan. 9, 1900, *Letters*, p. 260; Pinker to Crane, London, Feb. 26, 1900, ALS in Columbia University Libraries.
Crane began a bad series of hemorrhages on April 1. When he next had a remission, Cora indulged in self-deceptive hopes but he proceeded to make a will. Stallman, *Crane*, pp. 501–504, provides a detailed account.
[119] Shortly after her return, as she sent lists of questions to Pinker, she named "Moonlight on the Snow" among the stories for which she wanted to know about possible English publication. She touched on other matters before getting around to: "And please say what you want to give Harpers—what stories—for the English edition of 'The Monster.' Remember there is a book of short stories to be gotten together as well. Would it do to offer them one more short story?" (London [August, 1900], ALS in Dartmouth College Library).

pay furniture movers or to pay for her London lodgings, and Pinker was her only source. When he was unable to sell stories about which he found it hard to be enthusiastic, she took back his remaining manuscripts and turned instead to G. H. Perris and his Literary Agency of London. Perris, whose tone in his letters was that of an intelligent, sympathetic man, had evidently had experience with the bereaved; as if in kindness, he offered to handle Cora's business for 15 per cent commission. Luckily, she was a woman of the world and knew enough to instruct him that she would pay the usual 10 per cent.[120] She had better luck on another front, for Reynolds had, in the hard months of Crane's final illness, quietly overlooked the past and begun working again on his behalf.[121] But income from magazine sales only trickled in, and income from books hardly came at all. Exactly a year went by between her instructing Pinker to send the promised stories—including "Twelve O'Clock" and "Moonlight on the Snow"—to Harper's London office and their reporting back to the agent that they had finally secured authorization from New York to pay royalties on English editions to Crane's English executor. Deposit at the British Museum was made on February 23, 1901, and Cora left England at the end of April apparently without having received any royalties.[122]

The reason Cora had been anxious about the *Monster* was that she wished to make another book of short stories out of Crane's

[120] "I shall go over what ms. I have of my late husbands and send the stories for you to sell for me, but of course you will not charge me 15%. 10% is the usual rate of commission every where" (Cora Crane to Perris, London, Sept. 13, 1900, ALS in Yale University Library). Cora had been warned by her first experience in dealing with the man: "Dear Sir: I have qualified your form of receipt for the story 'The Squire's Madness', as I cannot believe you offer only £10—for *all* rights. I need the money, at once, & so if you think that is all you can offer for both American & English *serial* rights, I will except the £10— but I cannot let you have book rights as well" (same, Aug. 28, 1900, ALS in Yale University Library).

[121] Relations with Reynolds were reopened by the agent with a routine report on a manuscript still on hand (Reynolds to Crane, New York, Jan. 9, 1900, TLS in Columbia University Libraries), and by April regular communication was resumed. Instructions to Perris to see that Reynolds got story copy in New York (Cora Crane to Perris, London, Nov. 2, 1900, ALS in Yale University Library) brought him a number of stories that Pinker had already tried to sell to American magazines, with embarrassing consequences for Reynolds (Reynolds to Cora Crane, New York, Dec. 14, 1900, TLS in Columbia University Libraries).

[122] Cora Crane to Pinker, London, Oct. 3, [1900], TLS in Dartmouth College Library; F. W. Slater to Pinker, London, Oct. 3, 1901, TLS in Dartmouth College Library.

remaining manuscripts. The miscellaneous volume *Last Words* which she put together disclosed to her the bitter truth about where she stood financially. It was sold in England to Digby, Long and Company, presumably after Crane's former publishers had been tried and found uninterested, and the English executor under Crane's will saw to it that Cora got twenty pounds immediate payment for her services in putting the book together. Though the book was announced in the *Publishers' Circular* of March 29, 1902, copyright deposit was not made until May 16. The hope of a simultaneous American edition would sufficiently explain the delay, and the frustration of that hope gave the final turn to Crane's business history. In October, 1900, Reynolds had virtually sold the prospective volume to Frederick Stokes for a fifty-pound advance on a 15 per cent royalty, except that the publisher wanted to see at least a good sample of the copy. "The trouble I think will be just here," Reynolds reported. "Some of the stories that you have selected are really sketches. . . . Some of the stories don't seem to me fully up to Mr. Crane's standard." And one device that he recommended was that she send the four stories which added bulk to the London *Monster* in order that they might add quality to the American *Last Words*.[123] When Cora then requested a one-hundred-pound advance, Stokes declined the book. In the spring of 1901 Reynolds managed to sell the volume to Henry T. Coates of Philadelphia.[124]

On May 14 Reynolds reported to Cora that he had collected the two-hundred-fifty-dollar advance, and he went on to say: "Remembering that I paid to Judge [William] Crane some money that I received for a story from the Cosmopolitan entitled 'The

[123] W. H. Crane to Reynolds, New York, Nov. 11, 1901, TLS in University of Virginia Library; Reynolds to Cora Crane, New York, Oct. 23, 1900, TLS in Columbia University Libraries; same, Dec. 28, 1900, TLS in Columbia University Libraries.

[124] Joseph Coates must also have known something about widows and estates, for he asked Reynolds for assurance of copyright ownership (Philadelphia, April 12, 1901, TLS in University of Virginia Library), and Cora replied to the agent promptly: "Will you please say to Henry T. Coates and company of Philadelphia, that I own the exclusive book rights of the book of short stories which I am selling to them. Mr. Crane never sold book rights of short stories except those sold to Harpers by yourself" (London, April 26, 1900, ALS in University of Virginia Library). She obviously thought that ended the matter, but subsequent events evidently persuaded the cautious Mr. Coates to let his advance go and not publish the book.

Great Boer Trek' I asked Judge Crane, as executor of Mr. Stephen Crane's will, if he had any objection to my paying such money to you. He replies that while he is not prepared to say he objects, at the same time he does not consent to such payment." His postscript—"Judge Crane said he should be glad to talk the matter over with you"—led Cora to be too hopeful concerning her own rights and her brother-in-law's fraternal sentiments. As American executor, he could recognize all the informal loans he had made to his brother as prior claims on the estate to be paid at once. He took care of himself easily enough, but so long as there were other possible debts, he saw no way to distribute any money from the estate to the widow. The situation seemed to be stalemated, with each of the interested parties forbidding Reynolds to give the check to the other. In July, however, the Judge began a new gambit. He asked for the list of stories that would make up the American edition of *Last Words* and made known his curiosity as to whether it would prove identical with that of the volume contracted for in England. There were further letters that seemed to get nowhere, but at last on October 21 William Crane announced his control of the situation:

As my official letters are only ancillary letters testamentary, I wrote to the English executor for instruction and learned from him that the same stories had been sold in England under the same title and that Mrs. Crane had made no claim to their ownership. On the other hand, she had filed a claim for compensation for her work in getting them into shape.

As nearly as I can make out, I have no right to consent that this money shall be paid to her.

On November 6 he repeated his statement of fact, making the point that Cora Crane had made no particular claim to ownership in her dealing with the English sale of *Last Words*, but only a claim for services: "I have written Mrs. Crane that she'd better consent that the moneys in your hands be paid to me, but have received no reply to my letter. I think, under the circumstances, you'd better pay the amount to me. You may take this letter as my agreement to indemnify you against any further payment to her." On November 19 he acknowledged receipt of a check from

Reynolds.[125] Coates never published the volume. It is possible that timidity about copyright kept him from crossing Cora Crane; it is doubtful that he recovered any of his advance from William Crane. By the time the book came out in England, Cora was back in Jacksonville—without youth, without hope, without the élan that had kept her in the old days from being character- ized by her seamy business. Though she was now on the down- ward slope, she held tenaciously to the memories—and the man- uscripts—which in the long run identified her with the best part of her life.

Some of the work in *Last Words* can be dated early and some late, but when there is no particular evidence the case may be truly ambiguous. The general evidence points in both directions. Early manuscripts were available because William Crane had been caught, at the time of Stephen's burial and Cora's family visit, in an unpredictable tide of warmth and spontaneity. He obviously came to resent his uncharacteristic behavior. In one of his final letters to Reynolds about the book, he reviewed what had happened: "Mrs. Stephen Crane gathered up from various sources and particularly among the brothers and sisters of de- ceased, various unpublished stories in manuscript," and thus con- firmed, among other things, that some of the literary remains dated from 1896 or earlier. Cora Crane, on the other hand, since her dignity and solvency did not have a very solid base, tried courageously to bluff a little. When she described her manuscript holdings to Perris, she declared, "Some of the stories are of Mr. Crane's latest," and she could show enough new work to make her statement seem to cover more than it did. The internal evi- dence is sometimes as equivocal as the external. It is hard to tell an early piece left in raw draft because it was unpromising from a late and somewhat weary attempt to see if anything more was to be got out of an old vein. Such a story is "A Man by the Name of Mud." It offers a final glimpse of the two Kids whose play made Crane's imaginary Mexico City a great place to be young in. In New York they lose their gaiety, and the reason is that a woman

[125] Reynolds to Cora Crane, New York, May 14, [1901—stationery with "1900" printed at the dateline was used], ALS in Columbia University Libraries; W. H. Crane to Reynolds, New York, July 13, 1901, TLS in University of Virginia Library; same, Oct. 21, and Nov. 6, 1901, ALS in University of Virginia Library; same, Nov. 19, 1901, TLS in University of Virginia Library.

has come between them. The offstage Kid—lending support to John Berryman's suggestion that the inseparable pals are simply Crane's self-projection twinned, the story gives no clue as to which Kid is which—has fallen in love with a chorus girl, courted her with becoming ingenuousness, and then in one blasé moment of wondering about her fidelity, offends her unforgivably. The on-stage Kid, "morose and unapproachable," is ragged by friends who think he is down because he misses his special comrade, but the problem lies elsewhere: "Once in a while he seemed to perceive certain futilities and lapsed then immediately into a state of voiceless dejection." Gossip turns him from "his harrowing scrutiny of the amount of pleasure he achieved from living" to contemplation of the particular case. The Kid who suffers dejection in general is virtually interchangeable with the Kid whose name is mud with the girl he loves. And yet the story is not a psychological projection merely, since it stands also as literary evidence that Crane's Wild West convention, whatever its possibilities within its artificial limits, was too narrow to be useful for rendering the experience of city life or even of that simplest human complication, sex. Though the story seems to be the work of a tired writer nearing the end of his career, it could have come from a young man experimenting to find what his fictional technique could and could not do.[126]

"A Poker Game," despite its lack of prairies and cowboys, belongs more clearly with Crane's Western stories; it seems to be a tall tale first and only after that a personal fantasy. Young Bobbie Cinch, whose father had the merit to corner the market in bay rum and bequeath him twenty-two million dollars, comes from Chicago to New York in search of fun. In that unfallen city the most natural entertainment is to call on his father's old friend Henry Spuytendyvil, who "owns all the real estate in New York save that previously appropriated by the hospitals and Central Park," and to pass a quiet evening at poker. The narrative focus on the tension of the poker game suggests the early Crane of 1895 or 1896, and the turning of phrases adds to the

[126] W. H. Crane to Reynolds, New York, Nov. 11, 1901, TLS in University of Virginia Library; Cora Crane to Perris [London, around September, 1900], ALS in Yale University Library.

Last Words (London, 1902), pp. 258–259. The misprint "lapsed them" has been corrected to "lapsed then."

probability: "Theatrically speaking, straight flushes are as frequent as berries on a juniper tree but as a matter of truth the reason that straight flushes are so admired is because they are not as common as berries on a juniper tree." When Spuytendyvil, after losing heavily, draws a straight flush, he tries to bluff his way to a great recovery by opening the betting low. Bobbie Cinch has a straight flush too, though lower than his opponent's. By every law of logic he should be tempted to disaster, but his good nature proves to be his luck. "Well, Mr. Spuytendyvil, I can't play a sure thing against you," he says, and instead of raising the bets, he calls. Character, chance, and fate coincide, as they did in "The Five White Mice," or "The Blue Hotel," or "Moonlight on the Snow." The plot does not date the story. Early or late, the fancy of unlimited wealth might have amused the hard-pressed Crane. Early or late, he had the imagination not only of disaster but also of generosity. If this is an early tale, it still can be taken as representative of Stephen Crane's *Last Words*.

J. C. L.

TEXTUAL INTRODUCTION
THE OPEN BOAT

I

MOST of the stories in the present collected volume come from *The Open Boat*. The bibliographical details of the initial appearance of all stories in magazines or in newspapers are provided in the second section of this textual introduction. *The Open Boat*, however, merits special treatment.

Copyright for the American edition was applied for and deposit made in the Library of Congress on April 18, 1898. As early as September 11, 1897, *Publishers' Weekly* had carried a 'just ready' notice, but the formal advertisement appeared in the issue of April 16, 1898, for the April 18 publication.

The description of this edition is as follows:

The Open Boat | And Other Tales of Adventure | By | Stephen Crane | Author of "Red Badge of Courage," | "The Third Violet," etc. | [leaf type-ornament] | New York | Doubleday & McClure Co. | 1898

Collation: [1–21]⁸ [22]⁴, pp. [i–viii] [1–2] 3–336. Text paper is laid unwatermarked with horizontal chainlines 31 mm. apart; leaf measures 6⅞₆ × 4⅛₆", all edges trimmed. Laid endpapers unwatermarked with vertical chainlines 20 mm. or 31 mm. apart. (Harvard AC 85.C8507.898a, with the binding state with the two dots, has the front flyleaf with vertical chains but the back with horizontal.)

Contents: p. i: half-title, 'The Open Boat | And Other Tales of Adventure'; p. ii: blank; p. iii: title; p. iv: 'Copyright, 1898, by | DOUBLEDAY & McCLURE CO.'; p. v: 'TO | THE LATE WILLIAM HIGGINS | AND TO CAPTAIN EDWARD MURPHY AND | STEWARD C. B. MONTGOMERY | OF THE SUNK STEAMER | COMMODORE'; p. vi: blank; p. vii: Contents; p. viii: blank. p. 1: 'The Open Boat | A Tale Intended to be after the Fact: | Being the Experience of Four Men | From the Sunk Steamer | "Commodore" '; p. 2: blank. pp. 3–336: text, beginning 'The Open Boat'.

Binding: Green cloth, silver and black design of sea and an open boat, continuing onto the spine, with title on front cover within a rule-frame in black outlined letters: 'THE OPEN | BOAT | Stephen Crane.' Spine: '|| THE | OPEN | BOAT | DOUBLEDAY | AND | MᶜCLURE CO.' Back cover: blank.

Three states of the binding have been observed, and just possibly a fourth. In the first the publisher's name at the base of the spine measures 15⁄32″ from top to bottom of the three lines, and two short horizontal lines appear under the superior 'c' of 'MᶜCLURE'. In the second, the measurement is 11⁄32″ and only a single line appears under the 'c'. The third state is readily recognizable by two dots under the 'c' and a measurement of 11⁄32″. In what may doubtfully be a fourth state two horizontal lines are under the 'c' as in the first, but the measurement appears to be 14⁄32″. However, a distinction this small in measurement is too uncertain to be positive that a different binding-up from the first state is actually present. The first state with the 15⁄32″ measurement is represented at the University of Virginia Library by the Barrett copy PS1449.C8506 1898 (551440), which has laid endpapers with vertical chainlines 31 mm. apart. The second is owned by Professor Matthew J. Bruccoli and has vertical chainlines 20 mm. apart. The third is the University of Virginia's McGregor copy A1898.C.706 (281462), with the two dots and vertical chainlines 20 mm. apart. The fourth, unless it is actually a duplicate of the first, is Barrett 551439, with vertical chains 31 mm. apart. The Columbia University Libraries copy B812.C85.U2 1898 agrees with the McGregor copy. The three University of Virginia copies have been collated on the Hinman Machine and show no variation in the plates. The evidence of type-batter is insufficient to demonstrate whether these are representative of different printings or else are merely separate bindings-up of the same printing.

Dust Jacket: Light gray paper. '[within a rule frame] | THE OPEN BOAT | AND OTHER STORIES | By STEPHEN CRANE | Author of "The Red Badge of Courage" | The opening story recounts the author's | own experiences in a shipwreck off the coast | of Florida, and is a most vivid and dramatic | presentation of the behavior of a company of | castaways fighting to the last limit of physical |

endurance against a destruction that, in spite of | everything, seems inevitable. Several of the | stories portray the adventurous life of the South-|western frontier. | [short rule] | DOUBLEDAY & McCLURE CO. | NEW YORK'. Spine: 'THE | OPEN | BOAT | DOUBLEDAY | & McCLURE | CO.' Back cover: blank.
Price: One dollar.

Simultaneous publication on April 18, 1898 (with deposit in the British Museum), occurred for the English edition published by Heinemann at a price of six shillings. The original eight stories in the American edition are grouped in a different order under the section title "Minor Conflicts," and nine previously published stories and sketches are added with the section title "Midnight Sketches."

The Open Boat | and Other Stories | By | Stephen Crane | Author of "The Red Badge of Courage," "The Little Regiment," | "The Third Violet," etc. | London | William Heinemann | 1898

Collation: [A]⁴ B-I⁸ K-U⁸, pp. [i–viii] [1–3] 4–301 [302–304] + publisher's catalogue in 16's, pp. [1–2] 3–32, dated March, 1898. Text paper laid unwatermarked with vertical chainlines 25 mm. apart; leaf measures 7½ × 5", all edges untrimmed. Wove endpapers.

Contents: p. i: half-title, 'The Open Boat | and Other Stories'; p. ii: advertisement for 12 novels; p. iii: title; p. iv: '*All rights reserved*'; p. v: 'To the Memory of | THE LATE WILLIAM HIGGINS | and to | CAPTAIN EDWARD MURPHY and STEWARD C. B. MONT-GOMERY | Of the sunk steamer "Commodore." '; p. vi: blank; p. vii: Contents; p. viii: blank; p. 1: 'Part I | Minor Conflicts'; p. 2: blank; text, pp. 3–207; p. 208: blank; p. 209: 'Part II Midnight Sketches'; p. 210: blank; pp. 211–301: text; p. 302: colophon, 'RICHARD CLAY & SONS, LIMITED, | LONDON & BUNGAY.' pp. 303–304: advertisements, 'STEPHEN CRANE'S WORKS'.

MINOR CONFLICTS

The Open Boat, p. 3
A Man and Some Others, p. 41
The Bride Comes to Yellow
    Sky, p. 65
The Wise Men, p. 85

The Five White Mice, p. 107
Flanagan, p. 129
Horses, p. 155
Death and the Child, p. 175

MIDNIGHT SKETCHES

An Experiment in Misery, p. 211   The Men in the Storm, p. 227

Binding: Light apple-green cloth, with title on front cover in blue: 'THE OPEN BOAT'. *Spine*: in gold, 'THE | OPEN BOAT | STEPHEN CRANE | HEINEMANN'. *Back cover*: blind, Heinemann's monogram. The catalogue is not present in all copies.

University of Virginia-Barrett PS1449.C8506 1898a (551441) has the autograph inscription on the front endpaper: 'Dear Mrs Moreton Frewen: You, with the rest of the world, have herein a further proof of my basic incapacity. However there are some stories of Americans and some stories of America in the book which may remind you of somebody better but, in any case, allow me to present my esteem   Stephen Crane February 7, 1899.' In the upper left of the inside cover is Cora Crane's inscription, 'From the Library of Brede Place'.

A new binding, designed by William Nicholson, was used after June, 1900, in tan linen: *Front cover*: design of lifeboat in black and red, with title [black] 'The Open Boat | [red] *By Stephen Crane*'. *Spine*: [black] The | Open | Boat | [red] *By Stephen* | *Crane* | [black and red: windmill device] | [black] *Heinemann*'. *Back cover*: lifeboat design. Owned by Professor Bruccoli.

The sheets for 575 copies, less catalogue, were sold to the Times Book Club on March 20, 1906, and issued in an orange binding, lettered in black. *Front cover*: 'The Open Boat | *By Stephen Crane*'. *Spine*: 'The | Open Boat | *By Stephen* | *Crane* | [seal of Times Book Club]'. *Back cover*: blank. The endpapers are wove. University of Virginia-Barrett PS1449.C8506 1898d (574819). Professor Bruccoli has a similar copy but bound in blue with black lettering.

Heinemann published a Colonial edition on April 20, 1898, consisting of 1,500 copies of a new printing from the same plates on thin wove paper, issued in paper wrappers at 2/6 and in cloth at 3/6. The front wrapper reads: '𝕳𝖊𝖎𝖓𝖊𝖒𝖆𝖓𝖓'𝖘 𝕮𝖔𝖑𝖔𝖓𝖎𝖆𝖑 𝕷𝖎𝖇𝖗𝖆𝖗𝖞 | [short rule] | The Open Boat | And Other Stories | BY | STEPHEN CRANE | *Author of "THE RED BADGE OF COURAGE,"* ETC. | LONDON | WILLIAM HEINEMANN | *Published for sale in the British Colonies and India only* | *⁎* *This volume may also be had in Cloth Binding, price Three Shillings* | *and Sixpence*'.

Back wrapper: advertisements on recto and verso, as on verso of front wrapper.

Title-page: 'THE OPEN BOAT | AND OTHER STORIES | BY | STEPHEN CRANE | AUTHOR OF | "THE RED BADGE OF COURAGE," "THE LITTLE REGIMENT," | "THE THIRD VIOLET," ETC. | LONDON | WILLIAM HEINEMANN | 1898'

Collation: same as the trade printing; wove paper, all edges trimmed.

Contents: p. i: '**Heinemann's Colonial Library of Popular Fiction.** [underlined] | *Issued for sale in the British Colonies* | *and India, and not to be imported* | *into Europe or the United States* | *of America*.'; p. ii: 'BY THE SAME AUTHOR | UNIFORM WITH THIS VOLUME | [five book titles] | LONDON: WILLIAM HEINEMANN | 21 BEDFORD STREET, W. C.'; p. iii: title; p. iv: '*All rights reserved*'; p. v: dedication, etc., as in trade edition, excluding added catalogue.

Special Collections Columbia University Libraries copy is from Crane's own collection. The front wrapper is signed by Cora Crane, 'Stephen Crane 6, Milborne Grove | The Boltons | S. W.' On the title Cora wrote, 'This book belongs to Mrs Stephen Crane | 6, Milborne Grove. The Boltons | S. W.' Laid in is a duplicate fold of the title and dedication leaves.

The 3/6 cloth copy is in red, stamped in black. Front cover: '[within blind rule-frame] The Open Boat'. Spine: '|| The | Open | Boat || Stephen | Crane | Heinemann || '. Back cover: Heinemann device within blind rule-frame. Owned by Professor Bruccoli.

These Colonial Edition sheets, the first leaf (pp. i–ii) canceled, were also bound in dark olive-green cloth, the front and back covers blank, the spine reading in gold, 'THE | OPEN | BOAT | STEPHEN CRANE'. The endpapers are wove paper. University of Virginia-Barrett, copy 1 (551443), copy 2 (551442).

As remarked, machine collation on the Hinman Collator discloses no textual variants in the three Barrett copies of the American trade edition; Professor Bruccoli has machine-collated a Heinemann trade edition against his Colonial Edition copy to establish that no textual variation in the plates is present. The documentary form without variation of both the American and English editions appears to be established.

The individual sections of the textual introduction detail the facts about variant readings and the transmission of the texts from magazine or newspaper to book form. The cumulative evidence indicates that Crane exercised some supervision over the Heinemann edition in that he established the desired order of the tales and provided the printer's copy himself. The authoritative variant readings found in this edition on the whole appear to stem more from annotations that Crane made in the printer's copy than from alterations marked in proof. It is probable that his proofreading was casual and that he had revised the copy as he finally wished when he submitted the clippings from English magazines. Admittedly, the documents preserved do not permit a distinction to be made between copy-annotations and proof-alterations when the printer's copy was a clipping. However, in the several stories that were not printed in magazines early enough for printed copy to be supplied Heinemann, like "The Wise Men," "The Five White Mice," and "Death and the Child," comparison of the text with the periodical publication in England and the United States does not suggest that any Heinemann variant reading is authorial and made in proof. In short, the evidence indicates some care with revision of copy but little or no care thereafter in altering the text in proof. However, for all its value in providing this small number of Crane's textual revisions, the Heinemann edition in other respects is no better than its copy, and it preserves the various errors that developed in the English magazine publications that were assembled for the printer.

No evidence suggests that Crane supervised in any way the production of the American edition, other than providing copy where American magazine versions were not available to Doubleday & McClure. The order of the stories seems to have rested, ultimately, with the convenience of the publisher, and it seems probable that when printed copy was available Crane merely noted sources and let the company obtain the clippings. Yet quite definite evidence suggests that Crane read proof for this volume and noted a very few revisions. These changes were made with no relation to the marking of copy for the Heinemann edition (readings which never reached the American edition) and hence are completely independent. Fortunately, there is only one case where Crane altered the same reading (differently) in the two editions. The proof-revisions are casual in the Doubleday & McClure edition, but one or more changes seem to occur in many stories. The difficulty, of course, is to identify proof-changes among relatively indifferent readings that might easily be compositorial or editorial variants.

From the collection *The Monster* published by Harper's in the United States in 1899 comes "The Blue Hotel," and from the expanded Heinemann *Monster* of 1901 come "Twelve O'Clock" and "Moonlight on the Snow." The bibliographical descriptions of these editions appear in Volume VII of this edition, TALES OF WHILOMVILLE, 3–4. The evidence is clear that whether or not Crane read proof for the American edition of *The Monster*, he made no alterations. The English edition was posthumous. From *Last Words* (1902) the present collection draws "A Poker Game." The bibliographical description of *Last Words* and an account of its publishing history will appear in Volume VIII of the Virginia edition.

II

THE PACE OF YOUTH

"The Pace of Youth," syndicated by Bacheller, Johnson & Bacheller, appeared in two parts in various American newspapers, usually on January 17–18, 1895. Six of these newspaper versions have been identified: the Dayton (Ohio) *Daily Journal*, January 17, 1895, p. 4, and January 18, p. 4 (N^1); *Kansas City Star*, January 17, p. 8, and January 18, p. 7 (N^2); *Nebraska State Journal*, January 18, p. 5, and January 19, p. 5 (N^3); New York *Press*, January 18, p. 7, and January 19, p. 7 (N^4); *Minneapolis Tribune*, January 18, p. 4, and January 19, p. 4 (N^5); and, in a single number, later, the San Francisco *Examiner*, June 30, p. 39 (N^6).[1]

The story was mailed to the newspapers evidently in the form of proofs since each does its own typesetting from a common copy. The syndicate sent out mats for the two-column illustration in Part I with the legend ' "YOU'D BETTER ATTEND STRICTLY TO YOUR BUSINESS" ' and the one-column illustrations in Part II with the legends ' "YOU WERE ANGRY WITH ME YESTERDAY" ' and ' "OH! JOHN!—NOT—THE REVOLVER" '. Curiously, the mats for the

---

[1] The Bacheller, Johnson name appears only in the Dayton *Daily Journal* and the New York *Press*; the other papers content themselves with the simple notice, *Copyright, 1895.*

two-column illustrative title common to both parts may differ. In the form signed by the same initials as the Part 1 illustration (N¹,N³,N⁵) the three central characters are shown at their duties at the merry-go-round, whereas in the unsigned *Kansas City Star* (N²) variant Stimson's hack is shown pursuing the lovers' buggy.² The special heading was not used by N⁴ or N⁶.

So far as is known this story did not appear in any American or English magazine. In an autograph inventory list of twenty-seven stories that Crane made up (in the summer of 1897 according to Professor Levenson), "The Pace of Youth" is the first, where it is noted as 4,000 words and its publication as *Bacheller*. The next notation would seem to be in the autograph contents list for the Heinemann *Open Boat* volume where it is number eight in the added stories ("Midnight Sketches") both in the original order and in the renumbering that revised the order. This list is dated by Professor Levenson as about December, 1897. Finally, in an autograph list perhaps to be dated January, 1898, and headed *Midnight Sketches*, in the revised order, it is properly eighth as it was to appear in the Heinemann edition, pp. 279–295. Under this list is noted a total of about 20,000 words and the statement, *All these stories appeared in the N.Y. Sunday Press or the Bacheller Syndicate.*

The Heinemann book version appears to derive from the American syndicated newspaper text—almost certainly from the basic proof and not from some clipping.³ The possibility cannot be ignored, however, that a fresh typescript was made up for Heinemann from a proof in order to provide copy for the revised

---

² It would be mere speculation that the *Star* heading was originally planned for the second part and the *Daily Journal* type of mat for the first part.

³ The natural inference is that the basic Bacheller proof served as Heinemann copy. First, in the initial autograph list, which for some stories provides the magazine names in which they were published, "The Pace of Youth" is listed simply as *Bacheller*. Second, in only two relatively indifferent variants does the Heinemann version (E1) join a collated newspaper text (N) in an aberrant reading against the others, and neither of these offers significant evidence. At 11.38 E1 joins all newspapers except the *Press* (N⁴) in reading *clenched* for *clinched* although *clinched* is Crane's peculiar and invariable usage and ought to have stood in the basic copy in order to have been reproduced in the *Press*. Finally, E1 joins the *Press* at 10.34 in omitting *d———*; but independent censorship may seem best to explain this agreement. No connection can exist between the *Press* version and E1 owing to the serious cuts present in the *Press* but not in E1 or the other newspapers, as well as the failure of E1 to agree with any other unique *Press* reading save that at 10.34.

version in the book, and indeed some slight evidence may suggest that this happened, although demonstration is impossible. On the other hand, the Heinemann text—given the English house styling—is fairly close to N in a number of accidentals. It is clear, nonetheless, that Crane revised the copy before it was printed in E1. Over forty substantive variants distinguish E1 from its copy. A few of these are fairly clearcut cases of E1 sophistication as at 11.6 where the subjunctive *were* is substituted for N *was*. A few are downright errors, as the change from *man* to E1 *woman* at 9.11 and probably of *crowd* to *crowds* at 10.2. A few are uncertain and suspect, such as the transposition *associated long* in E1 at 10.15 for *long associated*, and perhaps the excision of *all* before *suddenly* at 11.22. One curious group alters *the* to *a*.[4] The majority, however, attack the central problem of stylistic precision and spareness. The favorite early word *mystic* is expunged at 6.15 and 8.18, as also in "One Dash—Horses" (18.35, 21.5); nouns substitute for pronouns (7.12), also as in "One Dash—Horses"; one word will replace a phrase, as *ardently* for *with great feeling* (9.22); commonplace words are varied, as in *fine* for *great* (7.26) but *fine* then removed at 9.4 and *great* at 9.32; adjectives are pruned, as *tired* before *brain* (6.26); and in general various obvious phrases are excised, as *holding the basket for* (8.4), *and they were gone* (10.32), or *his horse* (11.19). With greater precision, at 5.15 the lovers communicate what they *felt*, not what they *wished*; at 9.29 Lizzie is properly *indignant*, not *angry*; at 10.14 the father has a *cloud*, not a *storm* of rage in his eye; at 10.21 Stimson's denunciations are *kingly*, not *imperial*; and, most interestingly, at 12.12 Stimson *understood*, not *pursued*, the power of the lovers' young blood. The more than usual care that Crane expended on preparing this early story for the Heinemann collection may have resulted from the fact that no previous opportunity had been afforded to work over its style in an intermediate publication.

The newspaper texts vary unauthoritatively from one another in a number of readings. The chief offender is the New York *Press* (N⁴), which cut the story severely, with occasional rewriting. That this remarkable variance is editorial, and not the result

---

[4] At 4.18, 10.8, 12.7 (twice), 12.25. N *a* becomes E1 *the* at 5.21. See the Textual Note to 4.18 for a discussion of this series of changes.

of different copy, is indicated not only by the general concurrence of its accidentals with those of other newspapers but also by its publication, with a Bacheller copyright notice, on the same date (or rather a day later) as the general release. Moreover, the evidence that saving space, as well as fancied literary improvement, was the desideratum is furnished by the long excision at 5.22–6.32, for when the narrative is resumed the reference at 6.34 to *these contortions* is meaningless without the cut material at 6.27–32. The San Francisco *Examiner* (N⁶) makes one cut in order to adjust the space. Otherwise the newspapers print the text complete. The verbal variation is mainly inadvertent, but real editorial attention was provided (by Willa Cather?) in the *Nebraska State Journal,* not always with happy results.

Since the basic copy furnished the newspapers is the earliest text that can be reconstructed from the evidence, it represents the form nearest in its accidentals to the author's lost manuscript. A wide-ranging search has not turned up enough newspaper versions to reconstitute (with the less certain help of E1) the lost Bacheller proof with absolute certainty in every detail of the accidentals; nevertheless, in the vast majority of such readings the present edition furnishes a text that is more faithful to this archetype than any single preserved document can be. Into the texture of these authoritative accidentals [5]—for which N¹, the Dayton *Daily Journal,* has been selected as copy-text for its general concurrence with majority opinion—are inserted the altered substantives from the 1898 Heinemann edition (E1) that appear to be Crane's own revisions. The resulting eclectic text, therefore, attempts to reproduce in all details of substantives and of accidentals the actual marked N printer's copy that Crane gave to Heinemann.[6] If, instead, the Heinemann copy was a typescript made up from a marked set of proofs, its accidentals would not be authoritative. Hence the accidentals of the master proof remain the nearest to authority that can be recovered.

[5] That is, the accidentals herein printed are the most authoritative that can be recovered by a reconstruction of the archetype. The Bacheller proof itself may have been based on a professional typescript and thus could have been at two removes from the full authority of the lost manuscript.

[6] This is to assume (a) that this copy was a set of the Bacheller proofs (or, less likely, a clipping from some particular newspaper), and (b) that any corrections Crane may have made in the Heinemann proof must be indistinguishable for the purposes of textual reconstruction from those he is conjectured to have made in the copy furnished the printer of the book.

ONE DASH—HORSES

"One Dash—Horses," syndicated by Bacheller, Johnson, & Bacheller, appeared in two parts in a few American newspapers on January 3–4, 1896 (as in the *Kansas City Star* and the *Nebraska State Journal*) or—skipping Sunday—on January 4, 6 (as in the *Philadelphia Press*). The Bacheller, Johnson copyright notice was printed in these newspapers and also, later, in the *Pocket Magazine* publication but not in the English magazine, the *New Review*. The story was mailed to the newspapers in proof form since each appears in a different typesetting. Mats for illustrations accompanied the copy. In Part I single-column cuts occur with the legends 'He Shadowed His Master Along the Dimming Trail in the Fashion of an Assassin' and 'The Light of a Torch Was Flared Into the Room'. In Part II two similar cuts appear with the legends 'Jose's Moans and Curses Amounted to a University Course in Theology' and 'The Fat Mexican Fairly Groveled on His Horse's Neck'. None of these illustrations is signed.

The first English publication was in the *New Review*, XIV (February, 1896), 140–151; in the United States the Bacheller-owned *Pocket Magazine* printed it in III (June, 1896), 70–101, the newspaper syndication having been exhausted. Neither version is illustrated. Finally, it was included in the 1898 *Open Boat* collections in America (A1, pp. 105–138, third in the order) and in England (E1, pp. 155–174). In the *New Review* and in the English *Open Boat* the title was "Horses"; [7] in the book the story was seventh in the group entitled "Minor Conflicts."

The newspaper texts (N), set from the same basic copy, vary only slightly, no more than is normal for texts that radiate from

---

[7] In the manuscript inventory made up probably in the summer of 1897 the story appears as number 22, of 5,000 words, published in the *Pocket Magazine*. In the manuscript table of contents for the Heinemann *Open Boat* it is third on the list, but was eventually numbered 7, the word count is given as 5,000, and the publication as the *New Review*. Although originally inscribed in this contents draft as 'One Dash Horses', the *One Dash* has been deleted, probably to bring the book title into accord with the plain "Horses" of the *New Review*. This acceptance of what was originally an unauthoritative form of the title was due, no doubt, as Professor Levenson conjectures, to the unfamiliarity of the phrase in England. The unfamiliarity was not confined to England, as a matter of fact. Alone among the observed newspaper versions, the New Orleans *Daily Picayune* used a special cut of its own for the title, this cut reading 'ONE DASH WITH HORSES.'

a common original. The *Pocket Magazine* (PM) version was set
from this same proof or, less likely, from a newspaper clipping.[8]
The general concurrence of PM with the newspaper substantives, and also the accidentals, indicates sufficiently that an
independent typescript or manuscript could not have been its
copy.[9] In this connection the paragraphing is of prime significance. The newspaper paragraphing (the same as PM's) differs
from that in the *New Review* (NR) in cutting the text into very
small units suitable for the narrow measure of a newspaper
column. It would seem that the decision to syndicate in two parts
was made by the Bacheller firm. Unlike "The Pace of Youth" in
which a clearcut time-break in the narrative occurs between the
two parts and the book publication preserves the original part
numbering, "One Dash—Horses" Part II in the syndicated proof
starts in what must have been the middle of a paragraph in the
lost typescript copy.[10] Significantly, this unnatural paragraphing
is preserved in the *Pocket Magazine*, although without the part
number.

Apart from the reading *resemble* at 22.33 (see footnote 9
above) PM departs from the N and NR substantives only three
times. Two are quite innocuous: the substitution of *D——*at
15.11 for *Damn* and of *I'm* at 17.23 for *I am*. Since these
scarcely imply authorial intervention, the omission of *little* at
16.32 can be taken as a transmissional error. The late date of
PM publication and this textual evidence combine to certify that
PM is a simple linear reprint of the basic N proof. In turn, the
American *Open Boat* collection is a close reprint of PM. Only

---

[8] The exact copy is not to be determined, although the normal inference would
be that the magazine used the Bacheller proof. The *Pocket Magazine* error
resemble at 22.33 (see footnote 9 below) may support this hypothesis. In no case
does the magazine follow an individual newspaper error.

[9] The one reading that might furnish contrary evidence occurs at 22.33. Here,
according to the reconstructed history of the text worked out below, the
concurrence of the *Pocket Magazine* (PM) and *New Review* (NR) in the error
resemble for the correct newspaper (N) *resembles* might be taken as indicating
that PM and NR shared a common copy that differed from the basic proof
behind N. However, this is the only shared reading that differs from N. The
explanation would seem to be that the erroneous *resemble* stood in the lost
typescript and was transferred from that to the typescript behind NR, and also
to the Bacheller proof whence PM derived it, but the collated newspaper texts
corrected the error independently. If a newspaper text with *resemble* were to
turn up, the case would be demonstrated.

[10] The break comes after 'Sometimes he thought he saw it move' (18.26). Part
II begins with an artificial new paragraph at 'As grim white sheets, . . .'

one of its three variants can have any significance,[11] the omission of *mystic and* at 18.35, which is discussed in the Textual Note to 18.35 in connection with the E1 revision. It seems clear that this is an authentic proof-correction in A1, one of the relatively few that appear in the volume.

Between the American and the English lines a marked division in the textual tradition represented by over fifty substantive variants as well as by a quite different paragraphing system takes place. Certain of these variants are clearly part of the anglicizing of the text, such as the substitution of *lines* at 24.28 for the unfamiliar American term *dashes*; the subjunctive *were* at 18.20 for *was*; the English form *towards* at 18.20 for *toward* (the copy-form otherwise being retained), *linesman* for *lineman* at 19.16, possibly *of opinion* for *of the opinion* at 15.18, *about* for *around* at 22.30, and *something* for *somewhat* at 24.16. To these may be added the tinkering with *sort of an outpost* [12] at 22.4, and probably the 'correction' of the characteristic Crane split infinitive *to profoundly impress* at 24.5 and of the slightly awkward *gulped again* for *again gulped* (24.37), both of which may be NR sophistications. For the special case of the alteration of *the knife* at 18.22 to *a knife* see the Textual Note to 4.18 in "The Pace of Youth." A few appear to be positive NR errors, like the repetition of *nothing* at 20.4 when *nor* is required.

The remainder, with a few indifferent exceptions,[13] seem to represent an earlier state of the text than the N,PM readings. Significant in N is the development of a kind of revision already seen in the E1 revisions in "The Pace of Youth" which consists of the substitution of a character's name for the personal pronoun, as at 17.25, 18.31, and 19.24, or in the substitution of *The fingers of Richardson* for *The American's fingers* at 20.7. Occasional phrases are added in the N,PM line, such as *As a matter of truth* (22.26) or *at this time* (19.38) or *for the horse* (20.1–2); only a few are deleted, such as *panic-stricken* before *servant* (22.4). But the revision here in N,PM is not, as in "The

[11] The other two are trivial and unauthoritative: *farther* for PM *further* (15.18) and the sophistication *bent* for *bended* (21.7).

[12] Here the idiomatic *an* was also omitted by the *Nebraska State Journal*, as was *a* at 23.11 independently.

[13] Such, perhaps, as *and the night* in NR for *and night* (18.19), or *round* for *around* (24.15), or the rearrangement *He felt the effect of this cold dawn in his blood* (19.7).

Pace of Youth," several years after composition; instead, it probably took place in the typescript just before it was sent to the Bacheller printer. Although these additions often make for closer syntactical connections, some are directed at greater precision, as in the added *the folds of* (16.18), *as rigidly* (17.26–27), or *one of the favorite methods* for *a favorite method* (24.38–39).

Since the American newspapers printed the story in early January and it appeared in the English *New Review* in February, time must be allowed in any reconstruction of events for the negotiation of English sale as well as for magazine printing. Hence it might seem either that Bacheller had a new typescript made up from Crane's typescript and sent it abroad for English sale or that, after setting Crane's typescript into the newspaper basic copy, he sent Crane's typescript across the ocean. The evidence is not certain but what there is inclines one to the first alternative. That is, if Crane's typescript (x) was mailed to England only after it had been used as American printer's copy, no reason would seem to exist why Bacheller should not have sent an early proof instead. On the evidence of the paragraphing, he did not. Moreover, certain of the alterations that appear to be unauthoritative in NR may actually have been created by the typist, thus relieving the British compositor of at least some of the errors that mark the NR text. In favor of the second alternative is the generally close resemblance of the punctuation, although it is true that the NR accidentals are likely to differ more from reconstructed N and from PM than do PM from N, or the different texts of N from each other. In choosing the first alternative, one must assume the transmission through the second typescript of the errors *wrist* for *waist* (15.36), *tomale* for *tamale* (17.10), and *resemble* for *resembled* (22.33), by no means an impossible requirement however. On the whole, the time element and the oddity of sending the printer's copy typescript instead of the proof make it seem slightly more probable to conjecture that the *New Review* text was set from a typescript prepared for the English market immediately on the purchase of Crane's typescript and before Crane's later revised typescript was sent to the printer to produce the N basic copy.[14]

[14] This hypothesis also allows for the possibility that Crane first delivered to Bacheller, Johnson a carbon (x^2) of his typescript (x^1) for copying while he

The Heinemann *Open Boat* (E1) was set from a copy of NR, as stated in the draft contents list. Seven substantive variants appear in E1, two of which interestingly parallel Crane's distaste for his early use of *mystic* already illustrated in the E1 revision of "The Pace of Youth." [15] One corrects an error in NR that must have been present in the Crane typescript—*wrist* for *waist* (15.36). The rest are stylistic, and more doubtful, although all but one have been accepted in the present text.[16] Otherwise, since E1 repeats all of the NR variants from N,PM, it perpetuates the earlier version of the text, plus some NR unauthoritative changes, despite the handful of final revisions.

The one text that without question appears to have been set from Crane's typescript, even though it reproduces several errors demonstrably present in that typescript,[17] is the Bacheller proof insofar as it can be reconstructed from the evidence of the collated newspaper texts. This becomes the copy-text, therefore, as representing the earliest recoverable archetype, even though of inferior authority to the lost manuscript. The physical copy-text itself is the version in the *Philadelphia Press* (N¹) for January 4, 1896, p. 11, and January 6, p. 10, which is perhaps the closest in its accidentals to the lost master proof that is being

---

kept his original for further revision before releasing it for American publication.

[15] In E1 at 18.35 N,NR *mystic* becomes *vibrating*, and at 21.5 *mystic* is changed to *fabulous*.

[16] It seems reasonable to accept E1 *threats* substituted for N,NR *menace* (18.26) as more authorial than compositorial in origin. Given the emphasis on *silver eyes* in "Three Miraculous Soldiers" (VI, TALES OF WAR) at 43.18, 21–22, and at 45.7, the E1 dropping of *silver* before *coins* as a description of eyes (21.33) might seem disturbing; but José's eyes are not glittering at night, as in "Three Miraculous Soldiers," and hence the variant may pass as a revision. Since *singular* is one of Crane's favorite adjectives, like *mystic* or *fine*, its omission at 17.17 is perhaps the most doubtful of all of the above E1 variants. Its excision can be justified only on the conjectural ground that Crane was trying to reduce his dependence upon this adjective, as he manifestly was doing with *mystic*, even though no concrete evidence to this effect is found elsewhere except for a marked diminution of its use in his later writing. The general substantive authority of E1 for many of these changes may encompass these six, therefore, even though some reservations must inevitably accompany such a decision. At 22.29 E1 *the bridle* for *his bridle* appears to be an error and is rejected.

[17] It must be remembered that Crane did not do his own typing and thus that the typescript he may have submitted to Bacheller, Johnson would have been a professional one in which variation from his manuscript would have been present in accidentals as well perhaps as in some substantives.

reconstructed for the purposes of this edition. This N^1 copy-text has been emended as necessary for the reconstruction by collation with the texts in the *Kansas City Star* (N^2), January 3, p. 7, and January 4, p. 7; *Nebraska State Journal* (N^3), January 3, p. 5, and January 4, p. 5; *Buffalo Commercial* (N^4), January 3, p. 4, and January 4, p. 4; and New Orleans *Daily Picayune* (N^5), the two parts in one on January 5, p. 22.

The *Pocket Magazine* text, deriving from this same master proof, is of equal authority with these individual newspapers if we assume, what seems probable, that PM was set from the syndicate proof itself and not from some newspaper clipping. Insofar as the *New Review* version appears to be at one more remove from the original typescript than is N,PM, it is of secondary authority to N,PM in the accidentals. However, since NR radiates from x^1, the Crane typescript (or perhaps from its carbon x^2), it is collateral with N,PM and may be consulted in cases of doubt. Its substantives represent an earlier stage of composition than do those in N,PM, but the possibility must be kept in mind that some may reproduce the true readings in cases where N,PM may be suspect because of proof deviation from the typescript reading. (Moreover, the NR accidentals may on occasion retain more faithfully than N,PM the forms of x. Hence the NR paragraphing is adopted in the present edition as more faithful to the original manuscript than the proof, which seems to have been adjusted in its more frequent paragraphing for the narrow newspaper measure.) Finally, into the generally more authoritative accidentals of N,PM, as ordinarily represented by the copy-text, the *Philadelphia Press*, have been introduced the six substantive variants of E1 that are taken to represent Crane's final revisory intentions. The resulting eclectic text, then, reconstructs no physical copy that could ever have existed [18] but prints the closest documentary approximation of Crane's intentions in respect to his accidentals as well as the two rounds of substantive revision that he made in this story.

[18] In this respect the situation is unlike that of "The Pace of Youth," in which the edited text attempts to reproduce the actual printer's copy for E1.

THE WISE MEN

"The Wise Men" appeared in the United States in cut form as unnumbered pages 1–19 in *The Lanthorn Book* (LB), described as 'Being a Small Collection of Tales and Verses Read at The Sign o' the Lanthorn 126 William Street New York' (Williams and Starrett, no. 19). Crane's story was the first piece; works by John Langdon Heaton, Irving Bacheller, Willis Brooks Hawkins, Post Wheeler, Charles B. Lewis, and Charles Kelsey Gaines followed. The edition was limited to 125 copies and contributions were autographed by the authors. Except that it was in 1898, the date of publication of this collection is unknown: the book carries a copyright notice but the Copyright Office has no record of registration. Williams and Starrett conjecture: "Since Crane was in the United States for an extended period only during November and December of 1898, it seems likely that this book must have appeared during that time" (p. 40). This speculation seems to be based upon the authorial signing of copies; if so, the evidence would, indeed, be to the contrary. It is believed that Crane autographed very few of the books, and thus it is possible that he may have signed copies while in New York for the few days between landing on April 21, 1898, and his departure for Cuba; or else, perhaps just as likely (in case *The Lanthorn Book* was published later than April), he signed only what were still available, or were offered him, on his return in November and December. In short, no external evidence exists that can serve as the basis for anything but guesswork about the date of publication of this collection. Fortunately, the date is not of paramount textual significance since the facts of the transmissional history of the text are not affected by questions of priority in publication.

In England the story appeared in the *Ludgate Monthly*, April, 1898, pp. 594–603 (LM), illustrated by John H. Bacon,[19] and then, as the fourth story, in pages 87–105 of Heinemann's English edition of *The Open Boat* (E1) deposited in the British

---

[19] The decorative title cut shows the Kids with Pop at the bar. The three illustrations have the legends 'THE KIDS HAD MUCH BUSINESS WITH CERTAIN ORANGE, RED, BLUE, PURPLE AND GREEN BILLS', 'ONCE A KID PUT HIS HEAD OUT OF THE WINDOW', and 'THE OLD MAN SPUN TOWARDS THE TAPE LIKE A MADMAN'.

Museum on April 18, 1898.[20] In the Doubleday & McClure *Open Boat* (A1) the story occupied pages 213–246 and was placed sixth.

Collation discloses that the English and the American appearances follow different textual traditions. In substantive readings alone over twenty variants separate LM,E1 from LB,A1; and to these may be added nine significant accidentals variants. Some of the substantives are no more than such small differences in form as LB,A1 *'im* versus LM,E1 *him*, or *toward* versus *towards*, or *didn't* versus *did not*. But others range from the LM,E1 omission of words such as *some* (29.15), *now* (30.35), and *time* (33.3); the alteration of forms as between singular and plural in LB,A1 *are* versus LM,E1 *is* (26.29) or *mustache* versus *moustaches* (28.5); to verbal substitution such as LB,A1 *seats* for LM,E1 *chairs* (27.14), *throng* versus *crowd* (36.32); or syntactical rearrangement as in LB,A1 *Nobody but us gets in on this* versus LM,E1 *Nobody gets in on this but us* (30.14). Such accidentals differences as the four agreements of LB,A1 against LM,E1 in paragraphing, or in *four-thirty* as against 4:30, or in the commas as against the dashes that alter meaning at 35.3, or in the position of the dashes at 37.23–24 join with the substantive variants to indicate a common origin for the LB and A1 texts different from the common origin for the LM and E1 texts.

The few individual variants between LM and E1 suggest compositorial or editorial changes instead of authorial intervention; and, indeed, the differences do not indicate that Crane proofread either one of the English texts. On the other hand, these and other variants appear to preclude the possibility of a linear relationship such as setting one from proof of the other. Such subtle differences in meaning created by variant punctuation as the dash following *Mexico* in LM at 26.10 instead of the E1 (and LB,A1) comma, the omission of the apostrophe after *San Anton'* in LM but not in E1 (28.23), perhaps the LM error *clinch* for E1 (and LB,A1) *cinch*, but certainly LM *Hang* for E1 (and LB,A1) *Damn*, demonstrate effectively that E1 could not have been

---

[20] In the manuscript table of contents for the Heinemann edition the story was originally listed as sixth but then renumbered to be the fourth. Its word count was given as 5,500, but no place of publication was assigned. In the 1897 inventory it was placed seventh, the word count was given as 5,000, and the notation was made 'Ms at Hartwood'.

derived from a proof of LM. On the other hand, the paragraph indention in E1 at 31.10 whereas LM joins LB and A1 in run-on text, the refinement of the possessive *yards'* in E1 versus LM *yards* (LB,A1 *yard*) at 31.21, but particularly the variant *fallen* in E1, quite acceptable in its meaning, for LM (and LB,A1) *falling* at 37.22 suggest very strongly that a proof of E1 did not serve as copy for LM. This hypothesis may be buttressed by the general LM concurrence with LB and A1 in the use of commas, colons, or periods to introduce dialogue as against the unusual E1 dash. Although the variation is sufficient to discourage the possibility of a linear relationship as from proof-copy, it is neither so numerous nor of such a nature as to be of prime significance when compared with the generally quite exact concurrence of LM and E1. Hence the conjecture is reasonable that their relationship is one of radiation from a common source. That is, either one appears to have been set from the manuscript and the other from a typescript made from it, or else one was set from a typescript and the other from its unaltered carbon.[21]

The case for the relationship of the two American editions is not quite so definite, but the evidence suggests that they, in turn, radiate from a different typescript made in England from the manuscript. It is not probable that LB proof served as copy for A1 in the light of the LB omission of *broad* at 27.18 and of *and* at 32.12, whereas they are present in A1, LM, E1; the acceptable singular *means* at 28.14 versus *mean* in the others; the superficially plausible *buckskins* for *buskins* at 36.3; and the run-on text at 35.29 for a paragraph in A1, LM, E1.[22] On the other hand, the evidence is equally strong that proof or an example of the A1 pages could not have served as copy for LB. Numerous A1 variants from the basic typescript are not found in LB; however,

21 "The Five White Mice," we know, was set in E1 from manuscript, but no sale was made to an English periodical, although an attempt may well have been made: the exact derivation is impossible to decide. The only evidence that seems to bear on the problem may be rejected as too finespun. For instance, LM throughout prints the interjection *oh* as *o* (an occasional English characteristic) whereas E1 prints *oh*. But at 30.3 E1 reads uniquely, *O*. Since the spelling *oh* is customary in E1 elsewhere as well, it might be possible to speculate that here E1 printed O under the influence of copy, which could have been a typescript styled O by the English typist. See also footnote 27 below.

22 Of course, the cuts in LB would also preclude this arrangement ordinarily; but if these were made in proof, then this evidence would be valueless. Fortunately the other pieces of evidence are not subject to this difficulty.

if one were to conjecture that these are changes made in A1 proof, then the variant paragraphing in which A1 differs uniquely from LB, LM, and E1 at 29.36, 31.1, and seven other places may be accounted contrary evidence. Moreover, the punctuation system of A1—with particular reference to the use of semicolons and especially to the half-dozen and more times that the two texts differ in the sentence use of a semicolon or of a period and capital—is time and time again different in cases where LB agrees with LM and E1. The evidence makes it clear that LB could not possibly have derived from any form of A1.

The analysis of the American tradition turns on the question of whether LB was set from a manuscript and A1 from a typescript made from it, or one from a typescript and the other from its carbon.[23] To a limited extent the evidence seems contradictory. In accidentals, with particular reference to the punctuation system, LB and A1 differ from each other much more markedly than do LM and E1 from each other. Yet a considerable amount of this difference is compositorial in A1, as manifested by A1's frequent variation in cases where LB agrees with LM and E1, and thus where LB must represent the general manuscript forms as reflected in one or more typescripts, or possibly the forms of some archetypal typescript. The only significant evidence in this respect, then, would concern LB variation from what seems to be the typescript tradition in a manner that could relate it to the lost manuscript itself.

In a number of instances the LB system of comma punctuation approximates Crane's characteristic lightness more closely than do the other three texts, particularly in the lack of a comma separating the two parts of a double predicate created by the

[23] Reconstruction of the underlying printer's copy for all four texts is severely inhibited by the lack of all external evidence about the writing and sale of "The Wise Men." No preserved letter mentions the story. From the slip in "The Five White Mice" fair-copy manuscript at 46.24,26 in which the otherwise invariably capitalized *Kid* is inscribed *kid*, we may conjecture that its earlier manuscript had *kid* throughout as does "The Wise Men." If this is so, it is probable that the manuscript immediately behind the printer's copy for "The Wise Men" was the early original and not a revised and retranscribed manuscript like "The Five White Mice." On the other hand, some alterations must have been made to bring "The Wise Men" into conformity with the revised manuscript of "The Five White Mice." For instance, the manuscript alterations at 40.9–10 illustrate that the name *Casa Verde* was invented during the inscription of the fair copy and differed from the original name, yet in "The Wise Men" the name for Freddie's saloon is *Casa Verde*.

carrying-over of the same subject, as in *Under them small stray dogs go furtively into the café and are shied into the street again by the waiters* (27.1–2) where LM, E1, and A1 have a comma after *café*. But for every example of this lightness in LB, a contrary can be found, usually—and this has some significance —in the omission of a comma in LM,E1 as against its appearance in LB,A1. Moreover, qualitatively these LM,E1 occurrences are often superior in the value of their evidence since they concern not so much the conventional places for light or heavy punctuation but specific constructions where Crane, on the evidence of his manuscripts, was more likely than not to omit pointing. A typical example is the uncharacteristic enclosure of parenthetical *perhaps* in commas by LB and A1 but their omission in LM,E1 at 26.11. More significant is the extremely characteristic omission in LM,E1 at 26.21 of a comma between two adjectives preceding a noun, as in *smooth infantile faces* versus the LB,A1 comma. Crane seldom punctuated participial phrases ending a clause, as in LM,E1 *the tall form of old Pop himself awaited them smiling with broad geniality* (27.17–18) compared with the less characteristic comma in LB,A1 after *them*. In the description of dialogue Crane's manuscripts normally do not have a comma to separate the verb from some appended phrase. Hence at 27.18–19 the three other texts are more characteristic than LB in reading *"Well, my boys, how are you?" he cried in a voice of profound solicitude*, whereas the LB comma after *cried* would be rare in holograph. These examples could be multiplied many times to stand against the cases where the concurrence of LM, E1, and A1 must be taken as evidence of the basic copy readings (not necessarily always representing the forms of the lost manuscript, of course), readings that—curiously—seem to represent a heavier system than the light punctuation in LB that would often approximate Crane's own peculiarities.

The evidence, though conflicting as indicated, is subject to certain significant statements, however. First, although LB is often lighter than the concurrence of LM, E1, and A1, it also joins A1 with considerable frequency in being heavier than the agreement of light LM,E1 and in this respect seems to reflect a basic difference in the American and English copy. Thus no such overwhelming trend toward a distinctive manuscript system can be detected in LB, against the other authorities, as to lead irresistibly to the conviction that it was set from a copy that was markedly different in its form from theirs.[24] Second, despite the frequent uniqueness of LB's punctuation as against the agreement of the others, the also frequent concurrence of LB and A1 against LM and E1 suggests such a considerable similarity in the copy behind each as to constitute the sharing of an American tradition for their copy, just as LM and E1 share an English tradition in a common original for substantives as well as for accidentals. It can be only speculative, but the number of cases in which the two traditions oppose each other in the sharing of characteristics of an often minor and indifferent nature suggests the strong possibility that the American radiation was perhaps from a typescript and its carbon, or (less likely) one typescript derived from another.[25]

[24] That is, no doubt exists that in a number of cases LB does indeed print what might well have been the characteristics of the lost manuscript, as in the omission of a comma before *and* in a series of adjectives at 34.17. But these are neither so consistent nor so much in the majority as not to be susceptible of explanation as compositorial variants that happen to coincide with Crane's habits. Indeed, LB departs uniquely about as much as does A1 from the basic tradition as established by agreement of three of the four authorities: it happens only that LB departs in the direction of light punctuation instead of heavy. Moreover, LB is not always consistent. It is true that in refusing to hyphenate *side streets* at 33.1 LB seems to reflect the original copy more faithfully than the hyphenated form of the other three, if we may trust the evidence of 34.36 where LM and E1 (though not A1) join it in the unhyphenated form. But the reverse may happen. At 29.31 LB in *cocksure* departs from LM,E1,A1 *cock-sure*, but at 37.35 joins the others in the hyphenated form. Of course, Crane himself was far from consistent in his word-division. In "The Five White Mice" manuscript the first inscription of the word is *cock-tails* but thereafter always *cocktails*. It would be mere guesswork to wonder whether the first occurrence could not have reflected the earlier manuscript he was copying and whether he had changed his practice in the interval. Since we do not have the manuscripts, the evidence of *Maggie cock-tail* versus *George's Mother cocktail* is no doubt of little value.

[25] It is only the lack of external evidence about the sale of "The Wise Men" and its perhaps largely noncommercial printing in LB (which may not have been Reynolds' doing) that permits even speculation that a manuscript could have found its way to America. Thus every scrap of possible evidence for a hypothetical manuscript copy for LB must be mentioned. Perhaps little significance inheres to the LB period at 37.20–21 where the LM,E1,A1 form is an exclamation point: *Pop had hurled himself against the tape—victor!* Crane's manuscripts are often less full of these exclamation points than the printed versions made from them; but LB compositorial preference may well have operated here. One preservation of manuscript faulty grammar in LB might be argued for in *There was occasional grunts and groans* (35.23) versus LM,E1,A1 *were*. On the other hand, the LM,E1 tradition may preserve in another place a

Two specific pieces of evidence may be taken as supporting this position that LB and AI were set from a typescript and its carbon or else one typescript immediately derived from the other. First, the evidence mentioned in footnote 25 above: The correction of the false grammar *is set* as in LM,EI to *are set* in LB,AI (26.29) might represent independent editorial or compositorial intervention in LB and in AI, but the simpler explanation is that this is only one of the twenty or more substantive differences between the two typescripts that are responsible for dividing the English and the American lines of the text.[26] Second, LB and LM agree in reading *city of Mexico* at 26.10 whereas in EI and AI the reading is *City of Mexico*. It may be significant that in "The Five White Mice" although the preserved manuscript reads *City*, which is followed by the American line of the text in the New York *World* and in AI, the English line of the text as represented solely by EI reads *city*. If *city of Mexico* may be taken as an anglicizing in EI "The Five White Mice," then the LB concurrence with LM in *city* is less likely to repeat a manuscript form or else to derive from a transcript prepared in England that throughout read *city*. Instead, the EI capitalization at 26.10 suggests that the copy for both lines of the text read *City* but was subject to independent styling, as in LB, or in the EI *city* (as in LM) at 35.34. Independent styling, then, can associate AI and EI, or else LM and LB; but assumptions can often be made that distinguish such fortuitous concurrences from agreements stemming from similar readings in the two lines of printer's copy.

We arrive, then, at the textual hypothesis that two typescripts were prepared in England from the manuscript, probably at somewhat different times,[27] each seemingly with its carbon.[28]

---

case of false grammar, characteristic of Crane, that could have been smoothed out in the LB,AI tradition (see Textual Note to 26.29). The difficulty about LB *buckskins* for the LM,EI,AI *buskins* must also be faced, for which see the Textual Note to 36.3.

[26] That is, since it is difficult to conjecture that LM and EI would independently alter their typescript *are* to *is*, we must assume that the copy behind them read *is*. Crane is well known for his uncertain grammar; hence it is the more probable that the one typescript copied *is* from the manuscript and the other typist altered it to *are* than that the manuscript read *are* and the typist of the English copy made the error *is* (assuming that one English copy was not the manuscript itself). If so, the American line of the text must stem from a typescript in both its branches LB and AI.

[27] The possibility that one typescript was prepared from the other cannot be overlooked. If the omission of words in the LM,EI line does not represent

Whether a local typist typed one version and then sent the manuscript to Robert McClure, who had his own typescript and carbon made or whether the local typist (or McClure) typed up two copies with their carbons is not to be ascertained.[29] If the

authorial alteration, then the typescript behind LB,A1 cannot have been copied from that behind LM,E1. On the other hand, difficult as it is to assess, one may say that the accidentals readings that clearly stood in different forms in each typescript are more numerous than one might suppose would result from a typescript copied from another and thus already styled in part. In this connection, too, the fact that LM,E1 on various occasions seems closer to Crane's normal manuscript characteristics than LB,A1 would militate against a copying in the opposite direction. The mixed nature of either textual tradition leads more naturally to the hypothesis of independent radiation by two typescripts from the manuscript. For instance, the misunderstanding of the text reflected in the punctuation in the English line at 35.3 would more normally result from typing from a manuscript with uncertain pointing than from a typescript behind LB,A1; moreover, this concurrence in error would not appear to permit the manuscript itself and its typescript to be hypothetical copy for one English text or the other.

[28] Although the total evidence seems to point in the direction of two typescripts each radiating independently from the manuscript, evidence that could be explained as resulting from one typescript deriving from the other must be noticed. This evidence consists of common errors, corrected only in A1 proof, that must either represent the faithful reproduction of mistakes in the manuscript or else are mistakes made by the typist of one transcript and copied by the other. Just possibly, A1 *conference* for LB,LM,E1 *confidence* is a revision, not a correction at 29.2; but the error *Book* for *Bank* (30.9) common to LB,LM,A1 is a curious one (*bank* is correctly found at 28.9), and at 38.3 the LB,LM,E1 *hello* for *hollo* or *hallo* or *halloo* is less readily referable to the manuscript. Here an additional complication arises in that the inappropriate exclamation point after *hello* in LM,E1, which must derive from the manuscript, is omitted in favor of a normal comma in LB,A1—although this substitution could have been made as readily by a typist of the manuscript as one copying the typescript that was to be used for LM,E1. Then there is the LB,LM,E1 error *roads* for *rows* (36.7). If these four errors are to be taken as anything other than evidence for the derivation of one typescript from the other, they must have been present in the manuscript whence each typescript independently derived them. In this connection it is not necessary to conjecture that they could have resulted from just such a late fair copy as was made in "The Five White Mice" manuscript. We do not know why the manuscript of "The Five White Mice" became the printer's copy and why only the one typescript and (conjecturally) its carbon were made to send to America. It would be mere guesswork that a typescript was necessary for "The Wise Men" because the manuscript was in the original early state and not sufficiently legible. It may well be that the need to procure copy for the *Ludgate Monthly* publication operated here, provided it were understood that the copy was made early with periodical sale in view. But then why no such copy was made for "The Five White Mice" comes in question unless we are to suppose that Crane held off from this expense while waiting to see if the story could be sold in America to an international magazine and thus passed the point where English periodical sale was possible for publication before the book.

[29] Crane either could not or would not type. We know that typescripts of the manuscripts were sometimes made after January, 1899, by Cora (and also, later, by Edith Richie), for economy's sake perhaps. Sometimes a manuscript was sent to his agent to have a typescript made as needed.

twenty-odd substantive variants between the two traditions represent only unauthoritative departures from the manuscript in
one or the other, then no assumptions about their respective
verbal authority can be made. On the other hand, if at least some
of the variants can be assigned as corrections and revisions
made in one typescript and its carbon, but not in the other, some
conjecture is possible. Certain of these variants like the use of
towards in LM,E1 and of *toward* in LB,A1 are certainly house
styling and should have no reference at all to the typescript
forms. Other differences must derive from the typists, such as
the normalization, or correction, of grammar in LM,E1 *kinds* for
LB,A1 *kind* (32.36) or in LB,A1 *are* for LM,E1 *is* (26.29).
Presumably a typist was responsible for the LM,E1 form *him*
instead of *'im* (29.33, 30.11, 37.14), although correction here in
LB,A1 is also a possibility; for the normalization in LM,E1 to
daren't of *daresn't* (31.28); for the variant *until* in LB,A1 and
till in LM,E1 (33.14); for the error in LM,E1 *arrangement* for
LB,A1 *arrangements* (33.8); and for the normalization in LB,A1
did not of LM,A1 *didn't* (29.7) that more probably stood in the
manuscript. No direction of change can be observed in these,
and none could be expected.

It is possible to suspect anglicization in the use of *yards* (LM)
or *yards'* (probably compositorial in E1) for the American idiom
hundred yard dash (31.21); in the addition of *and* before the
final element in the characteristic Crane series of LB,A1 *no
crowds, lights, noise* (33.5);[30] and possibly in the LM,E1 word
chairs for *seats* (27.14). The LB,A1 *throng* (36.32) removes the
repetition of *crowd* from 36.31 but may represent a real revision
and not a sophistication.[31] Two omissions, at 26.19 and 33.3,
may represent revisions in LB,A1 copy about as readily as errors
in the LM,E1. The omission (or addition) of *that* at 32.37 is
almost completely indifferent (see the Textual Note to 29.38).
On the whole, the typescript behind the American line seems to
have somewhat more general substantive authority than that
behind the English, whether because of English sophistication of
idiom or else outright errors and omissions. Indeed, the overall
impression is that the copy behind LM,E1 was not gone over by

---

[30] See, for instance, 33.23–24: *rain on flowers, grass, leaves.*
[31] For *throng* elsewhere, see 33.22.

Crane, whereas that for America was very possibly reviewed before it was mailed to Reynolds (or to Robert McClure).

Two further textual problems still need discussion. The text of LB, though clearly enough so much in the tradition of A1 as to represent a typescript and its carbon (no evidence is available to determine which would have been which), has omissions at 27.2–8, 27.19–23, 29.14–18 totaling some 147 words. These are in descriptive passages that do not affect the narrative. That they are found intact in LM, E1, and A1 indicates that they were present in the manuscript from which both typescripts were made. Since LB is apparently to be associated with a typed copy of some kind, and not with the manuscript itself, LB with its omissions cannot represent the original form of the story subsequently expanded; hence the omissions must be cuts. The problem arises whether they were authorized by Crane as improvements or whether they were editorial. No evidence bears on this vexed question. We do not know whether Crane sent both typescript and carbon to Reynolds and Reynolds sold the story to Bacheller's *Lanthorn Book*, or whether Crane presented the copy to *The Lanthorn Book* himself, on request for a story. No correspondence is preserved that so much as mentions "The Wise Men." Under these circumstances it would be dangerous indeed to delete these passages from an established text on the mere speculation that their omission represented an afterthought on Crane's part and thus his final intention.[32] It is at least possible that they are the result of editorial cuts to make the material fit within a limited space.[33]

The final problem concerns the substantive variants in A1 that depart from the typescript readings as represented by the agreement of LB, LM, and E1. Although it is perhaps unusual to find Crane adding in revision instead of excising, that various of these are true revisions can scarcely be doubted either on their own evidence or on the evidence of their place in the textual transmission of the story. The only real question is whether they represent changes made in the copy before typesetting or else alterations in proof, especially since they are more extensive in

[32] No other unique reading in LB seems to come from authorial change, although some readings shared with A1 appear to represent authorial review.

[33] The story ends at the foot of the recto of the final leaf, with a blank page on its verso, as is customary in *The Lanthorn Book's* layout.

number and scope than changes made in other stories in the American collection.[34] Unfortunately, internal evidence cannot settle the matter and all external evidence is wanting. One may only comment that such frequent and consistent changes as the capitalization of *Kids* combine with the special nature of the literary revisions and additions to suggest the greater possibility of marked copy than of such unusual changes in proof, but proof-alterations as a theory are by no means to be barred.

Although each of the four authorities is theoretically equal in respect to the accidentals, E1 seems to represent the best single authority in that it joins LB and LM most frequently to offer a majority opinion while at the same time having fewest unique divergences in its general accidentals system. E1 has been chosen as the copy-text, therefore. With some caution, shared LB,A1 accidentals that seem most clearly to represent Crane's usual manuscript characteristics have been admitted as emendations, and with even greater caution a very few accidentals shared by LB and LM against E1 and A1. Since the textual analysis seems to indicate that the basic copy from which derive LB and A1 may have been reviewed and altered slightly, substantive emendations shared by LB and A1 are freely admitted. Finally, since the analysis also shows that A1 was either revised in proof or by a further review of its copy before being sent off to Doubleday & McClure, the unique A1 substantive variants are ordinarily adopted unless evidence of some weight suggests that they are compositorial or editorial changes without authority.

THE FIVE WHITE MICE

"The Five White Mice" first appeared in a heavily cut version in the New York *World*, April 10, 1898, p. 32 of the Sunday supplement (W), only eight days before copyright was applied for and deposit made by the American publisher of *The Open Boat*. In this collection the story is placed eighth and last and occupies pages 301–336. In the inventory list of summer, 1897, the story is sixth, its word count is given as 5,000, and the notation is

---

[34] These relatively extensive changes may suggest that the manuscript of "The Wise Men" had not been worked over in a fair copy as was that for "The Five White Mice."

made, 'Ms at Hartwood'. In the provisional list of contents for the Heinemann edition it had been placed seventh but was then renumbered fifth, in which position it was published in Part I, "Minor Conflicts." In the manuscript contents list the wordage is again given as 5,000 but no notation of publication appears.

At some unknown date Crane gave to Joseph Conrad the holograph manuscript that had served as Heinemann printer's copy. In 1912 Conrad inscribed the following on a prefixed leaf: "This MS. | Given to Joseph Conrad by | Stephen Crane is now made | over by J. Conrad to Mʳ John | Quinn for safe keeping in his | collection of MS and to | dispose of in the future as he | may think fit. | J. C. 1912 | Capel House | Orlestone | Nʳ Ashford | Kent | England." It is now preserved as HM 3995 in the Henry E. Huntington Library in San Marino, California.

This manuscript consists of twelve numbered leaves of un-ruled foolscap laid paper measuring 328 × 205 mm., water-marked Britannia in an oval with the countermark CARISBROOK | SUPERFINE.[35] The writing, on rectos only, is in blue ink with corrections and revisions in the same ink. However, on folio 10 a strange hand with a different pen has interlined a necessary *not* at 49.24, has corrected *temple* at 50.8 to *house*, and has interlined *fatally* above deleted *fattaly* at 50.13. The hand is not Cora's nor is it Conrad's; however, since all texts carry these readings the corrections must have been inserted before the typescript that was sent to Reynolds in New York was made up from this manuscript. At the upper right of the first leaf, on a slant, is written in an unidentified hand, 'Wᵐ Heinemann | 21, Bedford Sᵗ | W. C.' In pencil, in a different hand, to the left of the title is written the first compositor's name, J. Ecclestone, and the notation, 5,000 words. On a slant at the upper left of folio 4 is another compositor's name, Palmer, and similarly placed on folio 9 is C. Wright.[36] Unsigned printer's brackets occur on folios 5, 6, 9, and 11, in each case signifying a line-ending in the Heinemann text. The first marks the ending of

---

[35] This is the same paper used for the manuscript of " 'Showin' Off' " in the *Whilomville Stories*, which Professor Levenson has dated in March, 1899 (VII, TALES OF WHILOMVILLE, liii).

[36] If as seems probable these represent the exact takes of each compositor—since each begins a leaf with a new paragraph—Ecclestone set 39.1–42.13, Palmer 42.14–48.3, and Wright 48.4–52.7.

the line that is fifth from the foot on page 115 of the book, the
second marks the second line from the foot on page 117, and the
third and fourth the last lines on pages 123 and 126. Folios 2–12
were numbered in blue crayon 74–84, but these have been
crossed out and in blue crayon 40–50 have been substituted.[37] On
each verso Crane wrote the word count in ink in his usual
manner, circling the count for each leaf and then separately
adding it to the cumulative total for a final count of 4,960 on the
verso of folio 11. Folio 12 is blank on the verso.

As Professor Levenson remarks in his Introduction, a manuscript of "The Five White Mice" was among those stored at
Hartwood before Crane went to England; hence the Huntington
manuscript, on British paper which he is known to have used in
England, cannot represent the original but must be a revised fair
copy that Crane wrote out in December, 1897, since a typed
version seems to have been in Reynolds' hands before January
14, 1898 (*Letters*, pp. 169, 171).

That the Heinemann *Open Boat* text (E1) was set from this
manuscript is demonstrated by the printer's markings that check
with physical characteristics of the E1 edition. In thirteen readings E1 departs uniquely from readings shared by MS, W, and
A1.[38] The first five of these appear in the stint of Ecclestone (six,
if one counts 41.5 as one must), and the remaining eight in that
of Palmer. Wright's stint contains no such variants. Of these, the
variants *dinners* (40.19) and *shoulders* (42.2) are clearly errors; the curious *organ-mellow tones* (40.15) is almost certainly

---

[37] It is difficult to equate these printer's markings with the English order,
despite the fact that they must represent the position of the story in the
assembled copy that was being set into page proof. If one takes the second
blue-crayon numbering as representing the final order, then "The Open Boat"
has 13 pages of printed copy, "A Man and Some Others" 7 pages, and "The Bride
Comes to Yellow Sky" 12 pages, for a total of 32 pages. But the typescript for
"The Wise Men" must have taken more than the 6 remaining pages before "The
Five White Mice" starts with 39. If each magazine leaf were merely foliated, not
paged, in blue crayon, then an excessive space is left unless "The Wise Men"
typescript could have taken about 20 pages. The original blue-crayon numbering
is no more explicable in terms of the early than of the late order. One can only
conclude that the printer (or Heinemann) numbered copy as it was received,
perhaps, or in some now lost order, and that the present numbers do not
necessarily represent the order of typesetting.

[38] These occur at 40.1, 40.15, 40.19, 40.22, 42.2, 42.16, 42.19, 43.13, 44.23,
46.24–25, 47.4, 47.7, 47.38. To these may be added the E1 variant from MS at
41.5, an obvious sophistication, in which A1 independently joins.

unauthoritative, and *foolish-wise* (44.23) appears to be a sophistication (see the Textual Note), as does the change from dialect to normal *want to* at (47.7). The remaining nine are indifferent. Five of these represent omissions of words that are not strictly necessary (four of these are in Palmer's stint); the others represent such slight changes as *within* to *in* (40.22) or *his last throw* to *the last throw* (42.16). No demonstration is possible, of course, that certain of these indifferent readings are not proof-corrections; but no one reading in the thirteen (properly fourteen) requires such an explanation. Moreover, the concentration of these variants fairly evenly in the work of only two of the three compositors is suspicious, and even more suspicious is the heavy concentration of four of the five omissions in the stint of a single compositor, Palmer. On the whole, although the evidence does not bar the very slight possibility of proof-correction, an editor can scarcely be encouraged to accept any of these variants as authorial, and hence they have been rejected in the present text.[39]

Enough unique variants join the New York *World* (W) and the Doubleday & McClure *Open Boat* (A1) against MS and E1 to demonstrate that the American texts could not have been set from English proof (corrected or uncorrected) and that they must radiate, like E1, from the MS, presumably from the typescript prepared in England to send to Reynolds in New York. That at least some of these W,A1 variants are authorial is suggested by their special nature, such as the necessary corrections *bottom-up* for MS,E1 *bottom-down* (42.20) or *circus-box* for *theatre-box* (43.8), and also such changes as the addition of *high* at 51.19 and the alteration of *unscathed* to *scatheless* at 41.39 (see *scatheless* in "The Open Boat," 75.33). The typescript sometimes led both W and A1 into error, as most noticeably in the change from MS,E1 *in* to *on* (41.1) and from *Frishco* to *'Frisco* (51.35), or in the minor sophistication *Come 'ere* for *Comere* (45.1).[40] That a proof of A1 could not have been the

---

[39] Although the evidence is perhaps too slight for generalization, it may be significant that elsewhere the clearcut authorial variants in E1 seem, on the whole, to derive from marked-up printer's copy of already published stories, and not from proof-correction. It cannot be demonstrated that Crane actually read proof on the Heinemann *Open Boat*.

[40] Probably another sophistication is *They've* for MS,E1 *They* (44.1). The W,A1 reading *general* for MS,E1 *genial* (42.33) is suspicious because of the

printer's copy for W is indicated by such a reading as A1 *bent* (40.3, 48.9) for the characteristic Crane *bended* which W shares with MS and E1.[41] The numerous unique errors in W, as well as its severe cuts and variant paragraphing, preclude the possibility of the use of a proof of W as A1 copy, a speculation not encouraged by the date of the W appearance anyway.

The only two workable hypotheses are that A1 and W were set from the same Crane typescript and its carbon, or else that one was set from the Crane typescript and the other from a copy of this that Reynolds ordered for separate sale.[42] Unfortunately, no evidence seems to point in one or the other direction. Given the miserable newspaper setting of W, it would be superfluous to blame at least some of the errors on a careless typist. The paragraphing variants in W are seemingly created by the compositor in order to break up the longer paragraphs to adjust to the narrow newspaper column. On the other hand, the only two paragraphings in which A1 differs from W, MS, and E1 (44.8, 45.7) are clearly the result of printer's styling since each begins a new paragraph after dialogue. The few unique A1 substantive variants are either errors that any compositor could make, like *stake* for *shake* (40.28), or sophistications like *bent* for *bended* (40.3, 48.9), the alteration of *'em* to the consistent *'m* (44.4), or the addition of *a* to the phrase *too bloody combat* (50.33). Although it is possible that one or two of the neutral unique A1 variants resulted from the same casual proofreading that Crane seems to have given some other stories in A1, none is so clearly authorial as to demand acceptance, and all have been rejected.

Where some occasional authority does seem to exist is in the shared readings of W and A1 against MS and E1, which can have derived from no other source than the Crane typescript sent to Reynolds. Four substantive variants that are unusual enough to suggest more care than a typist would expend have been noticed above at 41.39, 42.20, 43.8, and 51.19. Less certain

---

possibility of misreading by the typist, and it has been rejected in the present edition (see the Textual Note).

[41] The variant paragraphing in which W agrees with MS and E1 contra A1 is also strong evidence against this hypothesis, as well as the various unique A1 readings that cannot all be proof-corrections since some are obvious errors.

[42] In theory Reynolds could have kept the Crane typescript as a file copy and had a typescript and carbon made for sale from this.

because more probable as a typist's misreading is the shift from MS *genial* (a favorite word with Crane) to W,A1 *general* (42.33). Although the hypothesis may be too finespun, at least a chance exists that as he read over the typescript and made these few corrections and changes before mailing it to Reynolds, Crane took some slight care with the drunken speech such as the change of *around* to *round* (45.11),[43] a speculation perhaps assisted by the typescript variant *ain'* for *ain't* at 46.23 and, though more doubtfully, by *Cer'ly* (W) or the partly sophisticated *Ce'r'ly* (A1) for *Cerly* (45.13).

The textual situation shaped by this evidence is a reasonably clear one. The Huntington manuscript must be chosen as the copy-text since it alone can be the ultimate authority for the accidentals. A survey of the unique E1 variants, as well as those unique with A1, does not preclude authorial alteration in proof of a few indifferent readings, but since no positive evidence is anywhere present in either book version they have both been rejected as substantive authorities when unique readings are in question. Except for the obvious correction of MS errors, therefore, only the few shared variants by W and A1 thought to represent authorial changes made in the typescript before mailing to Reynolds, and not typist's errors, have been admitted as emendations of the basic manuscript substantive text.

A listing of the alterations made in the manuscript during the inscription and in review is placed in the apparatus following the Historical Collation.

A MAN AND SOME OTHERS

"A Man and Some Others" was mailed to Crane's agent, Paul Reynolds, on September 9, 1896, from Hartwood, and acknowledged by Reynolds on September 11, who informed Crane that "I have spoken to one of the large papers down town and they have asked me to let them consider it for a day or two." The story was accepted by the *Century* (Cy) where it appeared in LIII (Febru-

[43] Emended in the present edition to *'round*. The alternative is to take it that an English typist altered MS *around* to the more typical idiom, found in other stories as English compositorial sophistication.

ary, 1897), 601–607, with a full-page illustration by Frederic Remington and the legend ' "HELLO, JOSÉ!" ' on page 600. As early as October 24, 1896, the editor Gilder was discussing with Reynolds changes already made in the story at his request: he thanks Crane for removing the hackneyed *crown of thorns* but expresses himself as particularly sorry that Crane had not changed *B'Gawd*. It may be that these changes were made in the copy returned by Gilder for alteration before typesetting, for on November 10 Reynolds assured Gilder that the *Century* had indeed received the proofs from Crane and that he would write to Crane about the removal of *gawd*. This word was apparently still a sticking point with Crane despite his acquiescence in the other changes requested earlier, but it is interesting to see that it finally emerges as *B'G——* (66.11), with or without his consent.

Despite Crane's expressed hope to Reynolds that he would sell the English rights for £25 and Reynolds' handwritten postscript to his typed letter of September 11 that he was writing to a literary agent in London, no English magazine appears to have bought the story, probably because the *Century* with its English issue would have controlled international rights. Thus it was printed next as the second story in the American *Open Boat* collection of 1898 (A1), pages 65–103; and simultaneously in the English *Open Boat* (E1), pages 41–64 where it is also second but in the distinctive English section called "Minor Conflicts." [44] Both book versions were set independently from *Century* clippings. Probably in the copy for E1 Crane made four substantive changes, none of which is present in A1, and probably in the proof for A1 he made one substantive change that is also unique. Otherwise both book versions are remarkably exact reprints of their *Century* copy, with very few accidentals changes.

The copy-text for this edition is the *Century*, which derives directly from the lost manuscript or typescript. Into these copy-text accidentals that are the most authoritative preserved are inserted the substantive revisions of the two book editions. It is interesting to see that Crane was still intent, as in "The Pace of

[44] In the manuscript inventory of the summer of 1897 the story is the fourth listed, it is given as 7,000 words, and the publication is noted as the *Century*. In the manuscript table of contents for the Heinemann edition it was originally fourth but was renumbered to be the second. The same information is supplied as in the earlier inventory.

Youth" and "One Dash—Horses," to remove all appearances of the word *mystic*. However, the curious substitution of *a* for *the* found in these earlier stories does not occur in the E1 "Man and Some Others" despite such phrases as *drew himself up in the manner affected by the villain in the play* (53.23).

THE OPEN BOAT

The only periodical publication of "The Open Boat" was in *Scribner's Magazine*, XXI (June, 1897), 728–740 (Sc). The next appearance was in the American (pp. 1–63) and London (pp. 1–39) editions of the collection *The Open Boat*. In Crane's inventory of the summer of 1897 the story was placed third and was stated to be 9,000 words; Scribner was given as the publisher. In the manuscript table of contents for the London edition it appears first and is also numbered 1, the same information being appended.

The copy for both book versions was, independently, the *Scribner's* text. The English edition (E1) contains a few authoritative revisions, probably made in the copy, such as are found in the other stories in this collection. There can be little doubt that the addition of *impudently* at 75.35 is authorial, or the substitution of *Holland* at 91.6 for *Algiers*. Under these circumstances the general authority of the E1 substantives supports the omission of *low*, which had been repetitive, at 76.5. On the other hand, the change of *command* to *commanded* at 69.2 and the addition of *the* before *breaking* at 85.33 seem to be examples of English styling. The most doubtful E1 variant of any real significance is the omission at 84.18–19 of *with the thing*, which seems required.

The more sporadic nature of the authorial proof-revision in the American collection (A1) is carried over to "The Open Boat." We may be willing to take it that the correction in the last line of "Bingen on the Rhine" (85.24) could be authorial despite the fact that Crane had passed it in the E1 copy. If so, then it is likely that the nearby substitution of *it* for the repetition *the fact* (85.28) is also authoritative, although the case must always remain a doubtful one. The other variants are even more doubtful. It may be that Crane himself corrected the error *waves* at

89.21 to *wave* (as also in E1), although a compositor might well have taken responsibility for such a change. The other A1 variants are indifferent and, in the light of the general nature of the Crane revisions throughout A1, more probably compositorial sophistications than authorial alterations.[45] Among these only the change of *doubtlessly* at 69.38 to *doubtless*, with parenthetical commas, may cause any real concern.

The *Scribner's Magazine* version becomes the copy-text since it is the nearest to the lost manuscript and hence most authoritative in its accidentals. The accidentals of A1 and E1 are derivative and can have no authority except in the unidentifiable cases where Crane may have chosen to modify them.[46] Into the texture of these accidentals are introduced those E1 variants thought to be authorial revisions, and also the necessary A1 corrections. The resulting text, thus, attempts to reproduce the marked printer's copy for E1 but with a few helpful editorial changes, and a possible A1 proof-correction or two.

FLANAGAN AND HIS SHORT FILIBUSTERING ADVENTURE

"Flanagan and His Short Filibustering Adventure" was printed first in the *Illustrated London News*, CXI (August 28, 1897), 279–282 (ILN), illustrated by G. Montbard.[47] In the United States its periodical appearance was in *McClure's Magazine*, IX (October, 1897), 1045–1052 (McC). In the 1898 American *Open Boat* (A1) it was the fourth story, occupying pages 139–179. The inventory of the summer of 1897 had listed it as second, with *McClure's* as the place of publication. In the manuscript table of contents for the Heinemann *Open Boat* (1898) it was originally placed second but then renumbered as sixth, in

---

[45] These are the change of *was* to *were* (75.25)—something of a refinement for Crane—of *awaken* to *awake* (82.29, 84.19), and of *warmed* to *warm* (82.13). The A1 omission of Sc 'said the captain' at 75.19 could be a simple though necessary editorial correction.

[46] Whether Crane or not, someone used intelligence in dealing in A1 with the Sc,E1 *From a black line it became a line of black and a line of white, trees, and sand* (75.5). The dash in A1 *and a line of white—trees and sand* materially clarifies the modification.

[47] Montbard provided a three-column heading showing the sinking ship with its lifeboats and two two-column illustrations with the legends *'The stoker smote his mate with an iron shovel, and the man fell headlong over a heap of coal'* and *' "There," said the captain. "That's Jupiter Light on the Florida coast" '*.

which position it was published by Heinemann (E1), pages 129–134. In the draft contents list it was also noted as 6,000 words and the magazine was given as the *Illustrated London News*.

The copy for the Heinemann book version was a clipping from the *Illustrated London News*, but the text was slightly revised by Crane, probably in this printer's copy. At 102.38 a careless original implication that all the small boats unloading the cargo off the Cuban coast would operate as a unit is repaired. At 107.16 the number of lifeboats is reduced from three to two, for if a dozen Cuban officers and the first mate could be accommodated in one (106.10–12), then the fifteen of the crew would launch only one other. A word is altered at 105.30 and 108.2; a sentence is added at 107.3. Otherwise, E1 diverges from ILN substantively only at 102.13 when by its omission of *to* ILN had manifestly been in error, and at 102.28 in the correction to *gong* of the ILN misprint *gang*. Except for these five cases of revision and two of correction, E1 follows its corrupt copy and is thus a derived text with only limited authority.

The copy for A1 was a clipping of *McClure's*. Although the examples are less certain than in some other stories of this collection, a correction and a revision appear to have been made during a casual proofreading (see the Textual Notes to 101.37 and 103.5–6).

Both ILN and McC are within the same textual line, their variants the result of typist or of compositorial transmission with few qualifying even as possibilities for authorial attention. At least eight seem to be positive errors in ILN; [48] at least seven more are clear cases of house styling or anglicization.[49] Another group is relatively indifferent but without positive suggestion of

---

[48] The added ILN question marks at 106.4 and 108.11 corrupt the text in a most insensitive manner; the addition of *the* at 108.8 sophisticates a typically idiomatic construction favored by Crane; the omission of *to* at 102.13 and of *and* at 107.4 created errors that E1 tried to patch; and there is little to be said in favor of *it'll* for *I'll* (101.26) or *everybody* for *anybody* (104.2). The weak repetition of *of the Foundling* at 104.6 must be wrong.

[49] ILN *were* for *was* (94.14, 95.17) is representative of the first; illustrating the second are *coals* for *coal* (98.29), *on* for *in* (99.35), *stoke-hold* for *stoke-hole* (101.24), and *northwards* for *northward* (104.24). The omission of *the* at 105.24 may be simple error but appears to be an anglicization; the substitution of *splashed* for *plashed* at 107.26 may be a mere misunderstanding.

authorial intervention.[50] On the other hand, in one reading, at least, ILN is manifestly correct as against McC. For instance, *floundered* must be right, and not McC *foundered* (99.5), as a description of the *Foundling* crossing *the blazing bright meadow of an ocean* toward Cuba. In two instances (99.8, 104.25) it is clear that ILN preserves profanity censored in McC; and almost certainly, on this evidence, the omission of an entire line in McC —*"Hell!" said the beaming Flanagan* (105.14)—was triggered by censorship and not by any literary criterion.

Five cases remain where material might have been added in McC or excised in ILN. One is very brief indeed, consisting only of the absence in ILN of the McC phrase *donned wraps and* (108.2–3) when the dancers left for the beach; the others consist of one or more complete sentences of descriptive material. That these are authorial cuts to tighten the story is faintly possible, but it would be equally possible to suggest that they are authorial additions. Fortunately a purely mechanical explanation seems to be indicated. These particular omissions all occur, suspiciously, toward the end of the story; and examination discloses that they are confined to the last two columns of the final page of ILN, which ends without a line to spare at the foot of the third and last column.[51] Hence it would seem almost certain that they may be assigned as editorial cuts in ILN to reduce the story's ending to the dimensions of the printed page on which has been inserted a large two-column extraneous illustration. If

---

[50] ILN substitution of *from* for *of* (93.16) seems to represent sophistication to reproduce the conventional Shakespearian phrase; *conditions* for *condition* (105.29) also substitutes a more conventional reading. Whether McC *the law* (94.12) is correct and ILN has omitted *the* in order to conform to the rest of the series is debatable; no one can tell whether *which* should be present or absent at 98.26; whether the captain tells the leader of the Cubans *"I'll wait for you"* (McC) or *"I'll wait"* (ILN) at 102.25; or whether the chief engineer tells the captain *"We can never beach her"* (McC) or *"We can never beach"* (106.13–14) in ILN. It is probable that the English compositor preferred the phrase *on tip-toe* as a matter of idiom at 100.35 and that McC is not in error in reading *walked tip-toe*. That the captain in the lifeboat knocked his head against the gunwale as in McC (107.20) seems preferable to ILN *hand* despite a distant parallel to *hand* in "The Blue Hotel" (149.33). The only such variant that might be thought to have a critical basis for judgment is the omission of *black* in ILN at 103.11, which could be argued for as an authorial attempt to avoid a repetition of the *black shadow* of the Spanish gunboat and the *black shadow* of the *Foundling* at 103.1.

[51] Indeed, the *finis* requires a line that lies below the normal makeup of the page.

this is so, then Crane had nothing to do with any variant between McC and ILN, and very likely he read proof on neither
before its appearance. Under these conditions the substantive
differences in the two magazine texts appear to derive from the
transmissional process, with the result that one or other of each
variant must represent either the correct reading or a corruption,
and not an authoritative revision. This conclusion simplifies the
editorial problem considerably, since decisions need not be made
to distinguish specific cases of authorial intervention from transmissional error (except for the unique E1 variants).

The question of the proper copy-text is complicated by the
absence of all external evidence bearing on the nature of the
copy submitted to both magazines. We know, from Professor
Levenson's Introduction, that on leaving Florida Crane had only
a week in New York before sailing for London on March 20,
1897, and then traveling to Greece. We know that on March 16
he wrote he was in the middle of a story *which I am bound to
finish before I leave,* that this story can only be "Flanagan," and
that McClure's would have had first option on its purchase. But
choice among several possibilities is quite speculative. We do not
know, for instance, whether he did indeed finish the story before
he sailed on March 20, and if so whether he left it with
McClure's in manuscript form and received or was mailed a
carbon of a typescript made up by the publisher; whether he
himself had a typescript made up for submission to McClure's
before he sailed and kept his own carbon; or whether he took the
manuscript with him to London and only on his return from
Greece at the end of May mailed a typescript to McClure's.[52]
General probability, at any rate, suggests that it was McClure's
which sold the English magazine rights to the *Illustrated London
News* (after normal purchase from Crane of international
rights), in which case we should expect McC to have been set
from a typescript and ILN quite possibly from its carbon, or
from an immediately derived typescript. Although specific evi-

[52] Such a guess would help explain the delay in McClure's publication until
October even though the *Illustrated London News* was able to bring it out in
August. However, one might speculate that McClure's could have had other
reasons. For example, since *Scribner's* had printed "The Open Boat" in June, it
might well occur to McClure to hold back an obviously derived story to prevent
immediate comparisons.

dence in favor of this possibility is largely wanting in the two magazine texts, yet negative evidence is not strong enough to prevent its use as an editorial working hypothesis.[53]

McClure's and the *Illustrated London News*, therefore, appear to radiate independently from a common original at perhaps the same distance and thus no choice between them as copy-text can be made on acceptable evidence that one stands in closer relation to the manuscript than the other. Under these conditions each is theoretically of equal authority for the accidentals as for the substantives and—whichever is selected as the copy-text— editorial choice may be made on a conservatively eclectic basis according as Crane's characteristics in accidentals (and also substantives) appear to penetrate more clearly the veil of the respective house stylings, or compositorial transmission. It seems more convenient to select the *McClure's Magazine* version as the copy-text since (although almost certainly set from typescript) it represents certain features of Crane's American style more faithfully than the product of an English printing shop. However, particularly in the lightness of the punctuation in certain specific practices, ILN seems to approximate more closely what one would expect the manuscript to have transmitted to the basic typescript, and in such cases the ILN readings have been used, with more than usual freedom, to emend the copy-text. (The *McClure's* compositor[s] had a particular passion for parenthetical punctuation that was alien to Crane's habits. Indeed, some of the McC styling is so unusual that in various cases even A1, set from McC on a straight reprint basis, fortuitously reverts by its own styling to the ILN accidentals.)

[53] It is true that a few ILN variants might be taken as misreadings, such as *it'll* for *I'll* or *hand* for *head*, and one other strongly suggests the reproduction of a manuscript alteration. At 104.5 McC reads, *This strange manœuver by the* Foundling *first dealt consternation on board*, whereas in ILN the sentence goes, *This strange manœuvre by the* Foundling *first dealt consternation on board of the* Foundling. It is tempting indeed to speculate that *by the Foundling* was an interlined revision of an original sentence, *This strange manœuver first dealt consternation on board of the* Foundling, in order to adjust it to the subsequent *Later the manœuver of the* Foundling *dealt consternation on board of the gunboat*, and the deletion of the original phrase was not recognized by the ILN compositor. But even if this were true (although it might have been no more than a simple memorial confusion), a typist could have misread the manuscript similarly, but *McClure's* corrected in proof. In short, the odds against ILN having been set from manuscript are very long indeed, especially when the external evidence is considered.

The unique substantive alterations of E1 are clearly authorial and hence are brought into the copy-text in order to provide Crane's final intentions—in these respects. However, the specific authority of the E1 revisions does not extend to the false 'approval' given the ILN corruptions by the E1 reprint of its copy. The present text is eclectic, therefore, in that it attempts a limited reconstruction of the typescript behind the *McClure's* version on the combined evidence of McC and ILN and then introduces from E1 what appear to be Crane's substantive changes written on the ILN clipping sent to Heinemann for the 1898 collection.

THE BRIDE COMES TO YELLOW SKY

"The Bride Comes to Yellow Sky" was published in the United States in *McClure's Magazine*, x, 377–384,[54] and in England in *Chapman's Magazine*, ix, 115–126, both in February, 1898. With the *McClure's* text as copy (either in the form of a clipping or of proof) it appeared as the fifth story in the 1898 American *Open Boat*, pages 181–212; and with *Chapman's* as copy (clipping or corrected proof) as the third of the "Minor Conflicts" in the 1898 Heinemann *Open Boat*, pages 65–84.[55]

As Professor Levenson has remarked, the evidence that McClure had placed "The Little Regiment" in *Chapman's* in June, 1896, for simultaneous publication with *McClure's Magazine* leads naturally to the hypothesis that Crane had sent copy for "The Bride" to Robert McClure in the London office, who relayed it to New York and very probably sold the English rights

[54] In addition to an illustrative heading of the couple leaving the station at Yellow Sky, E. L. Blumenschein drew various illustrations for the *McClure's* text. These have the legends: '*He sat with a hand on each knee, like a man waiting in a barber's shop*'; ' "*—and at the moment that the old man fell down stairs with the bureau in his arms, the old woman was coming up with two scuttles of coal, and, of course—*" '; '*Jack Potter*'; '*Scratchy Wilson*'; '*The man yelled, and the dog broke into a gallop*'; ' "*I ain't got a gun on me, Scratchy, . . . Honest, I ain't.*" '; and ' "*Married!*" '.

[55] In the manuscript table of contents for Heinemann it was originally fifth in order but has been renumbered third; it was listed as of 4,500 words and the copy was noted as *Chapman's*. In a letter from Cora to Reynolds, Sept. 29, 1898, some months after the April book publication, she states that she has transferred copyright to Heinemann, who is sueing *Illustrated Bits* for plagiarism of the story.

to *Chapman's*. The vexed question is whether Crane sent Robert McClure the manuscript and the London office had typescripts, or a typescript and its carbon, prepared for *McClure's* and for *Chapman's*, or whether Crane had a typescript and its carbon prepared and sent off the two copies himself.[56]

The exact circumstances are of interest chiefly because the two magazine texts differ in a number of readings, the origin, authority, and direction of which must be decided before a text can be contrived. Certain of these variants probably originated with the British compositor, such as *Chapman's* (Ch) *sledging* for *McClure's* (McC) *sledding* (117.4), *plate armour* for *armor-plate* (116.11), *yells* for *yowls* (116.25), or *train* for *coach* (109.8). Others might as readily have originated with the American compositor as with faulty copy, such as *glee, and reproach* for Ch *glee, reproach* (112.5–6) so characteristic of Crane, the assignment of *But* as part of the dialogue (115.21), or the misreading *could* for Ch *would* (112.2) or *his* for *this* (118.31). On the other hand, a few Ch variants could qualify as authorial revisions of satisfactory original readings, or—in one or two cases, hypothetically—incomplete or misread authorial revi-

[56] What evidence there is does not run counter to the hypothesis that one magazine was set from a typescript and the other from its carbon or from a closely derived typescript. Except for the paragraphing, which is house-styled in *Chapman's* to mark off the dialogue, the accidentals of both magazine appearances are fairly close to each other. Both agree in the use of parenthetical dashes, and *Chapman's* twice agrees with the four uses of a semicolon in *McClure's* and only once uses a semicolon where *McClure's* has none. As for commas, sometimes *McClure's* shows the heavier formal punctuation (as it did in "Flanagan"), and sometimes *Chapman's*: it is obvious that both have undergone some house styling to make Crane's impressionistic punctuation more regular. The possibility that one magazine was set from the manuscript itself and the other from a typescript is too remote to consider seriously. It is true that *Chapman's* exhibits at least one error that seems to derive from a manuscript misreading: at 116.10 its *fillings* for *fittings* may have come from the misreading of a word in which Crane had failed (as he was likely to do) to cross his internal *t*'s. (An instance occurs in the Huntington Library manuscript of "The Five White Mice" [fol. 2, l. 12] in which *cigarettes*, if set literally, would have come out as *cigarelles*.) Possibly the misprint *seeming* at 120.6 for *McClure's* *seemingly* derives from some manuscript difficulty, as may *Southron* at 113.21 for *Southern*, *revolver* for *revolvers* at 117.19, or *environments* for *environment* at 119.21. On the other hand, a typist could misread the manuscript as readily as a compositor. Moreover, the only really good piece of evidence—that of *fillings*—was corrected in the Heinemann *Open Boat*, perhaps from context, and no doubt *McClure's* could have done the same if it had actually stood in the typescript.

sions.[57] Perhaps the most plausible cases of authorial intervention—and also of the direction of change—would be readings that remove or add repetitions. In "The Wise Men," as a parallel, some copy revisions seem to represent a most refined attempt at avoiding the original repeated use of descriptive words even though at a distance. This same literary intention accounts in "The Bride Comes to Yellow Sky" for the single authorial E1 copy change from Ch (barring the possible correction of *fillings*) when at 114.21 *solemn* in all other texts is altered to *morose* presumably to prevent an echo shortly after at 114.30 in the *solemn, chapel-like gloom* of the saloon. Given this hint, we might be able to see a similar intention behind certain variants between Ch and McC. For example, at 110.21–22 we read about the Pullman porter, *he bullied them with skill in ways that did not make it exactly plain to them that they were being bullied.* In the *McClure's* version of the next encounter in the dining car, *The patronage* [of the waiter] *entwined with the ordinary deference was not plain to them* (111.9–10), but in *Chapman's* occurs the change *the deference was not palpable to them.* Also to be taken into account is the reading of both texts at 117.12–13, *Plain from the low collar of his shirt, the cords of his neck. . . .* Again, at 111.4 the waiters' coats are *glowing white* in McC but *dazzling white* in Ch, a change that in some part could have been made to anticipate the use of *glow* at 112.25–26, *They looked at each other with eyes softly aglow.*

However, the last illustration does indeed seem to strain probability, and at 111.10 Ch *palpable* is not a word that Crane favored, admirable as it might seem to an English magazine editor unappreciative of Crane's idiomatic and repetitive *plain.* In view of other, more thematic repetitions in the story, such as the references to Potter's *brick-colored hands* at 109.11 and *brick-red hands* at 111.17 or to Wilson's identifying *maroon-colored shirt* at 116.28 and 118.29, probabilities may favor *Chapman's* editorial intervention here instead of authorial proof-revision. Such a hypothesis would affect even the change of *glowing* to *dazzling*

[57] Of course, any statement such as this must be accompanied by the recognition that in some few cases a compositorial variant may appear to be authorial. An author could add *calm* at 118.12, but a compositor could just as easily skip it; the repetition at 117.13 might have been a typescript fault and thus its omission perhaps not an authorial intervention; and so on.

by Ch in the description of the waiters' suits (111.4) despite the seeming aptness of the repetition with the *dazzling fittings of the coach* (110.8–9). On the other hand, the addition of *calm* in Ch's description of Potter's house, *the same still, calm front as had the other adobes* (118.11–12), may be taken as an originally designed echo of the earlier *The calm adobes preserved their demeanor at the passing of this small thing in the middle of the street* (117.15–16). If so—and the phrase emphasizes an important theme in Crane[58]—the omission of *calm* is a McC error (like the omission at 120.10) and not a Ch proof-revision.

The conclusion may be drawn, at the last, that these substantive variants in the *Chapman's* version in a few cases reproduce more faithfully than *McClure's* the underlying typescript and its carbon and thus may be accepted, but that Crane did not, seemingly, alter the copy for Ch (no doubt sold direct by Robert McClure and not by Crane himself). Crane may or may not have seen proof, and if he saw it he may or may not have made selective alterations. The case must be considered *not proved* for any authority in Ch other than that of its copy. At any rate, the two copies seem in the authority of their accidentals—which alone is in question for a choice of copy-text —to be at the same distance from the manuscript insofar as any evidence can be adduced.

The copy-text, hence, is most conveniently taken as *McClure's Magazine*, principally because the evidence suggests that the American compositor house-styled fewer accidentals than did the British. However, that there was styling by *McClure's* is evident; consequently, when *Chapman's* seems to preserve certain distinctive characteristics of Crane's normal accidentals texture, it has been used, though conservatively, to emend the *McClure's* copy-text. In most respects, also, McC may be taken as more closely preserving Crane's American idiom in the indifferent substantive variants than does Ch. Thus in such readings as McC *infrequently* but Ch *unfrequently* (110.25) or McC *upon* but Ch *on* (115.12), and so forth, when McC so far as is known does not go counter to Crane's general preferences it has also been chosen as the superior authority, on the odds, for the

---

[58] For Crane's earlier use of the relation of buildings to humans, see *Maggie*, Textual Introduction, in Vol. I, Bowery Tales, lxxxix–xc and references.

general run of the substantives. No substantive variation occurs between A1, the Doubleday & McClure *Open Boat*, and its
McC copy. The single E1 substantive variant (besides the correction of obvious error) in Heinemann's *Open Boat* from its *Chapman's* copy—that at 114.21—appears to be authoritative and is
adopted as a presumed copy-annotation such as elsewhere in E1
produced what may be accepted as Crane's final intentions. The
Virginia text, thus, attempts to reconstruct as nearly as the
preserved documents permit the typescript used as copy by
McClure's Magazine, with the addition of the Heinemann final
alteration.

DEATH AND THE CHILD

The earliest publication of "Death and the Child" was in the
English magazine *Black and White*, in two parts, on March 5
and March 12, 1898 (xv, 332–334, 368–370).[59] Each part had
an illustration drawn by Ernest Prater: the legend in the first
part is 'SEVERAL TIMES HE TURNED AND SHOUTED "COME ON!
COME ON!"', and in the second part, '"ARE YOU A MAN?"' In the
United States, *Harper's Weekly* printed the story a fortnight later
on March 19 and March 26, 1898 (XLII, 281–282, 297–298).
The only illustration, by E. Vickery, heads the first part, on page
282; untitled, it shows the Lieutenant pointing out the battle to
Peza. In both magazine versions section IV begins the second
part. The story shortly appeared in America as the seventh in the
1898 *Open Boat* collection, pages 247–300, and as the eighth
and last of "Minor Conflicts" in the Heinemann 1898 *Open Boat*,
pages 175–207.[60]

No typescript or manuscript is known to be preserved except
for one leaf, paged 3, housed in the Columbia University Libraries Special Collections. Written in Cora's hand and deleted by
two diagonal strokes and one horizontal, it represents the earliest known example of Crane's dictation to Cora if certain of the
Greek-Turkish war dispatches be excepted as possibilities. On
the back, in a fine pen and perhaps in Stephen's hand, are

---

[59] The title was, uniquely, "The Death and the Child."
[60] In the early 1898 manuscript contents list for the Heinemann *Open Boat*
"Death and the Child" is eighth in the original order and was numbered eight,
finally. Its word count is given as 8,000. The story appears in no other Crane
list.

deleted notations of wordage. First 1,695 is placed under 1,610 and added for a total of 3,305, to which 3,200 is added for a total of 6,505, and then 870 for a final total of 7,375. In a circle, in a now-grayish ink, is the deleted word count for the leaf, 320. Also present is the deleted notation 'Verse—The City'. The leaf owes its preservation to the fact that Cora used its verso for the second page of her review of the play *Peter the Great* (page 1 of the review had been written on a leaf of her inscription of part of the text of "The Blue Hotel"). The leaf is unruled laid foolscap countermarked 'CARISBROOK | SUPERFINE. The text is transcribed in Professor Levenson's Introduction.[61]

The nature of the copy that was provided for each of the four versions of the "Death and the Child" text requires analysis. The number of substantive variants between the four not attributable to typist or compositorial error is relatively small. Among these sufficient exist, however, to demonstrate that the transmissional history of the text divides between the two countries: that is, one master copy produced the American line and another the English line of the text. The nine readings that separate these two traditions are shared by *Harper's Weekly* (HW) and the 1898 Doubleday & McClure *Open Boat* (A1) as against the shared variants by *Black and White* (BW) and the 1898 Heinemann *Open Boat* (E1): 123.13 bronzed] very bronzed BW,E1; 124.11 with] by BW,E1; 126.21 -shaped] -shape BW,E1; 128.28 near] nearer BW,E1; 131.31 moved] curved BW,E1; 135.15 steep] sheep BW,E1; 138.25 a corner] the corner BW,E1; 139.3 unhumanly] inhumanly BW,E1; 141.6 and] *omit* BW,E1.

The Heinemann *Open Boat* (E1) contains thirteen unique substantive readings, of which seven are clearcut errors,[62] two are highly probable errors,[63] and the remaining four are so suspicious in their nature as to be assigned to compositorial error as well[64] in the absence of any positive evidence elsewhere in the collection that E1 variants resulted from Crane's proofreading.

---

[61] This leaf was discovered in the Columbia Special Collections by Lillian Gilkes and was described by Joseph Katz, *Stephen Crane Newsletter*, III (Spring, 1969), 1–2.

[62] These are E1 *in the* for *in* (121.23), *side* for *sides* (124.37), *them* for *him* (126.7), *clean* for *cleaned* (128.10), *only* omitted (132.9), *had* for *had had* (137.35), and *formula* for *formulæ* (140.29).

[63] These are E1 *round* for *around* (131.31) and *can* for *could* (135.32).

[64] These are all E1 omissions: of *fine* (136.25), *up* (137.3), *once* (137.12), and *wee* (141.19). The batch of omissions (three on one page of the original

In addition to its title, the *Black and White* text (BW) has eight unique variants, of which six are certain errors and two are probable.[65]

These unique separate errors in E1 and BW effectively demonstrate that the proof for one version could not have been the printer's copy for the other. On the other hand, if they are all independent printer's errors, they can have no bearing on the important matter of the relation of the copy of BW to that of E1. Paragraphing may sometimes provide useful evidence. In this respect both of the English prints are close. On two occasions (124.5, 134.1) BW paragraphs in connection with dialogue in a manner not shared by E1, and on two occasions (127.6, 136.6) E1 paragraphs narrative differently not only from BW but also from HW and A1. The BW paragraph variants appear to be compositorial house styling; whatever the origin of the E1 variant paragraphing, the agreement against E1 of the other three authorities indicates that the E1 styling has no relation to the basic printer's copy. In contrast, BW and E1 join in differing from HW and A1 nine times, of which three indentions are distinctive in having no relation to dialogue and hence appear to reflect a difference in the printer's copy shared by each group. This evidence joins with the nine substantive agreements between BW and E1 as against HW and A1—at least three or more of these being agreement in errors—to indicate very strongly indeed that, since proof for one is impossible as printer's copy for the other, either a typescript and its carbon or a fresh copy made from the original typescript served as printer's copy.[66] Of

---

and the others fairly closely clustered, including the omissions at 132.1 and 137.35 listed in footnote 62 above) reminds one of the similar cluster of omissions in the E1 text of "The Five White Mice," four of the five being in the work of one compositor, Palmer. Of the debatable four in "Death and the Child" only the omission of *fine* is really explicable, and that merely because of its repetition of *fine* from 136.23, which may or may not be designed. Modern sensibilities might query the adjective *wee*, but Crane had used it elsewhere, as in "The Open Boat" (73.9), and there is no reason to suppose that he would have thought it sentimental.

[65] These are *all-tender* for *all tender* (129.10), *informous* for *infamous* (131.16), *firmly down* for *down* (131.25), *in* for *at* (139.4), *benches* for *trenches* (140.6), *indications* for *indication* (140.20), and probably *into* for *in* (136.16) and *it's* for *it is* (136.23).

[66] One may remark that despite other evidence for an intimate connection between BW and E1 each appears to have undergone considerable compositorial styling (although it is true that the differences might in part result from a

the two choices the common errors may suggest, perhaps, that of
a typescript and its carbon as the one to be preferred, especially
given what can be recovered of the circumstances of the *Black
and White* sale, which point toward Crane's having negotiated
the matter directly. Thus he may have had a typescript and
carbon made professionally.[67]

The concurrence of the two American prints HW and A1 in
the nine substantive readings against BW and E1—one of these
a distinctive error [68]—as well as the three nondialogue differences between the two traditions in paragraphing indicate that,
like the English line, the American stemmed from some common
original of its own. As with the English, the unique readings in
each American authority prevent any hypothesis that the proof
of one could have been the printer's copy for the other. HW has
only five substantive readings in which it differs from the other
three texts. One of these is a manifest error, whereas the others
are relatively indifferent readings which in the circumstances
can have no authority.[69] On the contrary, A1 exhibits twenty-one
unique substantive variants from the other three texts, of which
seven are relatively clearcut errors,[70] six are probably compositorial sophistications,[71] three are indifferent variants,[72] and only

---

typescript copying). Thus in punctuation variants BW and E1 agree about fifty
times against HW and A1, whereas (to show how chance operates) BW and HW
agree with each other against E1 and A1 some eighteen times, and E1 and HW
agree against A1 and BW some eighteen times. On the other hand, if we take it
that as a general rule unique divergences in one text from the agreement of the
other three authorities are likely to indicate nonauthoritative house styling, BW
disagrees in punctuation about fifty-two times against the others and E1
disagrees some forty-one times. Statistics for variation in capitalization, word-division, and the association of independent clauses with semicolons or their
separation by periods are roughly similar.

[67] For a straw in the wind that the typist of the copy behind BW and E1 was
very likely British, see the Textual Note to 124.11.

[68] This is HW,A1 *steep* for BW,E1 *sheep* at 135.15.

[69] The error is HW *peasants* for *peasant* (126.8); the others are HW *have now*
for *now have* (124.5), *were* for *was* (124.14), *mountain* for *mountains*
(135.34), and *readjustments* for *readjustment* (140.4).

[70] These are A1's alteration of *that* from a relative to a demonstrative pronoun
(125.5) accompanied by what seems to be a consequential omission of *But*
(125.6), *struggle* for *straggle* (129.14), *conditions* for *condition* (132.24), *men*
for *man* (137.9), *clumsy* for *clammy* (139.8), and the omission of fourteen
necessary words *and so . . . misery* (130.14–15).

[71] A1 *been expressed only* for *only been expressed* (122.24), *all the* for *all*
(130.37), *an* for *a* (135.6), *concerted* for *connected* (136.12), *motion* for
motions (137.22), and *fearless and cherubic* for *fearless cherubic* (141.6).

[72] A1 *the* for *all the* (127.15), *known that* for *known* (129.9), and *on* for
onward (131.25).

five qualify as possible revisions.[73] The five differences in paragraphing between HW and A1 may be put down to compositorial styling of dialogue, in four cases HW creating a new paragraph against the concurrence of the other three texts in no indention [74] and in one (133.22) retaining the lack of paragraphing of the other texts against the A1 indention of dialogue.

In other respects HW and A1 appear to differ between themselves more markedly than do BW and E1. For example, although in punctuation variance from the other three authorities HW is the most conservative of all the texts with about twenty-nine differences, A1 shows roughly eighty-three such variations. HW ten times moves against the others in word-division, but A1 only five times. In capitalization HW differs some twenty-three times (although in only five words), whereas A1 varies from the rest only once. In the use of semicolons to join two independent clauses or of periods to make separate sentences of them, HW disagrees with the others five times but A1 an extraordinary total of twenty-seven times.[75] When these differences (which are rough counts, only) are viewed qualitatively, however, it is evident that they represent what has been encountered elsewhere in the volume when A1 could be assessed against known copy—that is, a very considerable amount of house styling, with especial reference to the joining of separate sentences by means of semicolons. On the other hand, since Reynolds was presumably sent only one copy, which must have been a typescript or its carbon, and since proof for one was not copy for the other, the problem arises whether Crane himself furnished McClure in London with the copy for A1, or whether Reynolds had a second copy made for the New York office from the text that had been sent him. If the latter, the question would then arise whether he sold the copy Crane had sent him to *Harper's Weekly* or whether he sold his new typescript and retained the Crane copy to pass on to Doubleday & McClure for A1.

It is unfortunate that neither external nor internal evidence can offer anything really conclusive to settle this important

---

[73] A1 *times* for *moments* (122.16), *dwelt . . . this* for *dwell . . . his* (123.30), *one explosion* for *an explosion* (123.36), and *was* for *had* (124.31).

[74] These are 122.27, 130.21, 133.20, and 133.25.

[75] The next highest total is BW, which disagrees in this respect eight times against the other texts.

point. Crane's letters to Reynolds can readily be interpreted as signifying that Crane himself, having sold the rights to McClure in London, was furnishing the copy; and indeed his reference as late as January 31, 1898, that McClure had not been sent copy might strengthen that supposition. The statements to Reynolds, and even the argument about placing "Death and the Child" in *The Open Boat* and not in *The Monster* (which shows that on February 7 Crane did not believe that Reynolds had taken the copy to McClure) are intended to be informatory and not hortatory. Since Reynolds had been told plainly in the letter accompanying Crane's mailing of the story in December that McClure had a 'call' on it, why he had not given the typescript to the publisher by early February is not to be explained if one supposes that he was intended to provide the copy. The external evidence, then, may favor—though not prove—the hypothesis that although the copy sent to Reynolds and the copy used by McClure were substantially identical, the split in their two forms occurred in England and not in America. No clearcut evidence offers a basis for placing either HW or A1 at a further remove from the lost archetype than the other; hence each must be, theoretically, of equal authority.[76]

On the evidence of the preserved manuscript page of the early draft, a distinction may be made between the fidelity of the accidentals of the English and American traditions to the lost final manuscript. Ten variants in punctuation exist between the text in the MS and in one or other of the printed texts. In the four cases where HW,A1 differ from BW,E1, the English texts reproduce the MS punctuation.[77] Thrice all four prints differ

[76] The evidence of the letters seems to point so strongly in this direction as to outweigh what may or may not be some slight contrary internal evidence. For example, A1 *clumsy* for *clammy* (139.8) may seem to have originated more naturally in a typist misreading handwriting than in a compositor misreading a typescript, as may *concerted* for *connected* (136.12) and possibly *men* for *man* (137.9). Moreover, there exists the mystery about the loss of fourteen words from A1 at 130.14–15. Eyeskip of a whole line has certainly occurred here, but whether by typist or by compositor is moot. On the other hand, it may be noticed that the unique characteristics of HW suggest radiation from two typescripts less than the one or two possibly suggestive characteristics in this direction found in A1. On the whole, the evidence is too uncertain for the formation of a hypothesis in favor of a typescript from a typescript.

[77] These are 124.1 *racket*ᴧ BW,E1 [*noise*ᴧ MS] versus a comma in HW,A1; 124.5 *war*ᴧ versus a comma in HW,A1; 124.11 *me.* versus an exclamation point in HW,A1; and 124.17 *fight*ᴧ versus a comma in HW,A1.

from the MS.[78] Once AI varies where the rest agree with the MS,[79] once HW varies uniquely,[80] and once BW, HW, and AI disagree with the MS,EI concurrence.[81] Since in the two cases where AI and HW vary uniquely, each increases the weight of the punctuation, and since in the four cases where BW and EI agree with MS they disagree with heavier punctuation in HW and AI, it is evident that—within the range of the available evidence—the punctuation of the BW,EI tradition is closer to the MS than is that of the HW,AI tradition. It would seem that when Crane worked over and rewrote his dictated manuscript, he did not materially, if at all, increase the weight of the light punctuation which he had presumably dictated to Cora and which is definitely a characteristic of his manuscripts. It follows that the two English texts, BW and EI, reproduce his punctuation system more faithfully than do the American texts. To this evidence must be added the more extreme variation of the American texts when either one differs from the agreement among the other three in punctuation or in other of the accidentals.

Fidelity to the accidentals of the lost manuscript and thus the choice of copy-text for the present edition must rest with BW and EI. As between BW and EI, however, the evidence indicates that EI has considerably fewer unique variants from the accidentals of the rest than does BW and is thus the more conservative and accurate copy-text.

On the other hand, the substantives of EI will need occasional emendation from the other authorities. Certain working principles can be formulated. No evidence suggests that either BW or HW was authorially proofread: the majority of their unique substantive readings are manifest errors and the relatively few indifferent readings do not carry the air of authority. These, then, can be ignored, as can the single reading in which, against all transmissional possibility, BW and AI by chance join in a

[78] At 124.4 all prints have a comma before *as* but MS has no comma; at 124.8 the prints have an exclamation point after *Yes* but MS a period; and at 124.17 where the MS has no punctuation after *fight* BW, HW, and AI join in a comma but EI has a dash.

[79] At 123.23 AI prints a comma after *measures* uniquely.

[80] At 124.10 HW uses an exclamation point after *way* whereas the rest have a period.

[81] At 123.23 oddly enough MS and EI place a comma after *clock* although the rest join in a dash.

contaminated plural at 125.31. On the other hand, the agreement of BW and E1 in a substantive reading against HW and A1 is no necessary sign of correctness, for the typescript behind HW and A1 may have reproduced the manuscript copy more faithfully than that behind BW and E1, and vice versa. Examination of the nine readings in this category does not suggest that Crane read over and corrected either basic typescript in a manner different from the other. The variants, thus, must be sophistications in the one, like the British idiom *struck by* in BW,A1 instead of *struck with*, or misreadings in the typescript like *steep* in HW,A1. But whatever the reason for the variance, the reading of one pair in any individual case must be right and the other wrong. Two degrees of correctness—one of these of revision—are not in question here.

Not one of the thirteen unique substantive variants in E1 is demonstrably an authorial copy-revision or proof-alteration. The evidence of the other stories in the Heinemann collection appears to be applicable here: no basis seems to exist for assigning E1 variants to proofreading; instead, stories where authorial revision occurs are confined to printed-copy texts annotated before being sent to Heinemann. Stories printed in E1 from typescript or manuscript copy do not exhibit authoritative revision from their other preserved texts. Although thirteen substantive errors is a rather high proportion to assign to E1, it may be that the careless compositor Palmer, whose work can be identified in "The Five White Mice," is responsible for the majority.[82]

In turn, twenty-one unique substantive variants is an exceptionally high proportion to find in A1, especially since only five of these, at the most, might qualify for consideration as possible proof-changes of the kind observed in various other stories in the American edition. Yet because of the lateness of submission of the copy to the publisher, it is possible that proof could not be sent to Crane and returned in time.[83] If this is so, the authority of

[82] "Death and the Child" occupies pages 177–207 in E1. Four of the substantive errors appear in pages 178–187; the remaining nine occur between pages 193–207. Of these nine, however, six are found in pages 200–207. This is the same sort of concentration observed in "The Five White Mice," and its significance would seem to be clear.

[83] It may be significant that "The Five White Mice," which follows "Death and the Child" as the final story in A1, has no identifiable proof-alterations. Its copy found its way to McClure only a little earlier than "Death and the Child."

even these five variants is suspect. In fact, although one of these five (*this* for *his* [123.30]) is a necessary correction, no other is required nor is the evidence in favor of Crane as the agent so distinctive as to enforce acceptance. The free alteration of the text that the compositor was capable of may be viewed in the two changes at A1 125.5,6. The most that can be said for the little group of possible proof-changes is that they cluster within three pages of the present edition (pages 252, 255, 256, and 258 of A1), but the confidently rejected pair at 125.5,6 represent the immediately following A1 variants and so could be included by the same line of reasoning. It is true, of course, that proof-correction is not wholly required as the source for authority. It is possible that the apparent delay in Crane's handing over printer's copy to McClure [84] could have offered him the opportunity to review the story in this typescript at a point after he had sent off the other texts and to alter the few clustered readings that called themselves to his attention. Nevertheless, in their kind this group does not distinguish itself sharply enough to demand acceptance as authoritative, whether made in the copy or in proof. Indeed, it may even be that the unusually high proportion of substantive error in A1 comes about because—unlike the other stories, with the possible exception of "The Five White Mice"—it was not proofread and various corrections were not made that restored the typescript readings. With some reluctance, therefore, the editor has rejected all A1 variants as unauthoritative and made use only of what may be regarded as necessary correction.

Despite the four equal authorities, their division into two traditions, each seemingly radiating from the manuscript and not one deriving from another, simplifies the editorial problem. The present edition, therefore, after an attempt to establish the readings, both substantive and accidental, of each textual line, is enabled by a synthesis to go in the back of these two typescripts and to recover in some part the basic readings of the lost manuscript.

---

[84] See the letter of Jan. 31, 1898, to Reynolds: "[McClure] has already 53000 words of a book—at least he has as soon as he gets a copy of Death and the Child." He had sent Reynolds a copy (which probably became HW) enclosed with a letter in early to mid-December, 1897.

THE BLUE HOTEL

"The Blue Hotel" first appeared in *Collier's Weekly* in two parts, on November 26 and December 3, 1896 (XXII, 14–16, 14–16), the division being made at 135.14. A drawing of the hotel by Jay Hambidge heads both parts, and each part contains a further illustration by the same artist, the first with the legend 'THE SWEDE HELD A HUGE FIST IN FRONT OF JOHNNIE'S FACE' and the second, 'THERE WAS HEARD THE CUSHIONED SOUND OF BLOWS'. The next and last appearance in Crane's lifetime was in *The Monster and Other Stories*, published in early December, 1899, by Harper and Brothers in New York and in late February, 1901, by the same firm in London, printed from the same plates without alteration.[85] None of the stories in this edition appears to have been proofread by Crane.

In the Columbia University Libraries Special Collections is preserved a leaf of an early draft of material covering 148.18–149.5 written by Cora from dictation.[86] This leaf is of ruled foolscap laid paper with the oval Britannia watermark. A red stain in the upper left corner does not interfere with the legibility. On the verso (i.e., on the side with Cora's later composition) are some word-count figures that belong with the original manuscript. First 250 (the word count of the page) is written, circled, and deleted. Then the sum of 250 is added to 1,400 for a total of 1,650, to which is added 970 for a final total of 2,620. Cora wrote the manuscript in a very black india ink. This paper is also found in a few of the *Whilomville Stories*. The text is printed in Professor Levenson's Introduction.

Since the 1899 collection *The Monster* provides a derived text set from *Collier's* without authorial revision, the only authority and copy-text for "The Blue Hotel" is the *Collier's Weekly* version, which is here reprinted with a few simple corrections drawn from A1, *The Monster*.

[85] For a bibliographical description of the New York and London editions, see Vol. VII, TALES OF WHILOMVILLE, 3–4.
[86] Cora was using the verso of this leaf as part of the paper supply for her review of the play *Peter the Great* by Lawrence Irving. The discovery by Lillian Gilkes was announced and analyzed by Joseph Katz, "An Early Draft of 'The Blue Hotel'," *Stephen Crane Newsletter*, III (Fall, 1968), 1–3.

TWELVE O'CLOCK

"Twelve O'Clock" appeared first—in its only known periodical form—in the *Pall Mall Magazine*, XIX (December, 1899), 462–468, illustrated by G. Grenville Manton.[87] This text was used for the book form in the 1901 Harper's London and New York reissue of *The Monster* collection (E2) where, on pages 191–206, it was the first of the four stories added in a new setting to the plates of the 1899 *Monster* first printing.[88]

The 1901 book collection (E2) is a straight reprint of the magazine text of "Twelve O'Clock," undoubtedly from a clipping. It makes a few literal errors, but in this posthumous collection none of the added stories shows any signs of revised copy prepared for publication, even though the autograph final list noticed in footnote 88 above demonstrates that Crane had this collection in mind before his death. Moreover, evidence exists that several changes made in proof have no authority either. The first page proofs are preserved in the Barrett Collection at the University of Virginia, marked '1ˢᵗ Pf.' in black ink in the upper left corner of the half-title and in the same unknown hand 'The Monster' in the lower left corner. Toward the head of the page is a blue-crayon figure '4' and below it the blue rubber stamp of the

[87] The Williams and Starrett bibliography of Crane is in error, on page 128, in listing this periodical as the *Pall Mall Gazette*. The story was noted as 'Copyright 1899 by Stephen Crane.' Manton furnished three illustrations with the legends ' "*Organise*," replied Roddie pompously. "*Organise*." '; ' "*Here's my money—come an' git it.*" '; and '*He had pitched headlong over the body of Big Watson.*'

[88] For a description of the 1899 and 1901 Harper printings, see Vol. VII, TALES OF WHILOMVILLE, 3–4. The story appears in two book lists that Crane made up, both now preserved in the Columbia University Libraries Special Collections. The order is uncertain but what may be the earlier, which seems to have been written out in early January, 1900, first lists the "Midnight Sketches" in the revised order as printed in the Heinemann 1898 *Open Boat*, for a total of 20,000 words, with the subscription 'All these stories appeared in the N.Y. Sunday Press or the Bacheller Syndicate.' Then below a line Crane lists nine stories with their word count and where published or whether unpublished. Fifth on this list is "Twelve O'Clock," given as the *Pall Mall Magazine* and as 2,500 words. The other list appears to be in preparation for the second English printing of *The Monster* in its expanded form. The three basic stories are noted, with their combined word count of 34,000. Then, in the order of eventual publication, appears "Twelve O'Clock" (here given as 3,000 words) and the other three, for a total of 10,500 words. Added as a fifth but without a word count, and below the 10,500 total line, is "Mad as a Hatter," no doubt to be identified with "A Tale of Mere Chance," which in the first list was ninth under the title of "The Pursuit of the Tiles."

printer William Clowes & Son with the date 'SENT OUT | 18 OCT OO'. In what is probably Cora's hand is the notation '3000 words'. Fifteen proof corrections are made in black ink, some of them, at least, almost certainly in Cora's hand. Various merely correct errors in the proof such as the omission of the sentence *"Mornin',"* *they answered in subdued voices* (172.16) or the omission of a period after *hand* (177.28). Some tinker with punctuation, such as the alteration of periods to exclamations after *me* (171.2,7) or of *Organise: that's* to *Organise. That's* (172.10). At 171.26 *their* is wrongly altered to *there* and it would seem that the change *Upside-down-F* to *Upside-down-P* is also a mistake. The omission of *up* twice in 171.18–19 seems to betray a misunderstanding of a common idiom, the change of *to one another* to *one to another* is an uncharacteristic refinement (174.6), and the insertion of *two* before *statues* (177.10) is otiose. On the whole, then, despite the change of *towards* to *toward* (176.4) and of *or* to *nor* (177.26), both of which might have come from a Crane manuscript, there is no firm evidence that Cora was referring to manuscript for her alterations although it seems evident that she was comparing the proofs against copy and bringing them into some conformity with the magazine text as well as indulging her own penchant for 'improvements.' Incidentally, this is also the pattern in the proofs for the remaining three stories, some of which contain better evidence against reference back to any manuscript authority. A list of the proof corrections in E2 follows the Historical Collation.

The copy-text and sole authority, therefore, remains the version published in the *Pall Mall Magazine* (PMM). A very few alterations of the PMM text to American forms or spellings are made editorially or, for convenience, by reference to E2 even though it is a completely derived text.

Moonlight on the Snow

"Moonlight on the Snow" was published in the United States in *Frank Leslie's Popular Monthly*, XL (April, 1900), 606–618,[89]

---

[89] F. P. Klix drew the illustrations, which have the following legends: 'I'M F'M WAR-POST'; 'IT'S THIS HERE GUN-FIGHTER BUSINESS'; 'SO YOU'VE COME UP TO THE

only two months before Crane's death, followed by book collection in England as the second of the four added stories in the 1901 Harper's *Monster and Other Stories*, pages 207–231. In the first of the autograph lists of stories discussed above in the section devoted to "Twelve O'Clock" it is the fourth, is noted as unpublished, and is optimistically reported as of 6,000 words. In the second list it appears in its correct position for publication after "Twelve O'Clock" and its word count is less optimistically given as 4,000.

The copy for the *Frank Leslie's Popular Monthly* text (FL) was probably a typescript at only one remove from the manuscript, since in its irregular paragraphing of dialogue and its generally light punctuation system it is often very close to the characteristics of Crane manuscripts. Worth some mention is the misnaming of Tom Larpent as Jack at 186.3, which may reflect not an inadvertency but an earlier choice not fully ironed out in the manuscript; also worth mention is the FL retention in its section numbers of the word 'Chapter,' irregularly found in Crane manuscripts.[90]

Although the 1901 *Monster* (E2) was deposited in the British Museum on February 25, 1901, and the proof for the four added stories was sent out on October 18, 1900 (as we know from "Twelve O'Clock"), the April, 1900, *Leslie's* printed text does not seem to have been the copy for the book. The exact nature of the document that was used by the E2 printer is, unfortunately, not susceptible of true demonstration. In certain of its accidentals E2 agrees closely with the magazine version, as in some of the semicolons and all of the FL dashes. Its departures from FL paragraphing are entirely associated with dialogue except for its continuous text at three places where FL seems to have introduced house-styling indentions in connection with dialogue. However, although E2 is ordinarily styled with a heavier punc-

SCRATCH ALL RIGHT, EH, BOBBY?'; 'AH, THE CROSS TRAIL STAGE APPROACHES. WHAT A SITUATION!'; 'THERE WAS A QUALITY TO THE SITUATION IN FRONT OF PILGRIM'S STORE WHICH MADE WAR-POST WISH TO STAMPEDE'; and 'THE LAST THING SEEN BY THE MEN IN THE CRYSTAL PALACE WAS THE BRONZE COUNTENANCE OF JACK POTTER AS HE BACKED FROM THE PLACE'.

[90] In *Whilomville Stories,* for example, *Chapter* is used for the sections after the first in the manuscript of "The Fight." The sections in "The Angel-Child" and "The Knife" manuscripts are called *Parts.* Ordinarily, however, Crane used simple roman numerals.

tuation system, at times its unusual lightness in pointing parenthetical matter and especially its occasional lack of a comma
between two adjectives before a noun preserve Crane's habits
more faithfully than does FL, which has certainly been styled by
the magazine editor. A few times each text normalizes dialect
found in the other, perhaps representing typist or compositorial
slips. At 186.3 E2 corrects (in its original setting) the FL misnaming of Larpent, noticed above.

In its substantives, however, E2 gives the distinct impression
of a considerably edited text, even in its proof form. The most
egregious case of interference is its use of the English *ill* for the
American *sick* at 187.24, and very likely its inclusion of Scratchy
Wilson with Potter in altering the singular FL *outsider* to *outsiders* at 190.6, accompanied by a change in the neutral *the* to
their in the next line. But equally obvious is the picking up of
state occasions from 183.12 and using it to alter FL *on occasion*
to *on state occasions* a few lines above at 183.8. The omitted
words, as *a* (180.23), *were* (181.19), *the* (185.33), and *a*
(188.6) are more likely than not to be errors, on the evidence of
similar omissions in "Twelve O'Clock" where both the proof and
the control printer's copy enable us to discriminate more accurately. Neutral variants of doubtful authority are the omission of
FL *in every way* (183.37) and the substitution of *were* for FL
had been (187.2).[91] The change of FL *had* to *was* at 187.20 was
a proof correction, however. In addition to 186.3, errors in FL are
found in correct form in E2 at 184.11, and also at 185.5 where a
necessary sentence omitted in FL by an eyeskip caused by other
nearby sentences beginning with *You* is printed intact both in
proof and in the book.

The collational evidence suggests, first, that no substantive
variant in E2 appears to be an authorial revision of an FL
reading and that the same may perhaps be said for FL, though
more doubtfully; second, that the number of substantive variants and of correct dialect forms in E2 may just possibly be
greater than one would expect to be produced by the printers if

[91] At 187.2 one might argue that FL had changed typescript *were* to *had been*
in order to avoid the repetition of *was*, the verb in *was to prey* of the main
clause; but it would be simpler to suggest the possibility that this *was* had
influenced the E2 compositor (or typist) into altering typescript *had been* for
conformity.

both texts had been set from identical forms of copy like a typescript and its carbon. However, against this undemonstrable impression may be placed the various coincidences in accidentals mentioned above, not the least of which is the closeness of FL *War-post* and E2 *Warpost* against presumed manuscript *War Post* as found in the preserved leaf of an early draft of the story. (The two autograph fragments are transcribed and discussed in Professor Levenson's Introduction.) The printed form here appears to derive from a common typescript original.[92]

This may be shrewd evidence in favor of a typescript and its carbon as the respective printer's copy for FL and E2, especially since it simplifies the transmissional history of the text, for which no external evidence is preserved. On the other hand, something may be said in favor of the opposite, that, instead, when printer's copy was required for the expanded *Monster*, the carbon was not available and a new typescript had to be made up from the manuscript.[93] Two typescripts would help to remove some of the onus for the E2 compositorial corruptions by allotting some to a typist. However, given the considerable corruption of the text found in the E2 "Twelve O'Clock" set from printed copy, the E2 setting of "Moonlight on the Snow" from the carbon of a typescript—which would invariably encourage more styling than printed copy—is not demonstrably inferior. Yet the number of times that E2 preserves dialect forms smoothed out in FL is somewhat dashing if both were set from identical copy.

The most difficult evidence to interpret comes in the FL spelling *Bobby* whereas E2 prints *Bobbie*. Crane's invariable ending for nicknames of this kind was *-ie*, although a compositor might rarely (as in *Maggie* 9.30) introduce a *-y* form. If *Bobby* stood in only one typed copy, then we should need to take it that the FL compositor followed his copy but the E2 compositor exercised his preference for *-ie*; if *Bobbie* stood in such a copy, the situation is merely reversed. The legend to the third illustration reads *Bobby*, but unfortunately we have no means of knowing whether

[92] Otherwise it would be unusual to have two typists transcribe manuscript *War Post* one as *War-post* and the other as *Warpost*.

[93] One can only guess in this matter. Perhaps the usual carbon had been mislaid, or perhaps it was not available in the office of Crane's agent or else was still in circulation among English magazines seeking a publisher who never appeared.

the artist made notes from (or was lent) the typescript or drew his information from an early proof. Although the dilemma might be somewhat reduced if the two could be hypothesized as repeating the forms in two different lines of the text independently stemming from the manuscript, it should be clear that speculation is idle about this spelling variant.

The answer, if one were possible, to the vexed question of the printer's copy for the two texts is of theoretical importance. For example, if both prints derive from a single typescript and its carbon (both presumably identical),[94] then the odds favor one form of a variant being right and the other wrong on the sole basis of compositorial error or editorial intervention. In such circumstances a partial reconstruction of the lost typescript is possible but no reconstruction of the manuscript from documentary evidence. However, if two typescripts radiate independently from a manuscript, then compositorial error is no longer mensurable except for the most obvious forms like typos since a compositor could be led into considerable error by faithfully following a corrupt typescript. Moreover, though in the first instance no documentary evidence could exist to isolate the cases when the typescript departed from the manuscript, in the second (allowing for compositorial error) one form is likely to reproduce the manuscript whereas the other does not. In these circumstances it is possible to attempt a synthesis of the documentary evidence that in some part will recover certain features of the manuscript behind the typescripts. The practical effect of this latter situation is ordinarily to promote the general authority of what might otherwise be thought a less trustworthy text, since even in the midst of carelessness and sophistication a bad typist can occasionally reproduce accurately a reading in the manuscript which the other typist (or compositor) has corrupted.[95]

[94] A slightly complicating factor here is that in some other stories Crane seems occasionally to have made changes in a copy that he did not mail out immediately, whereas the carbon dispatched earlier, say, and its print would not reflect these changes. That a few variants in the FL text represent some such casual alteration is possible, but only possible.

[95] For instance, an editor would normally take it that FL preserves the correct reading *stage coach* at 185.8 and that E2 (which is likely to omit words) is in error also in omitting *stage*. But he could feel limited confidence in this decision only if he held to the hypothesis that both FL and E2 were set from one source, a typescript and its carbon, because only on that hypothesis could the apparent omission of *stage* in E2 be associated with other omissions of an equally neutral

Fortunately, the question is not a crucial one in "Moonlight on the Snow," for no certain resolution is possible. As a working hypothesis, however, the present editor has taken the risky position that both authorities were set from a typescript and its carbon, since the forms of *War-post* and *Warpost* weigh heavily with him as more likely to stem from a single typed copy than from two copies made from a manuscript that read *War Post*.[96] The two texts, thus, are theoretically of equal authority. However, FL has been chosen as copy-text in some part because its American accidentals would normally be closer to Crane's than the English-set E2, and in some part because—despite its styling —FL does indeed reflect Crane's punctuation as well as spelling system more faithfully on the whole than its English counterpart. Nevertheless, when reason exists to suspect that E2 reproduces certain authorial accidentals habits with superior fidelity because of the interference of American house styling, the copytext has been emended to introduce the E2 authority. In general, the substantives of FL seem to be more authoritative than those of E2, and hence substantive emendation from E2 is confined to the few cases of positive error in FL and to dialect forms in E2 that have apparently been smoothed out in the American text. Where the variants are indifferent, the assumption has been made that they are more likely to result from E2 sophistication than from FL corruption.[97] The present text, therefore, attempts by a conservative synthesis of the two authorities to reconstruct as far as the documentary evidence permits the features of the typescript used as copy for *Frank Leslie's Monthly Magazine*.

Along with the other added stories in E2, the page proof for the E2 text of "Moonlight on the Snow" is preserved in the

---

kind that, cumulatively, add up to the assumption of error. If "Moonlight on the Snow" were set from a typescript and its carbon in the two authorities, one can weigh the chances for omission in error of the word in E2 as against those for addition in error in FL. But if the two go back to independent typescripts, then the question is more complex and the decision more difficult.

[96] Yet, to illustrate how cloudy evidence of this sort may be, all one need do is to postulate Crane dictating the final manuscript form to someone who adopted the spelling *Warpost* in copying the story by ear, and the whole value of this evidence vanishes.

[97] Even if the working hypothesis is faulty and FL and E2 derive from two independent typescripts, the evidence would suggest that any later typescript behind E2 would have been produced in an authorially unsupervised manner and that its rate of substantive error would be correspondingly high.

Barrett Collection at the University of Virginia. Its half-title has the same markings as "Twelve O'Clock" except that the word count is given as '5000 words' and the printer's date stamp is absent. The correcting hand appears to be that of Cora Crane. The ten proof alterations are listed in the apparatus following the Historical Collation.

A POKER GAME

The only appearance in print of "A Poker Game" was in the posthumous collection *Last Words* (Digby, Long & Co., 1902), pages 263–267 (E1), for which deposit was made in the British Museum on May 16, 1902, although it seems to have been ready for publication by late March. The title appears in no known example of Crane's various inventories or notes for collections.

The Barrett Collection in the University of Virginia Library preserves a black typescript on four leaves of ruled wove unwatermarked quarto paper, 265 × 208 mm., the rules 9 mm. apart,[98] now laminated for protection. The misspellings and certain special typing habits [99] identify this typescript with some certainty as made by Cora Crane. Various corrections in a black ink are found, some to add a necessary final letter or two in the right margin, some to form exclamation points from periods, and others to correct misspellings and to interline words omitted in error. These annotations are all in Cora's hand. Also in Cora's hand is the ink notation '1080 words' in the upper left corner of the first page, the addition of 'A' to the title—which may or may not be authoritative—and (on the verso of leaf 4, in pencil) the memorandum, 'A Poker Game | for book'. In another hand, in the upper right corner of the first leaf, is a blue-crayon '6'. No word counts are present on the versos nor is the story signed.

---

[98] This paper is identical with that used for the copy of "The Upturned Face" also in the Barrett Collection.

[99] These include her habit of breaking words arbitrarily at the right margin, when the typewriter (without margin release) could go no farther, and continuing with the remaining letters at the start of the next line (one example here), or—to avoid this practice—of deleting a partially typed word at the right margin and starting the next line with the word again. Occasionally she would not type the final letter or two in the right margin when prevented and leave it to hand correction later; however, this particular characteristic she shared with others who typed Crane's manuscripts for him.

Cora's annotations seem to have been made with care, although she missed the correction of various misspellings. That she was conscious of the need for accuracy in typing may be shown by the several occasions in which *currente calamo* she made corrections before typing the next word. A typical example comes at 192.22–23 where she originally typed 'It came to pass that they played' but then recognized her mistake and continued with 'just naturally played poker' and later deleted the first *played.* As another, at 194.12 she typed a wrong comma after *thing* but deleted it with a typed slant, presumably before continuing. The omitted word *moments* at 194.10 she caught on review and interlined in ink, probably at the time she was reading over the story to make the numerous ink corrections of missing letters and so on, just as she interlined at this time the missing *a* in *dimonds* at 194.4.

The origin of this typescript and its relationship to the text of *Last Words* is, fortunately, readily established. This is one of a collection of similar typescripts and carbons that was purchased originally from Henry Coates of Philadelphia, who reportedly had them from Paul Reynolds. Necessarily, these must represent part of the copy that Cora sent to the United States when negotiations were proceeding for the publication by Coates of *Last Words*, a project that was to be aborted in the end.

It is clear, therefore, that the carbon of this Barrett typescript served as printer's copy for the story in *Last Words*. Indeed, one little piece of evidence may be taken as establishing this natural inference. At 192.12 the Barrett typescript reads *corner on bay rum*, but Cora has altered the *on* in ink to *in. Last Words* faithfully reproduces the *on*, thus showing that Cora had not made this change when she reviewed the carbon.[100] Although the *Last Words* error of *diamond* for *diamonds* (194.4) cannot be imputed to a lack of clarity in the typescript, the error *those* for typescript *these* (194.8) is an easy one when the type is clogged; and it is also evident that some difficulty with the lack of clarity in the inking of the typescript must have caused the E1 misreading *fear, horror* for TMs *roar of horror* (194.15).

---

[100] Since *in* is the more common but *on* perfectly acceptable, it is probable that the change in TMs is unauthoritative and that the original reading of the typescript should be retained.

The Barrett typescript becomes the copy-text for the present edition, emended as necessary in its errors of punctuation and spelling by reference to E1, which may or may not have differed slightly in these respects from Cora's handwritten corrections. House styling of a faulty copy by the printer, however, is enough to account for the minor accidentals variants between the preserved carbon and the E1 text.

F. B.

TALES OF ADVENTURE

THE PACE OF YOUTH
I

STIMSON stood in a corner and glowered. He was a fierce man and had indomitable whiskers, albeit he was very small.

"That young tarrier," he whispered to himself. "He wants to quit makin' eyes at Lizzie. This is too much of a good thing. First thing you know, he'll get fired."

His brow creased in a frown, he strode over to the huge open doors and looked at a sign. "Stimson's Mammoth Merry-Go-Round," it read, and the glory of it was great. Stimson stood and contemplated the sign. It was an enormous affair; the letters were as large as men. The glow of it, the grandeur of it was very apparent to Stimson. At the end of his contemplation, he shook his head thoughtfully, determinedly. "No, no," he muttered. "This is too much of a good thing. First thing you know, he'll get fired."

A soft booming sound of surf, mingled with the cries of bathers, came from the beach. There was a vista of sand and sky and sea that drew to a mystic point far away in the northward. In the mighty angle, a girl in a red dress was crawling slowly like some kind of a spider on the fabric of nature. A few flags hung lazily above where the bathhouses were marshalled in compact squares. Upon the edge of the sea stood a ship with its shadowy sails painted dimly upon the sky, and high overhead in the still, sun-shot air a great hawk swung and drifted slowly.

Within the merry-go-round there was a whirling circle of ornamental lions, giraffes, camels, ponies, goats, glittering with varnish and metal that caught swift reflections from windows high above them. With stiff wooden legs, they swept on in a never-ending race while a great orchestrion clamored in wild speed. The summer sunlight sprinkled its gold upon the garnet canopies carried by the tireless racers and upon all the devices of

decoration that made Stimson's machine magnificent and famous. A host of laughing children bestrode the animals, bending
forward like charging cavalrymen and shaking reins and whooping in glee. At intervals they leaned out perilously to clutch at
iron rings that were tendered to them by a long wooden arm. At
the intense moment before the swift grab for the rings one could
see their little nervous bodies quiver with eagerness; the laughter
rang shrill and excited. Down in the long rows of benches,
crowds of people sat watching the game, while occasionally a
father might arise and go near to shout encouragement, caution-
ary commands, or applause at his flying offspring. Frequently
mothers called out: "Be careful, Georgie!" The orchestrion bellowed and thundered on its platform, filling the ears with its
long monotonous song. Over in a corner a man in a white apron
and behind a counter roared above the tumult: "Pop corn! Pop
corn!"

A young man stood upon a small, raised platform, erected in
the manner of a pulpit and just without the line of the circling
figures. It was his duty to manipulate the wooden arm and affix
the rings. When all were gone into the hands of the triumphant
children, he held forth a basket, into which they returned all
save the coveted brass one, which meant another ride free and
made the holder very illustrious. The young man stood all day
upon his narrow platform, affixing rings or holding forth the
basket. He was a sort of general squire in these lists of childhood. He was very busy.

And yet Stimson, the astute, had noticed that the young man
frequently found time to twist about on his platform and smile
at a girl who shyly sold tickets behind a silvered netting. This,
indeed, was the great reason of Stimson's glowering. The young
man upon the raised platform had no manner of license to smile
at the girl behind the silvered netting. It was a most gigantic
insolence. Stimson was amazed at it. "By jiminy," he said to
himself again, "that fellow is smiling at my daughter." Even in
this tone of great wrath it could be discerned that Stimson was
filled with wonder that any youth should dare smile at the
daughter in the presence of the august father.

Often the dark-eyed girl peered between the shining wires,

and, upon being detected by the young man, she usually turned her head away quickly to prove to him that she was not interested. At other times, however, her eyes seemed filled with a tender fear lest he should fall from that exceedingly dangerous platform. As for the young man, it was plain that these glances filled him with valor, and he stood carelessly upon his perch, as if he deemed it of no consequence that he might fall from it. In all the complexities of his daily life and duties he found opportunity to gaze ardently at the vision behind the netting.

This silent courtship was conducted over the heads of the crowd who thronged about the bright machine. The swift, eloquent glances of the young man went noiselessly and unseen with their message. There had finally become established between the two in this manner a subtle understanding and companionship. They communicated accurately all that they felt. The boy told his love, his reverence, his hope in the changes of the future. The girl told him that she loved him, that she did not love him, that she did not know if she loved him, that she loved him. Sometimes a little sign saying "Cashier" in gold letters, and hanging upon the silvered netting, got directly in range and interfered with a tender message.

The love affair had not continued without anger, unhappiness, despair. The girl had once smiled brightly upon a youth who came to buy some tickets for his little sister, and the young man upon the platform observing this smile had been filled with gloomy rage. He stood like a dark statue of vengeance upon his pedestal and thrust out the basket to the children with a gesture that was full of scorn for their hollow happiness, for their insecure and temporary joy. For five hours he did not once look at the girl when she was looking at him. He was going to crush her with his indifference; he was going to demonstrate that he had never been serious. However, when he narrowly observed her in secret he discovered that she seemed more blythe than was usual with her. When he found that his apparent indifference had not crushed her he suffered greatly. She did not love him, he concluded. If she had loved him she would have been crushed. For two days he lived a miserable existence upon his high perch. He consoled himself by thinking of how unhappy he was, and by swift, furtive glances at the loved face. At any rate he was in her presence, and he could get a good view from his perch when there was no interference by the little sign: "Cashier."

But suddenly, swiftly, these clouds vanished and under the imperial blue sky of the restored confidence they dwelt in peace, a peace that was satisfaction, a peace that, like a babe, put its trust in the treachery of the future. This confidence endured until the next day, when she, for an unknown cause, suddenly refused to look at him. Mechanically, he continued his task, his brain dazed, a tortured victim of doubt, fear, suspicion. With his eyes he supplicated her to telegraph an explanation. She replied with a stony glance that froze his blood. There was a great difference in their respective reasons for becoming angry. His were always foolish, but apparent, plain as the moon. Hers were subtle, feminine, as incomprehensible as the stars, as mysterious as the shadows at night.

They fell and soared, and soared and fell in this manner until they knew that to live without each other would be a wandering in deserts. They had grown so intent upon the uncertainties, the variations, the guessings of their affair that the world had become but a huge immaterial background. In time of peace their smiles were soft and prayerful, caresses confided to the air. In time of war, their youthful hearts, capable of profound agony, were wrung by the intricate emotions of doubt. They were the victims of the dread angel of affectionate speculation that forces the brain endlessly on roads that lead nowhere.

At night, the problem of whether she loved him confronted the young man like a specter, looming as high as a hill and telling him not to delude himself. Upon the following day, this battle of the night displayed itself in the renewed fervor of his glances and in their increased number. Whenever he thought he could detect that she too was suffering, he felt a thrill of joy.

But there came a time when the young man looked back upon these contortions with contempt. He believed then that he had imagined his pain. This came about when the redoubtable Stimson marched forward to participate.

"This has got to stop," Stimson had said to himself, as he stood and watched them. They had grown careless of the light world that clattered about them; they were become so engrossed in their personal drama that the language of their eyes was almost as obvious as gestures. And Stimson, through his keenness, his wonderful, infallible penetration, suddenly came into possession of these obvious facts. "Well, of all the nerves," he said, regarding with a new interest the young man upon the perch.

He was a resolute man. He never hesitated to grapple with a crisis. He decided to overturn everything at once, for, although small, he was very fierce and impetuous. He resolved to crush this dreaming.

He strode over to the silvered netting. "Say, you want to quit your everlasting grinning at that idiot," he said, grimly.

The girl cast down her eyes and made a little heap of quarters into a stack. She was unable to withstand the terrible scrutiny of her small and fierce father.

Stimson turned from his daughter and went to a spot beneath the platform. He fixed his eyes upon the young man and said: "I've been speakin' to Lizzie. You better attend strictly to your own business or there'll be a new man here next week." It was as if he had blazed away with a shotgun. The young man reeled upon his perch. At last he in a measure regained his composure and managed to stammer: "A—all right, sir." He knew that denials would be futile with the terrible Stimson. He agitatedly began to rattle the rings in the basket and pretend that he was obliged to count them or inspect them in some way. He, too, was unable to face the great Stimson.

For a moment Stimson stood in fine satisfaction and gloated over the effect of his threat. "I've fixed them," he said complacently, and went out to smoke a cigar and revel in himself. Through his mind went the proud reflection that people who came in contact with his granite will usually ended in quick and abject submission.

II

One evening, a week after Stimson had indulged in the proud reflection that people who came in contact with his granite will usually ended in quick and abject submission, a young feminine friend of the girl behind the silvered netting came to her there and asked her to walk on the beach after "Stimson's Mammoth Merry-Go-Round" was closed for the night. The girl assented with a nod.

The young man upon the perch holding the rings saw this nod and judged its meaning. Into his mind came an idea of defeating the watchfulness of the redoubtable Stimson.

When the merry-go-round was closed and the two girls started for the beach, he wandered off aimlessly in another direction, but he kept them in view, and as soon as he was assured that he had escaped the vigilance of Stimson, he followed them.

The electric lights on the beach made a broad band of tremoring light, extending parallel to the sea, and upon the wide walk there slowly paraded a great crowd intermingling, intertwining, sometimes colliding. In the darkness stretched the vast purple expanse of the ocean, and the deep indigo sky above was peopled with yellow stars. Occasionally out upon the water a whirling mass of froth suddenly flashed into view, like a great ghostly robe appearing, and then vanished, leaving the sea in its darkness, from whence came those bass tones of the water's unknown emotion. A wind, cool, reminiscent of the wave wastes, made the women hold their wraps about their throats and caused the men to grip the rims of their straw hats. It carried the noise of the band in the pavilion in gusts. Sometimes people unable to hear the music glanced up at the pavilion and were reassured upon beholding the distant leader still gesticulating and bobbing and the other members of the band with their lips glued to their instruments. High in the sky soared an unassuming moon, faintly silver.

For a time the young man was afraid to approach the two girls. He followed them at a distance and called himself a coward. At last, however, he saw them stop on the outer edge of the crowd and stand silently listening to the voices of the sea. When he came to where they stood, he was trembling in his agitation. They had not seen him.

"Lizzie," he began. "I——"

The girl wheeled instantly and put her hand to her throat. "Oh, Frank, how you frightened me," she said—inevitably.

"Well, you know I—I——" he stuttered.

But the other girl was one of those beings who are born to attend at tragedies. She had for love a reverence, an admiration that was greater the more that she contemplated the fact that she knew nothing of it. This couple with their emotions, awed her and made her humbly wish that she might be destined to be of some service to them. She was very homely.

When the young man faltered before them, she, in her sympathy, actually overestimated the crisis and felt that he might fall dying at their feet. Shyly, but with courage, she marched to the rescue. "Won't you come and walk on the beach with us," she said. The young man gave her a glance of deep gratitude which was not without the patronage which a man in his condition naturally feels for one who pities it. The three walked on.

Finally the being who was born to attend at this tragedy said that she wished to sit down and gaze at the sea, alone.

They politely urged her to walk on with them, but she was obstinate. She wished to gaze at the sea, alone. The young man swore to himself that he would be her friend until he died.

And so the two young lovers went on without her. They turned once to look at her.

"Jennie's awful nice," said the girl.

"You bet she is," replied the young man, ardently.

They were silent for a little time.

At last the girl said: "You were angry at me yesterday."

"No, I wasn't."

"Yes, you were, too. You wouldn't look at me once all day."

"No, I wasn't angry. I was only putting on."

Though she had, of course, known it, this confession seemed to make her very indignant. She flashed a resentful glance at him. "Oh, were you, indeed!" she said, with a great air.

For a few minutes she was so haughty with him that he loved her to madness. And directly this poem which stuck at his lips came forth lamely in fragments.

When they walked back toward the other girl and saw the patience of her attitude, their hearts swelled in a patronizing and secondary tenderness for her.

They were very happy. If they had been miserable they would have charged this fairy scene of the night with a criminal heartlessness, but as they were joyous, they vaguely wondered how the purple sea, the yellow stars, the changing crowd under the electric lights could be so phlegmatic and stolid.

They walked home by the lakeside way and out upon the water those gay paper lanterns, flashing, fleeting and careering, sang to them, sang a chorus of red and violet and green and gold, a song of mystic lands of the future.

One day when business paused during the dull, sultry afternoon, Stimson went up town. Upon his return he found that the popcorn man from his stand over in a corner was keeping an eye upon the cashier's cage, and that nobody at all was attending to the wooden arm and the iron rings.

He strode forward like a sergeant of grenadiers. "Where in thunder is Lizzie?" he demanded, a cloud of rage in his eyes.

The popcorn man, although associated long with Stimson, had never got over being dazed. "They've—they've—gone round to th'—th'—house," he said, with difficulty, as if he had just been stunned.

"Whose house?" snapped Stimson.

"Your—your house, I 'spose," said the popcorn man.

Stimson marched round to his home. Kingly denunciations surged, already formulated, to the tip of his tongue, and he bided the moment when his anger could fall upon the heads of that pair of children.

He found his wife convulsive and in tears.

"Where's Lizzie?"

And then she burst forth: "Oh—John—John—they've run away—I know they have. They drove by here not three minutes ago. They must have done it on purpose to bid me good-bye, for Lizzie waved her hand sad-like, and then, before I could get out to ask where they were going or what, Frank whipped up the horse."

Stimson gave vent to a dreadful roar. "Get my revolver—get a hack—get my revolver, d——, do you hear—what the devil——" His voice became incoherent.

He had always ordered his wife about as if she were a battalion of infantry, and despite her misery, the training of years forced her to spring mechanically to obey, but suddenly she turned to him a shrill appeal.

"Oh, John—not—the—revolver."

"Confound it, let go of me," he roared again and shook her from him.

He ran hatless upon the street. There was a multitude of hacks at the summer resort, but it was ages to him before he could find one. Then he charged it like a bull. "Up town," he yelled, as he tumbled into the rear seat. The hackman thought of severed arteries. His galloping horse distanced a large number of citizens who had been running to find what caused such contortions by the little hatless man.

It chanced as the bouncing hack went along near the lake, Stimson gazed across the calm, gray expanse and recognized a color in a bonnet and a poise of a head. A buggy was traveling along a highway that led to Sorington. Stimson bellowed: "There —there—there they are—in that buggy."

The hackman became inspired with the full knowledge of the situation. He struck a delirious blow with the whip. His mouth expanded in a grin of excitement and joy. It came to pass that this old vehicle, with its drowsy horse and its dusty-eyed and tranquil driver, seemed suddenly to awaken, to become animated and fleet. The horse ceased to ruminate on his state, his air of reflection vanished. He became intent upon his aged legs and spread them in quaint and ridiculous devices for speed. The driver, his eyes shining, sat critically in his seat. He watched each motion of this rattling machine down before him. He resembled an engineer. He used the whip with judgment and deliberation as the engineer would have used coal or oil. The horse clacked swiftly upon the macadam, the wheels hummed, the body of the vehicle wheezed and groaned.

Stimson, in the rear seat, was erect in that impassive attitude that comes sometimes to the furious man when he is obliged to leave the battle to others. Frequently, however, the tempest in his breast came to his face and he howled: "Go it—go it—you're gaining; pound 'im; thump the life out of 'im; hit 'im hard, you fool." His hand grasped the rod that supported the carriage top, and it was clinched so that the nails were faintly blue.

Ahead, that other carriage had been flying with speed, as from realization of the menace in the rear. It bowled away rapidly, drawn by the eager spirit of a young and modern horse. Stimson could see the buggy-top bobbing, bobbing. That little pane, like an eye, was a derision to him. Once he leaned forward and bawled angry sentences. He began to feel impotent; his whole expedition was the tottering of an old man upon the trail of birds. A sense of age made him choke again with wrath. That other vehicle, that was youth, with youth's pace, it was swift-flying with the hope of dreams. He began to comprehend those two children ahead of him, and he knew a sudden and strange awe, because he understood the power of their young blood, the power to fly strongly into the future and feel and hope again, even at that time when his bones must be laid in the earth.

The dust rose easily from the hot road and stifled the nostrils of Stimson. The highway vanished far away in a point with a suggestion of intolerable length. The other vehicle was becoming so small that Stimson could no longer see the derisive eye.

At last the hackman drew rein to his horse and turned to look at Stimson. "No use, I guess," he said. Stimson made a gesture of acquiescence, rage, despair. As the hackman turned his dripping horse about, Stimson sank back with the astonishment and grief of a man who has been defied by the universe. He had been in a great perspiration and now his bald head felt cool and uncomfortable. He put up his hand with the sudden recollection that he had forgotten his hat.

At last he made a gesture. It meant that at any rate he was not responsible.

ONE DASH—HORSES

RICHARDSON pulled up his horse and looked back over the trail where the crimson serape of his servant flamed amid the dusk of the mesquite. The hills in the west were carved into peaks, and were painted the most profound blue. Above them, the sky was of that marvelous tone of green —like still, sun-shot water—which people denounce in pictures.

José was muffled deep in his blanket, and his great toppling sombrero was drawn low over his brow. He shadowed his master along the dimming trail in the fashion of an assassin. A cold wind of the impending night swept over the wilderness of mesquite.

"Man," said Richardson in lame Mexican as the servant drew near, "I want eat! I want sleep! Understand—no? Quickly! Understand?" "Si, señor," said José, nodding. He stretched one arm out of his blanket and pointed a yellow finger into the gloom. "Over there, small village! Si, señor."

They rode forward again. Once the American's horse shied and breathed quiveringly at something which he saw or imagined in the darkness, and the rider drew a steady, patient rein, and leaned over to speak tenderly as if he were addressing a frightened woman. The sky had faded to white over the mountains and the plain was a vast, pointless ocean of black.

Suddenly some low houses appeared squatting amid the bushes. The horsemen rode into a hollow until the houses rose against the sombre sundown sky, and then up a small hillock, causing these habitations to sink like boats in the sea of shadow.

A beam of red firelight fell across the trail. Richardson sat sleepily on his horse while the servant quarreled with somebody —a mere voice in the gloom—over the price of bed and board. The houses about him were for the most part like tombs in their whiteness and silence, but there were scudding black figures that seemed interested in his arrival.

José came at last to the horses' heads, and the American slid stiffly from his seat. He muttered a greeting, as with his spurred feet he clicked into the adobe house that confronted him. The brown stolid face of a woman shone in the light of the fire. He seated himself on the earthen floor and blinked drowsily at the blaze. He was aware that the woman was clinking earthenware and hieing here and everywhere in the maneuvers of the house-wife. From a dark corner of the room there came the sound of two or three snores twining together.

The woman handed him a bowl of tortillas. She was a submissive creature, timid and large-eyed. She gazed at his enormous silver spurs, his large and impressive revolver, with the interest and admiration of the highly privileged cat of the adage. When he ate, she seemed transfixed off there in the gloom, her white teeth shining.

José entered, staggering under two Mexican saddles, large enough for building sites. Richardson decided to smoke a cigarette, and then changed his mind. It would be much finer to go to sleep. His blanket hung over his left shoulder, furled into a long pipe of cloth, according to a Mexican fashion. By doffing his sombrero, unfastening his spurs and his revolver belt, he made himself ready for the slow blissful twist into the blanket. Like a cautious man he lay close to the wall, and all his property was very near his hand.

The mesquite brush burned long. José threw two gigantic wings of shadow as he flapped his blanket about him—first across his chest under his arms, and then around his neck and across his chest again—this time over his arms, with the end tossed on his right shoulder. A Mexican thus snugly enveloped can nevertheless free his fighting arm in a beautifully brisk way, merely shrugging his shoulder as he grabs for the weapon at his belt. (They always wear their serapes in this manner.)

The firelight smothered the rays which, streaming from a moon as large as a drum head, were struggling at the open door. Richardson heard from the plain the fine, rhythmical trample of the hoofs of hurried horses. He went to sleep wondering who rode so fast and so late. And in the deep silence the pale rays of the moon must have prevailed against the red spears of the fire until the room was slowly flooded to its middle with a rectangle of silver light.

Richardson was awakened by the sound of a guitar. It was badly played—in this land of Mexico, from which the romance of the instrument ascends to us like a perfume. The guitar was groaning and whining like a badgered soul. A noise of scuffling feet accompanied the music. Sometimes laughter arose, and often the voices of men saying bitter things to each other, but always the guitar cried on, the treble sounding as if some one were beating iron, and the bass humming like bees. "Damn it—they're having a dance," muttered Richardson, fretfully. He heard two men quarreling in short, sharp words, like pistol shots; they were calling each other worse names than common people know in other countries. He wondered why the noise was so loud. Raising his head from his saddle pillow, he saw, with the help of the valiant moonbeams, a blanket hanging flat against the wall at the further end of the room. Being of the opinion that it concealed a door, and remembering that Mexican drink made men very drunk, he pulled his revolver closer to him and prepared for sudden disaster.

Richardson was dreaming of his far and beloved North.

"Well, I would kill him, then!"

"No, you must not!"

"Yes, I will kill him! Listen! I will ask this American beast for his beautiful pistol and spurs and money and saddle, and if he will not give them—you will see!"

"But these Americans—they are a strange people. Look out, señor."

Then twenty voices took part in the discussion. They rose in quavering shrillness, as from men badly drunk. Richardson felt the skin draw tight around his mouth, and his knee-joints turned to bread. He slowly came to a sitting posture, glaring at the motionless blanket at the far end of the room. This stiff and mechanical movement, accomplished entirely by the muscles of the waist, must have looked like the rising of a corpse in the wan moonlight, which gave everything a hue of the grave.

My friend, take my advice and never be executed by a hangman who doesn't talk the English language. It, or anything that resembles it, is the most difficult of deaths. The tumultuous emotions of Richardson's terror destroyed that slow and careful process of thought by means of which he understood Mexican. Then he used his instinctive comprehension of the first and universal language, which is tone. Still it is disheartening not to be able to understand the detail of threats against the blood of your body.

Suddenly the clamor of voices ceased. There was a silence—a silence of decision. The blanket was flung aside, and the red light of a torch flared into the room. It was held high by a fat, round-faced Mexican, whose little snake-like mustache was as black as his eyes, and whose eyes were black as jet. He was insane with the wild rage of a man whose liquor is dully burning at his brain. Five or six of his fellows crowded after him. The guitar, which had been thrummed doggedly during the time of the high words, now suddenly stopped. They contemplated each other. Richardson sat very straight and still, his right hand lost in the folds of his blanket. The Mexicans jostled in the light of the torch, their eyes blinking and glittering.

The fat one posed in the manner of a grandee. Presently his hand dropped to his belt, and from his lips there spun an epithet —a hideous word which often foreshadows knife-blows, a word peculiarly of Mexico, where people have to dig deep to find an insult that has not lost its savor. The American did not move. He was staring at the fat Mexican with a strange fixedness of gaze, not fearful, not dauntless, not anything that could be interpreted. He simply stared.

The fat Mexican must have been disconcerted, for he continued to pose as a grandee, with more and more sublimity, until it would have been easy for him to have fallen over backward. His companions were swaying in a very drunken manner. They still blinked their little beady eyes at Richardson. Ah, well, sirs, here was a mystery. At the approach of their menacing company, why did not this American cry out and turn pale, or run, or pray them mercy? The animal merely sat still, and stared, and waited for them to begin. Well, evidently he was a great fighter; or perhaps he was an idiot. Indeed, this was an embarrassing situation, for who was going forward to discover whether he was a great fighter or an idiot?

To Richardson, whose nerves were tingling and twitching like live wires and whose heart jolted inside him, this pause was a long horror; and for these men who could so frighten him there began to swell in him a fierce hatred—a hatred that made him long to be capable of fighting all of them, a hatred that made him capable of fighting all of them. A 44-caliber revolver can make a hole large enough for little boys to shoot marbles through, and there was a certain fat Mexican with a mustache like a snake who came extremely near to have eaten his last tamale merely because he frightened a man too much.

José had slept the first part of the night in his fashion, his body hunched into a heap, his legs crooked, his head touching his knees. Shadows had obscured him from the sight of the invaders. At this point he arose, and began to prowl quakingly over toward Richardson, as if he meant to hide behind him.

Of a sudden the fat Mexican gave a howl of glee. José had come within the torch's circle of light. With roars of ferocity the whole group of Mexicans pounced on the American's servant. He shrank shuddering away from them, beseeching by every device of word and gesture. They pushed him this way and that. They beat him with their fists. They stung him with their curses. As he groveled on his knees, the fat Mexican took him by the throat and said: "I am going to kill you!" And continually they turned their eyes to see if they were to succeed in causing the initial demonstration by the American. Richardson looked on impassively. Under the blanket, however, his fingers were clinched as rigidly as iron upon the handle of his revolver.

Here suddenly two brilliant clashing chords from the guitar were heard, and a woman's voice, full of laughter and confidence, cried from without: "Hello! Hello! Where are you?" The lurching company of Mexicans instantly paused and looked at the ground. One said, as he stood with his legs wide apart in order to balance himself: "It is the girls. They have come!" He screamed in answer to the question of the woman: "Here!" And without waiting he started on a pilgrimage toward the blanket-covered door. One could now hear a number of female voices giggling and chattering.

Two other Mexicans said: "Yes, it is the girls! Yes!" They also started quietly away. Even the fat Mexican's ferocity seemed to be affected. He looked uncertainly at the still-immovable American. Two of his friends grasped him gayly: "Come, the girls are here! Come!" He cast another glower at Richardson. "But this—," he began. Laughing, his comrades hustled him toward the door. On its threshold and holding back the blanket with one hand, he turned his yellow face with a last challenging glare toward the American. José, bewailing his state in little sobs of utter despair and woe, crept to Richardson and huddled near his knee. Then the cries of the Mexicans meeting the girls were heard, and the guitar burst out in joyous humming.

The moon clouded, and but a faint square of light fell through the open main door of the house. The coals of the fire were silent save for occasional sputters. Richardson did not change his position. He remained staring at the blanket which hid the strategic door in the far end. At his knees José was arguing, in a low, aggrieved tone, with the saints. Without the Mexicans laughed and danced, and—it would appear from the sound—drank more.

In the stillness and night Richardson sat wondering if some serpent-like Mexican was sliding toward him in the darkness, and if the first thing he knew of it would be the deadly sting of the knife. "Sssh," he whispered, to José. He drew his revolver from under the blanket and held it on his leg. The blanket over the door fascinated him. It was a vague form, black and unmoving. Through the opening it shielded was to come, probably, threats, death. Sometimes he thought he saw it move. As grim white sheets, the black and silver of coffins, all the panoply of death, affect us because of that which they hide, so this blanket, dangling before a hole in an adobe wall, was to Richardson a horrible emblem, and a horrible thing in itself. In his present mood Richardson could not have been brought to touch it with his finger.

The celebrating Mexicans occasionally howled in song. The guitarist played with speed and enthusiasm. Richardson longed to run. But in this vibrating and threatening gloom his terror convinced him that a move on his part would be a signal for the pounce of death. José, crouching abjectly, occasionally mumbled. Slowly and ponderous as stars the minutes went.

Suddenly Richardson thrilled and started. His breath, for a

moment, left him. In sleep his nerveless fingers had allowed his revolver to fall and clang upon the hard floor. He grabbed it up hastily, and his glance swept apprehensively over the room. A chill blue light of dawn was in the place. Every outline was slowly growing; detail was following detail. The dread blanket did not move. The riotous company had gone or become silent. Richardson felt in his blood the effect of this cold dawn. The candor of breaking day brought his nerve. He touched José. "Come," he said. His servant lifted his lined yellow face, and comprehended. Richardson buckled on his spurs and strode up; José obediently lifted the two great saddles. Richardson held two bridles and a blanket on his left arm; in his right hand he held his revolver. They sneaked toward the door.

The man who said that spurs jingled was insane. Spurs have a mellow clash—clash—clash. Walking in spurs—notably Mexican spurs—you remind yourself vaguely of a telegraphic lineman. Richardson was inexpressibly shocked when he came to walk. He sounded to himself like a pair of cymbals. He would have known of this if he had reflected; but then he was escaping, not reflecting. He made a gesture of despair, and from under the two saddles José tried to make one of hopeless horror. Richardson stooped, and with shaking fingers unfastened the spurs. Taking them in his left hand, he picked up his revolver and they slunk on toward the door. On the threshold Richardson looked back. In a corner, he saw, watching him with large eyes, the Indian man and woman who had been his hosts. Throughout the night they had made no sign, and now they neither spoke nor moved. Yet Richardson thought he detected meek satisfaction at his departure.

The street was still and deserted. In the eastern sky there was a lemon-colored patch. José had picketed the horses at the side of the house. As the two men came around the corner, Richardson's animal set up a whinny of welcome. The little horse had evidently heard them coming. He stood facing them, his ears cocked forward, his eyes bright with welcome.

Richardson made a frantic gesture, but the horse in his happiness at the appearance of his friends whinnied with enthusiasm. The American felt at this time that he could have strangled his well-beloved steed. Upon the threshold of safety, he was being betrayed by his horse, his friend. He felt the same hate for the horse that he would have felt for a dragon. And yet, as he glanced wildly about him, he could see nothing stirring in the street, nor at the doors of the tomb-like houses.

José had his own saddle girth and both bridles buckled in a moment. He curled the picket ropes with a few sweeps of his arm. The fingers of Richardson, however, were shaking so that he could hardly buckle the girth. His hands were in invisible mittens. He was wondering, calculating, hoping about his horse. He knew the little animal's willingness and courage under all circumstances up to this time, but then—here it was different. Who could tell if some wretched instance of equine perversity was not about to develop. Maybe the little fellow would not feel like smoking over the plain at express speed this morning, and so he would rebel and kick and be wicked. Maybe he would be without feeling of interest, and run listlessly. All men who have had to hurry in the saddle know what it is to be on a horse who does not understand the dramatic situation. Riding a lame sheep is bliss to it. Richardson, fumbling furiously at the girth, thought of these things.

Presently he had it fastened. He swung into the saddle, and as he did so his horse made a mad jump forward. The spurs of José scratched and tore the flanks of his great black animal, and side by side the two horses raced down the village street. The American heard his horse breathe a quivering sigh of excitement. Those four feet skimmed. They were as light as fairy puff balls. The houses of the village glided past in a moment, and the great, clear, silent plain appeared like a pale blue sea of mist and wet bushes. Above the mountains the colors of the sunlight were like the first tones, the opening chords of the mighty hymn of the morning.

The American looked down at his horse. He felt in his heart the first thrill of confidence. The little animal, unurged and quite tranquil, moving his ears this way and that way with an air of interest in the scenery, was nevertheless bounding into the eye of the breaking day with the speed of a frightened antelope. Richardson, looking down, saw the long, fine reach of forelimb, as steady as steel machinery. As the ground reeled past, the long, dried grasses hissed, and cactus plants were dull blurs. A wind whirled the horse's mane over his rider's bridle hand.

José's profile was lined against the pale sky. It was as that of a man who swims alone in an ocean. His eyes glinted like metal, fastened on some unknown point ahead of him, some fabulous place of safety. Occasionally his mouth puckered in a little unheard cry; and his legs, bended back, worked spasmodically as his spurred heels sliced the flanks of his charger.

Richardson consulted the gloom in the west for signs of a hard-riding, yelling cavalcade. He knew that whereas his friends the enemy had not attacked him when he had sat still and with apparent calmness confronted them, they would certainly take furiously after him now that he had run from them—now that he had confessed to them that he was the weaker. Their valor would grow like weeds in the spring, and upon discovering his escape they would ride forth dauntless warriors. Sometimes he was sure he saw them. Sometimes he was sure he heard them. Continually looking backward over his shoulder, he studied the purple expanses where the night was marching away. José rolled and shuddered in his saddle, persistently disturbing the stride of the black horse, fretting and worrying him until the white foam flew, and the great shoulders shone like satin from the sweat.

At last, Richardson drew his horse carefully down to a walk. José wished to rush insanely on, but the American spoke to him sternly. As the two paced forward side by side, Richardson's little horse thrust over his soft nose and inquired into the black's condition.

Riding with José was like riding with a corpse. His face resembled a cast in lead. Sometimes he swung forward and almost pitched from his seat. Richardson was too frightened himself to do anything but hate this man for his fear. Finally, he issued a mandate which nearly caused José's eyes to slide out of his head and fall to the ground like two coins. "Ride behind me—about fifty paces."

"Señor——" stuttered the servant. "Go," cried the American, furiously. He glared at the other and laid his hand on his revolver. José looked at his master wildly. He made a piteous gesture. Then slowly he fell back, watching the hard face of the American for a sign of mercy. Richardson had resolved in his rage that at any rate he was going to use the eyes and ears of extreme fear to detect the approach of danger; and so he established his servant as a sort of an outpost.

As they proceeded he was obliged to watch sharply to see that the servant did not slink forward and join him. When José made beseeching circles in the air with his arm he replied by menacingly gripping his revolver. José had a revolver, too; nevertheless it was very clear in his mind that the revolver was distinctly an American weapon. He had been educated in the Rio Grande country.

Richardson lost the trail once. He was recalled to it by the loud sobs of his servant.

Then at last José came clattering forward, gesticulating and wailing. The little horse sprang to the shoulder of the black. They were off.

Richardson, again looking backward, could see a slanting flare of dust on the whitening plain. He thought that he could detect small moving figures in it.

José's moans and cries amounted to a university course in theology. They broke continually from his quivering lips. His spurs were as motors. They forced the black horse over the plain in great headlong leaps. But under Richardson there was a little insignificant rat-colored beast who was running apparently with almost as much effort as it requires for a bronze statue to stand still. As a matter of truth, the ground seemed merely something to be touched from time to time with hoofs that were as light as blown leaves. Occasionally Richardson lay back and pulled stoutly at his bridle to keep from abandoning his servant. José harried at his horse's mouth, flopped around in the saddle and made his two heels beat like flails. The black ran like a horse in despair.

Crimson serapes in the distance resembled drops of blood on the great cloth of plain. Richardson began to dream of all possible chances. Although quite a humane man, he did not once think of his servant. José being a Mexican, it was natural that he should be killed in Mexico; but for himself, a New Yorker——
He remembered all the tales of such races for life, and he thought them badly written.

The great black horse was growing indifferent. The jabs of José's spurs no longer caused him to bound forward in wild leaps of pain. José had at last succeeded in teaching him that spurring was to be expected, speed or no speed, and now he took the pain of it dully and stolidly, as an animal who finds that doing his best gains him no respite. José was turned into a raving maniac. He bellowed and screamed, working his arms and his heels like one in a fit. He resembled a man on a sinking ship, who appeals to the ship. Richardson, too, cried madly to the black horse. The spirit of the horse responded to these calls, and quivering and breathing heavily he made a great effort, a sort of a final rush, not for himself apparently, but because he understood that his life's sacrifice, perhaps, had been invoked by these two men who cried to him in the universal tongue. Richardson had no sense of appreciation at this time—he was too frightened—but often now he remembers a certain black horse.

From the rear could be heard a yelling, and once a shot was fired—in the air, evidently. Richardson moaned as he looked back. He kept his hand on his revolver. He tried to imagine the brief tumult of his capture—the flurry of dust from the hoofs of horses pulled suddenly to their haunches, the shrill, biting curses of the men, the ring of the shots, his own last contortion. He wondered, too, if he could not somehow manage to pelt that fat Mexican, just to cure his abominable egotism.

It was José, the terror-stricken, who at last discovered safety. Suddenly he gave a howl of delight and astonished his horse into a new burst of speed. They were on a little ridge at the time, and the American at the top of it saw his servant gallop down the slope and into the arms, so to speak, of a small column of horsemen in gray and silver clothes. In the dim light of the early morning they were as vague as shadows, but Richardson knew them at once for a detachment of rurales, that crack cavalry corps of the Mexican army which polices the plain so zealously, being of themselves the law and the arm of it—a fierce and swift-moving body that knows little of prevention but much of vengeance. They drew up suddenly, and the rows of great silver-trimmed sombreros bobbed in surprise.

Richardson saw José throw himself from his horse and begin to jabber at the leader of the party. When he arrived he found that his servant had already outlined the entire situation, and was then engaged in describing him, Richardson, as an American señor of vast wealth who was the friend of almost every governmental potentate within two hundred miles. This seemed to profoundly impress the officer. He bowed gravely to Richardson and smiled significantly at his men, who unslung their carbines.

The little ridge hid the pursuers from view, but the rapid thud of their horses' feet could be heard. Occasionally they yelled and called to each other. Then at last they swept over the brow of the hill, a wild mob of almost fifty drunken horsemen. When they discerned the pale-uniformed rurales, they were sailing down the slope at top speed.

If toboggans half way down a hill should suddenly make up their minds to turn around and go back, there would be an effect somewhat like that now produced by the drunken horsemen. Richardson saw the rurales serenely swing their carbines forward, and, peculiar-minded person that he was, felt his heart leap into his throat at the prospective volley. But the officer rode forward alone.

It appeared that the man who owned the best horse in this astonished company was the fat Mexican with the snaky mustache, and, in consequence, this gentleman was quite a distance in the van. He tried to pull up, wheel his horse and scuttle back over the hill as some of his companions had done, but the officer called to him in a voice harsh with rage. "—!" howled the officer. "This señor is my friend, the friend of my friends. Do you dare pursue him, —? —! —! —! —!" These lines represent terrible names, all different, used by the officer.

The fat Mexican simply groveled on his horse's neck. His face was green; it could be seen that he expected death. The officer stormed with magnificent intensity: "—! —! —!" Finally he sprang from his saddle, and, running to the fat Mexican's side, yelled: "Go—" and kicked the horse in the belly with all his might. The animal gave a mighty leap into the air, and the fat Mexican, with one wretched glance at the contemplative rurales, aimed his steed for the top of the ridge. Richardson again gulped in expectation of a volley, for—it is said—this is one of the favorite methods of the rurales for disposing of objectionable people. The fat, green Mexican also evidently thought that he was to be killed while on the run, from the miserable look he cast at the troops. Nevertheless, he was allowed to vanish in a cloud of yellow dust at the ridge-top.

José was exultant, defiant, and, oh, bristling with courage. The black horse was drooping sadly, his nose to the ground. Richardson's little animal, with his ears bent forward, was staring at the horses of the rurales as if in an intense study. Richardson longed for speech, but he could only bend forward and pat the shining, silken shoulders. The little horse turned his head and looked back gravely.

THE WISE MEN:

A DETAIL OF AMERICAN LIFE IN MEXICO

THEY were youths of subtle mind. They were very wicked according to report, and yet they managed to have it reflect credit upon them. They often had the well-informed and the great talkers of the American colony engaged in reciting their misdeeds, and facts relating to their sins were usually told with a flourish of awe and fine admiration.

One was from San Francisco and one was from New York, but they resembled each other in appearance. This is an idiosyncrasy of geography.

They were never apart in the City of Mexico, at any rate, excepting perhaps when one had retired to his hotel for a respite, and then the other was usually camped down at the office sending up servants with clamorous messages. "Oh, get up and come on down."

They were two lads—they were called the Kids—and far from their mothers. Occasionally some wise man pitied them, but he usually was alone in his wisdom. The other folk frankly were transfixed at the splendor of the audacity and endurance of these Kids. "When do those two boys ever sleep?" murmured a man as he viewed them entering a café about eight o'clock one morning. Their smooth infantile faces looked bright and fresh enough, at any rate. "Jim told me he saw them still at it about four-thirty this morning."

"Sleep!" ejaculated a companion in a glowing voice. "They never sleep! They go to bed once in every two weeks." His boast of it seemed almost a personal pride.

"They'll end with a crash, though, if they keep it up at this pace," said a gloomy voice from behind a newspaper.

The Café Colorado has a front of white and gold, in which is set larger plate-glass windows than are commonly to be found in Mexico. Two little wings of willow flip-flapping incessantly serve as doors. Under them small stray dogs go furtively into the café, and are shied into the street again by the waiters. On the sidewalk there is always a decorative effect in loungers, ranging from the newly-arrived and superior tourist to the old veteran of the silver mines bronzed by violent suns. They contemplate with various shades of interest the show of the street—the red, purple, dusty white, glaring forth against the walls in the furious sunshine.

One afternoon the Kids strolled into the Café Colorado. A half-dozen of the men who sat smoking and reading with a sort of Parisian effect at the little tables which lined two sides of the room, looked up and bowed smiling, and although this coming of the Kids was anything but an unusual event, at least a dozen men wheeled in their seats to stare after them. Three waiters polished tables, and moved chairs noisily, and appeared to be eager. Distinctly these Kids were of importance.

Behind the distant bar, the tall form of old Pop himself awaited them smiling with broad geniality. "Well, my boys, how are you?" he cried in a voice of profound solicitude. He allowed five or six of his customers to languish in the care of Mexican bar-tenders, while he himself gave his eloquent attention to the Kids, lending all the dignity of a great event to their arrival. "How are the boys to-day, eh?"

"You're a smooth old guy," said one, eyeing him. "Are you giving us this welcome so we won't notice it when you push your worst whisky at us?"

Pop turned in appeal from one Kid to the other Kid. "There, now, hear that, will you?" He assumed an oratorical pose. "Why, my boys, you always get the best—the very best—that this house has got."

"Yes, we do!" The Kids laughed. "Well, bring it out, anyhow, and if it's the same you sold us last night, we'll grab your cash register and run."

Pop whirled a bottle along the bar and then gazed at it with a rapt expression. "Fine as silk," he murmured. "Now just taste that, and if it isn't the finest whisky you ever put in your face, why I'm a liar, that's all."

The Kids surveyed him with scorn, and poured out their allowances. Then they stood for a time insulting Pop about his whisky. "Usually it tastes exactly like new parlor furniture," said the San Francisco Kid. "Well, here goes, and you want to look out for your cash register."

"Your health, gentlemen," said Pop with a grand air, and as he wiped his bristling grey moustache he wagged his head with reference to the cash register question. "I could catch you before you got very far."

"Why, are you a runner?" said one derisively.

"You just bank on me, my boy," said Pop, with deep emphasis. "I'm a flier."

The Kids set down their glasses suddenly and looked at him. "You must be," they said. Pop was tall and graceful and magnificent in manner, but he did not display those qualities of form which mean speed in the animal. His hair was grey; his face was round and fat from much living. The buttons of his glittering white vest formed a fine curve, so that if the concave surface of a piece of barrel-hoop had been laid against Pop it would have touched each button. "You must be," observed the Kids again.

"Well, you can laugh all you like, but—no jolly now, boys, I tell you I'm a winner. Why, I bet you I can skin anything in this town on a square go. When I kept my place in Eagle Pass there wasn't anybody who could touch me. One of these sure things came down from San Anton'. Oh, he was a runner he was. One of these people with wings. Well, I skinned 'im. What? Certainly I did. Never touched me."

The Kids had been regarding him in grave silence, but at this moment they grinned, and said quite in chorus: "Oh, you old liar!"

Pop's voice took on a whining tone of earnestness. "Boys, I'm telling it to you straight. I'm a flier."

One of the Kids had had a dreamy cloud in his eye and he cried out suddenly. "Say, what a joke to play this on Freddie."

The other jumped ecstatically. "Oh, wouldn't it be, though. Say he wouldn't do a thing but howl! He'd go crazy."

They looked at Pop as if they longed to be certain that he was, after all, a runner. "Say, now, Pop, on the level," said one of them wistfully, "can you run?"

"Boys," swore Pop, "I'm a peach! On the dead level, I'm a peach."

"By golly, I believe the old Indian can run," said one to the other, as if they were alone in conference.

"That's what I can," cried Pop.

The Kids said: "Well, so long, old man." They went to a table and sat down. They ordered a salad. They were always ordering salads. This was because one Kid had a wild passion for salads, and the other didn't care much. So at any hour of the day or night they might be seen ordering a salad. When this one came they went into a sort of executive session. It was a very long consultation. Some of the men noted it; they said there was deviltry afoot. Occasionally the Kids laughed in supreme enjoyment of something unknown. The low rumble of wheels came from the street. Often could be heard the parrot-like cries of distant vendors. The sunlight streamed through the green curtains, and made some little amber-colored flitterings on the marble floor. High up among the severe decorations of the ceiling— reminiscent of the days when the great building was a palace—a small white butterfly was wending through the cool air spaces. The long billiard hall stretched back to a vague gloom. The balls were always clicking, and one could see endless elbows crooking. Beggars slunk through the wicker doors, and were ejected by the nearest waiter. At last the Kids called Pop to them.

"Sit down, Pop. Have a drink." They scanned him carefully. "Say now, Pop, on your solemn oath, can you run?"

"Boys," said Pop piously, and raising his hand, "I can run like a rabbit."

"On your oath?"

"On my oath."

"Can you beat Freddie?"

Pop appeared to look at the matter from all sides. "Well, boys, I'll tell you. No man is cock-sure of anything in this world, and I don't want to say that I can best any man, but I've seen Freddie run, and I'm ready to swear I can beat 'im. In a hundred yards I'd just about skin 'im neat—you understand—just about neat. Freddie is a good average runner, but I—you understand—I'm just—a little—bit—better." The Kids had been listening with the utmost attention. Pop spoke the latter part slowly and meaningly. They thought he intended them to see his great confidence.

One said: "Pop, if you throw us in this thing, we'll come here and drink for two weeks without paying. We'll back you and work a josh on Freddie! But oh!—if you throw us!"

To this menace Pop cried: "Boys, I'll make the run of my life! On my oath!"

The salad having vanished, the Kids arose. "All right, now," they warned him. "If you play us for duffers, we'll get square. Don't you forget it."

"Boys, I'll give you a race for your money. Bank on that. I may lose—understand, I may lose—no man can help meeting a better man. But I think I can skin 'im, and I'll give you a run for your money, you bet."

"All right, then. But, look here," they told him, "you keep your face closed. Nobody but us gets in on this. Understand?"

"Not a soul," Pop declared. They left him, gesturing a last warning from the wicker doors.

In the street they saw Benson, his cane gripped in the middle, strolling among the white-clothed jabbering natives on the shady side. They semaphored to him eagerly, their faces ashine with a plot. He came across cautiously, like a man who ventures into dangerous company.

"We're going to get up a race. Pop and Fred. Pop swears he can skin 'im. This is a tip. Keep it dark, now. Say, won't Freddie be hot!"

Benson looked as if he had been compelled to endure these exhibitions of insanity for a century. "Oh, you fellows are off. Pop can't beat Freddie. He's an old bat. Why, it's impossible. Pop can't beat Freddie."

"Can't he? Want to bet he can't?" said the Kids. "There now, let's see—you're talking so large."

"Well, you——"

"Oh, bet. Bet or else close your trap. That's the way."

"How do you know you can pull off the race. Seen Freddie?"

"No, but——"

"Well, see him then. Can't bet now with no race arranged. I'll bet with you all right—all right. I'll give you fellows a tip though —you're a pair of asses. Pop can't run any faster than a brick school-house."

The Kids scowled at him and defiantly said: "Can't he?" They left him and went to the Casa Verde. Freddie, beautiful in his white jacket, was holding one of his innumerable conversations across the bar. He smiled when he saw them. "Where you boys been?" he demanded, in a paternal tone. Almost all the proprietors of American cafés in the city used to adopt a paternal tone when they spoke to the Kids.

"Oh, been 'round," they replied.

"Have a drink?" said the proprietor of the Casa Verde, forgetting his other social obligations. During the course of this ceremony one of the Kids remarked: "Freddie, Pop says he can beat you running."

"Does he?" observed Freddie without excitement. He was used to various snares of the Kids.

"That's what. He says he can leave you at the wire and not see you again."

"Well, he lies," replied Freddie placidly.

"And I'll bet you a bottle of wine that he can do it, too."

"Rats!" said Freddie.

"Oh, that's all right," pursued a Kid. "You can throw bluffs all you like, but he can lose you in a hundred yard dash, you bet."

Freddie drank his whisky, and then settled his elbows on the bar. "Say, now, what do you boys keep coming in here with some pipe-story all the time for? You can't josh me. Do you think you can scare me about Pop? Why, I know I can beat 'im. He's an old man. He can't run with me. Certainly not. Why, you fellows are just jollying me."

"Are we though?" said the Kids. "You daresn't bet the bottle of wine."

"Oh, of course I can bet you a bottle of wine," said Freddie disdainfully. "Nobody cares about a bottle of wine, but——"

"Well, make it five then," advised one of the Kids.

Freddie hunched his shoulders. "Why, certainly I will. Make it ten if you like, but——"

"We do," they said.

"Ten, is it? All right; that goes." A look of weariness came over Freddie's face. "But you boys are foolish. I tell you Pop is an old man. How can you expect him to run? Of course, I'm no great runner, but then I'm young and healthy and—and a pretty smooth runner, too. Pop is old and fat, and then he doesn't do a thing but tank all day. It's a cinch."

The kids looked at him and laughed rapturously. They waved their fingers at him. "Ah, there!" they cried. They meant they had made a victim of him.

But Freddie continued to expostulate. "I tell you he couldn't win—an old man like him. You're crazy. Of course, I know you don't care about ten bottles of wine, but, then—to make such bets as that. You're twisted."

"Are we, though?" cried the Kids in mockery. They had precipitated Freddie into a long and thoughtful treatise on every possible chance of the thing as he saw it. They disputed with him from time to time, and jeered at him. He labored on through his argument. Their childish faces were bright with glee.

In the midst of it Wilburson entered. Wilburson worked; not too much, though. He had hold of the Mexican end of a great importing house of New York, and as he was a junior partner he worked. But not too much, though. "What's the howl?" he said.

The Kids giggled. "We've got Freddie rattled."

"Why," said Freddie, turning to him, "these two Indians are trying to tell me that Pop can beat me running."

"Like the devil," said Wilburson, incredulously.

"Well, can't he?" demanded a Kid.

"Why, certainly not," said Wilburson, dismissing every possibility of it with a gesture. "That old bat? Certainly not. I'll bet fifty dollars that Freddie——"

"Take you," said a Kid.

"What?" said Wilburson, "that Freddie won't beat Pop?"

The Kid that had spoken now nodded his head.

"That Freddie won't beat Pop?" repeated Wilburson.

"Yes. It's a go?"

"Why, certainly," retorted Wilburson. "Fifty? All right."

"Bet you five bottles on the side," ventured the other Kid.

"Why, certainly," exploded Wilburson wrathfully. "You fellows must take me for something easy. I'll take all those kind of bets I can get. Cer—tain—ly."

They settled the details. The course was to be paced off on the asphalt of one of the adjacent side-streets, and then, at about eleven o'clock in the evening, the match would be run. Usually in Mexico the streets of a city grow lonely and dark but a little time after nine o'clock. There are occasional lurking figures, perhaps, but no crowds, lights, noise. The course would doubtless be undisturbed. As for the policemen in the vicinity, they—well, they were conditionally amiable.

The Kids went to see Pop; they told him of the arrangements, and then in deep tones they said: "Oh, Pop, if you throw us!"

Pop appeared to be a trifle shaken by the weight of responsibility thrust upon him, but he spoke out bravely. "Boys, I'll pinch that race. Now you watch me. I'll pinch it."

The Kids went then on some business of their own, for they were not seen again until evening. When they returned to the neighborhood of the Café Colorado the usual evening stream of carriages was whirling along the *calle*. The wheels hummed on the asphalt, and the coachmen towered in their great sombreros. On the sidewalk a gazing crowd sauntered, the better class self-satisfied and proud, in their derby hats and cutaway coats, the lower classes muffling their dark faces in their blankets, slipping along in leather sandals. An electric light sputtered and fumed over the throng. The afternoon shower had left the pave wet and glittering. The air was still laden with the odor of rain on flowers, grass, leaves.

In the Café Colorado a cosmopolitan crowd ate, drank, played billiards, gossiped, or read in the glaring yellow light. When the Kids entered a large circle of men that had been gesticulating near the bar greeted them with a roar.

"Here they are now!"

"Oh, you pair of peaches!"

"Say, got any more money to bet with?"

The Kids smiled complacently. Old Colonel Hammigan, grinning, pushed his way to them. "Say, boys, we'll all have a drink on you now because you won't have any money after eleven o'clock. You'll be going down the back stairs in your stocking feet."

Although the Kids remained unnaturally serene and quiet, argument in the Café Colorado became tumultuous. Here and there a man who did not intend to bet ventured meekly that perchance Pop might win, and the others swarmed upon him in a whirlwind of angry denial and ridicule.

Pop, enthroned behind the bar, looked over at this storm with a shadow of anxiety upon his face. This widespread flouting affected him, but the Kids looked blissfully satisfied with the tumult they had stirred.

Blanco, honest man, ever worrying for his friends, came to them. "Say, you fellows, you aren't betting too much? This thing looks kind of shaky, don't it?"

The faces of the Kids grew sober, and after consideration one said: "No, I guess we've got a good thing, Blanco. Pop is going to surprise them, I think."

"Well, don't——"

"All right, old boy. We'll watch out."

From time to time the Kids had much business with certain orange, red, blue, purple, and green bills. They were making little memoranda on the back of visiting cards. Pop watched them closely, the shadow still upon his face. Once he called to them, and when they came he leaned over the bar and said intensely: "Say, boys, remember, now—I might lose this race. Nobody can ever say for sure, and if I do, why——"

"Oh, that's all right, Pop," said the Kids, reassuringly. "Don't mind it. Do your derndest and let it go at that."

When they had left him, however, they went to a corner to consult. "Say, this is getting interesting. Are you in deep?" asked one anxiously of his friend.

"Yes, pretty deep," said the other stolidly. "Are you?"

"Deep as the devil," replied the other in the same tone.

They looked at each other stonily and went back to the crowd. Benson had just entered the café. He approached them with a gloating smile of victory. "Well, where's all that money you were going to bet?"

"Right here," said the Kids, thrusting into their vest pockets.

At eleven o'clock a curious thing was learned. When Pop and Freddie, the Kids and all, came to the little side street, it was thick with people. It seems that the news of this great race had spread like the wind among the Americans, and they had come to witness the event. In the darkness the crowd moved, gesticulating and mumbling in argument.

The principals, the Kids, and those with them, surveyed this scene with some dismay. "Say—here's a go." Even then a policeman might be seen approaching, the light from his little lantern flickering on his white cap, gloves, brass buttons, and on the butt of the old-fashioned Colt's revolver which hung at his belt. He addressed Freddie in swift Mexican. Freddie listened, nodding from time to time. Finally Freddie turned to the others to translate. "He says he'll get into trouble if he allows this race when all this crowd is here."

There was a murmur of discontent. The policeman looked at them with an expression of anxiety on his broad brown face.

"Oh, come on. We'll go hold it on some other fellow's beat," said one of the Kids. The group moved slowly away debating. Suddenly the other Kid cried: "I know! The Paseo!"

"By jiminy," said Freddie, "just the thing. We'll get a cab and go out to the Paseo. S-s-sh! Keep it quiet; we don't want all this mob."

Later they tumbled into a cab—Pop, Freddie, the Kids, old Colonel Hammigan and Benson. They whispered to the men who had wagered: "The Paseo." The cab whirled away up the black street. There was occasional grunts and groans, cries of "Oh, get off me feet," and of "Quit! you're killing me." Six people do not have fun in one cab. The principals spoke to each other with the respect and friendliness which comes to good men at such times. Once a Kid put his head out of the window and looked backward. He pulled it in again and cried: "Great Scott! Look at that, would you!" The others struggled to do as they were bid, and afterward shouted: "Holy smoke! Well, I'll be blowed! Thunder and turf!"

Galloping after them came innumerable other cabs, their lights twinkling, streaming in a great procession through the night. "The street is full of them," ejaculated the old colonel.

The Paseo de la Reforma is the famous drive of the City of Mexico, leading to the Castle of Chapultepec, which last ought to be well known in the United States.

It is a broad fine avenue of macadam with a much greater quality of dignity than anything of the kind we possess in our own land. It seems of the Old World, where to the beauty of the thing itself is added the solemnity of tradition and history, the knowledge that feet in buskins trod the same stones, that cavalcades of steel thundered there before the coming of carriages.

When the Americans tumbled out of their cabs the giant bronzes of Aztec and Spaniard loomed dimly above them like towers. The four rows of poplar trees rustled weirdly off there in the darkness. Pop took out his watch and struck a match. "Well, hurry up this thing. It's almost midnight."

The other cabs came swarming, the drivers lashing their horses, for these Americans, who did all manner of strange things, nevertheless always paid well for it. There was a mighty hubbub then in the darkness. Five or six men began to pace off the distance and quarrel. Others knotted their handkerchiefs together to make a tape. Men were swearing over bets, fussing and fuming about the odds. Benson came to the Kids swaggering. "You're a pair of asses." The cabs waited in a solid block down the avenue. Above the crowd the tall statues hid their visages in the night.

At last a voice floated through the darkness. "Are you ready there?" Everybody yelled excitedly. The men at the tape pulled it out straight. "Hold it higher, Jim, you fool!" A silence fell then upon the throng. Men bended down trying to pierce the darkness with their eyes. From out at the starting point came muffled voices. The crowd swayed and jostled.

The racers did not come. The crowd began to fret, its nerves burning. "Oh, hurry up," shrilled some one.

The voice called again: "Ready there?" Everybody replied: "Yes, all ready. Hurry up!"

There was more muffled discussion at the starting point. In the crowd a man began to make a proposition. "I'll bet twenty——" but the throng interrupted with a howl. "Here they come!" The thickly packed body of men swung as if the ground had moved. The men at the tape shouldered madly at their fellows, bawling: "Keep back! Keep back!"

From the profound gloom came the noise of feet pattering furiously. Vague forms flashed into view for an instant. A hoarse roar broke from the crowd. Men bended and swayed and fought. The Kids back near the tape exchanged another stolid look. A white form shone forth. It grew like a spectre. Always could be heard the wild patter. A barbaric scream broke from the crowd. "By Gawd, it's Pop! Pop! Pop's ahead!"

The old man spun toward the tape like a madman, his chin thrown back, his grey hair flying. His legs moved like maniac machinery. And as he shot forward a howl as from forty cages of wild animals went toward the imperturbable chieftains in bronze. The crowd flung themselves forward. "Oh, you old Indian! You savage! You cuss, you! Dern my buttons, did you ever see such running?"

"Ain't he a peach! Well!"

"Say, this beats anything!"

"Where's the Kids? H-e-y, Kids!"

"Look at 'im, would you? Did you ever think?" These cries flew in the air blended in a vast shout of astonishment and laughter.

For an instant the whole great tragedy was in view. Freddie, desperate, his teeth shining, his face contorted, whirling along in deadly effort, was twenty feet behind the tall form of old Pop, who, dressed only in his—only in his underclothes—gained with each stride. One grand insane moment, and then Pop had hurled himself against the tape—victor!

Freddie, falling into the arms of some men, struggled with his breath, and at last managed to stammer: "Say, can't—can't that old—old man run!"

Pop, puffing and heaving, could only gasp: "Where's my shoes? Who's got my shoes?" Later Freddie scrambled panting through the crowd, and held out his hand. "Good man, Pop!" And then he looked up and down the tall, stout form. "Hell! who would think you could run like that."

The Kids were surrounded by a crowd, laughing tempestuously.

"How did you know he could run?"

"Why didn't you give me a line on him?"

"Say—great snakes!—you fellows had a nerve to bet on Pop."

"Why, I was cock-sure he couldn't win."

"Oh, you fellows must have seen him run before."

"Who would ever think it?"

Benson came by, filling the midnight air with curses. They turned to jeer him. "What's the matter, Benson?"

"Somebody pinched my handkerchief. I tied it up in that string. Damn it."

The Kids laughed blithely. "Why, hollo, Benson!" they said.

There was a great rush for cabs. Shouting, laughing, wondering, the crowd hustled into their conveyances, and the drivers flogged their horses toward the city again.

"Won't Freddie be crazy! Say, he'll be guyed about this for years."

"But who would ever think that old tank could run so?"

One cab had to wait while Pop and Freddie resumed various parts of their clothing.

As they drove home, Freddie said: "Well, Pop, you beat me."

Pop said: "That's all right, old man."

The Kids, grinning, said: "How much did you lose, Benson?"

Benson said defiantly: "Oh, not so much. How much did you win?"

"Oh, not so much."

Old Colonel Hammigan, squeezed down in a corner, had apparently been reviewing the event in his mind, for he suddenly remarked: "Well, I'm damned!"

They were late in reaching the Café Colorado, but when they did, the bottles were on the bar as thick as pickets on a fence.

THE FIVE WHITE MICE

FREDDIE was mixing a cocktail. His hand with the long spoon was whirling swiftly and the ice in the glass hummed and rattled like a cheap watch. Over by the window, a gambler, a millionaire, a railway conductor and the agent of a vast American syndicate were playing seven-up. Freddie surveyed them with the ironical glance of a man who is mixing a cocktail.

From time to time a swarthy Mexican waiter came with his tray from the rooms at the rear and called his orders across the bar. The sounds of the indolent stir of the city, awakening from its siesta, floated over the screens which barred the sun and the inquisitive eye. From the faraway kitchen could be heard the roar of the old French chef, driving, herding and abusing his Mexican helpers.

A string of men came suddenly in from the street. They stormed up to the bar. There were impatient shouts. "Come, now, Freddie, don't stand there like a portrait of yourself. Wiggle!" Drinks of many kinds and colors, amber, green, mahogany, strong and mild, began to swarm upon the bar with all the attendants of lemon, sugar, mint and ice. Freddie, with Mexican support, worked like a sailor in the provision of them, sometimes talking with that scorn for drink and admiration for those who drink which is the attribute of a good bar-keeper.

At last a man was afflicted with a stroke of dice-shaking. A herculean discussion was waging and he was deeply engaged in it but at the same time he lazily flirted the dice. Occasionally he made great combinations. "Look at that, would you?" he cried proudly. The others paid little heed. Then violently the craving took them. It went along the line like an epidemic and involved them all. In a moment they had arranged a carnival of dice-shaking with money penalties and liquid prizes. They clamorously made it a point of honor with Freddie that he too should play and take his chance of sometimes providing this large group with free refreshment. With bended heads like foot-ball players they surged over the tinkling dice, jostling, cheering and bitterly arguing. One of the quiet company playing seven-up at the corner table said profanely that the row reminded him of a bowling contest at a picnic.

After the regular shower, many carriages rolled over the smooth *calle* and sent a musical thunder through the Casa Verde. The shop-windows became aglow with light and the walks were crowded with youths, callow and ogling, dressed vainly according to supposititious fashions. The policemen had muffled themselves in their gnome-like cloaks and placed their lanterns as obstacles for the carriages in the middle of the street. The City of Mexico gave forth the deep mellow organ-tones of its evening resurrection.

But still the group at the bar of the Casa Verde were shaking dice. They had passed beyond shaking for drinks for the crowd, for Mexican dollars, for dinner, for the wine at dinner. They had even gone to the trouble of separating the cigars and cigarettes from the dinner's bill and causing a distinct man to be responsible for them. Finally they were aghast. Nothing remained within sight of their minds which even remotely suggested further gambling. There was a pause for deep consideration.

"Well——"

"Well——"

A man called out in the exuberance of creation. "I know! Let's shake for a box tonight at the circus! A box at the circus!" The group was profoundly edified. "That's it! That's it! Come on now! Box at the circus!" A dominating voice cried: "Three dashes— high man out!" An American, tall and with a face of copper red from the rays that flash among the Sierra Madres and burn on the cactus deserts, took the little leathern cup and spun the dice out upon the polished wood. A fascinated assemblage hung upon the bar-rail. Three kings turned their pink faces upward. The tall man flourished the cup, burlesquing, and flung the two other dice. From them he ultimately extracted one more pink king. "There," he said. "Now, let's see! Four kings!" He began to swagger in a sort of provisional way.

The next man took the cup and blew softly in the top of it. Poising it in his hand, he then surveyed the company with a stony eye and paused. They knew perfectly well that he was applying the magic of deliberation and ostentatious indifference but they could not wait in tranquility during the performances of all these rites. They began to call out impatiently. "Come now— hurry up." At last the man with a gesture that was singularly impressive, threw the dice. The others set up a howl of joy. "Not a pair!" There was another solemn pause. The men moved restlessly. "Come, now, go ahead!" In the end the man, induced and abused, achieved something that was nothing in the presence of four kings. The tall man climbed on the foot-rail and leaned hazardously forward. "Four kings! My four kings are good to go out," he bellowed into the middle of the mob and although in a moment he did pass into the radiant region of exemption he continued to bawl advice and scorn.

The mirrors and oiled woods of the Casa Verde were now dancing with blue flashes from a great buzzing electric lamp. A host of quiet members of the Anglo-Saxon colony had come in for their pre-dinner cocktails. An amiable person was exhibiting to some tourists this popular American saloon. It was a very sober and respectable time of day. Freddie reproved courageously the dice-shaking brawlers and, in return, he received the choicest advice in a tumult of seven combined vocabularies. He laughed; he had been compelled to retire from the game but he was keeping an interested, if furtive, eye upon it.

Down at the end of the line, there was a youth at whom everybody railed for his flaming ill-luck. At each disaster, Freddie swore from behind the bar in a sort of affectionate contempt. "Why this Kid has had no luck for two days. Did you ever see such throwin'."

The contest narrowed eventually to the New York Kid and an individual who swung about placidly on legs that moved in nefarious circles. He had a grin that resembled a bit of carving. He was obliged to lean down and blink rapidly to ascertain the facts of his venture but fate presented him with five queens. His smile did not change but he puffed gently like a man who has been running.

The others, having emerged scatheless from this part of the

conflict, waxed hilarious with the Kid. They smote him on either shoulder. "We've got you stuck for it, Kid! You can't beat that game! Five queens!"

Up to this time, the Kid had displayed only the temper of the gambler but the cheerful hoots of the players supplemented now by a ring of guying non-combatants caused him to feel profoundly that it would be fine to beat the five queens. He addressed a gambler's slogan to the interior of the cup.

> "Oh, five white mice of chance,
> Shirts of wool and corduroy pants,
> Gold and wine, women and sin,
> All for you if you let me come in—
> Into the house of chance."

Flashing the dice sardonically out upon the bar, he displayed three aces. From two dice in the next throw, he achieved one more ace. For his last throw, he rattled the single dice for a long time. He already had four aces; if he accomplished another one, the five queens were vanquished and the box at the circus came from the drunken man's pocket. All of the Kid's movements were slow and elaborate. For his last throw he planted the cup bottom-up on the bar with the one dice hidden under it. Then he turned and faced the crowd with the air of a conjuror or a cheat. "Oh, maybe it's an ace," he said in boastful calm. "Maybe it's an ace." Instantly he was presiding over a little drama in which every man was absorbed. The Kid leaned with his back against the bar-rail and with his elbows upon it. "Maybe it's an ace," he repeated.

A jeering voice in the background said: "Yes, maybe it is, Kid!"

The Kid's eyes searched for a moment among the men. "I'll bet fifty dollars it is an ace," he said.

Another voice asked: "American money?"

"Yes," answered the Kid.

"Oh!" There was a genial laugh at this discomfiture. However no one came forward at the Kid's challenge and presently he turned to the cup. "Now, I'll show you." With the manner of a mayor unveiling a statue, he lifted the cup. There was revealed naught but a ten-spot. In the roar which arose could be heard each man ridiculing the cowardice of his neighbor and above all the din rang the voice of Freddie berating everyone. "Why, there isn't one liver to every five men in the outfit. That was the greatest cold bluff I ever saw worked. He wouldn't know how to cheat with dice if he wanted to. Don't know the first thing about it. I could hardly keep from laughin' when I seen him drillin' you around. Why, I tell you, I had that fifty dollars right in my pocket if I wanted to be a chump. You're an easy lot——"

Nevertheless the group who had won in the circus-box game did not relinquish their triumph. They burst like a storm about the head of the Kid, swinging at him with their fists. " 'Five white mice'!" they quoted choking. " 'Five white mice'!"

"Oh, they are not so bad," said the Kid.

Afterward it often occurred that a man would suddenly jeer a finger at the Kid and derisively say: " 'Five white mice'."

On the route from the dinner to the circus, others of the party often asked the Kid if he had really intended to make his appeal to mice. They suggested other animals—rabbits, dogs, hedge-hogs, snakes, opossums. To this banter the Kid replied with a serious expression of his belief in the fidelity and wisdom of the five white mice. He presented a most eloquent case, decorated with fine language and insults, in which he proved that if one was going to believe in anything at all, one might as well choose the five white mice. His companions however at once and unani-mously pointed out to him that his recent exploit did not place him in the light of a convincing advocate.

The Kid discerned two figures in the street. They were making imperious signs at him. He waited for them to approach, for he recognized one as the other Kid—the 'Frisco Kid—there were two Kids. With the 'Frisco Kid was Benson. They arrived almost breathless. "Where you been?" cried the 'Frisco Kid. It was an arrangement that upon a meeting the one that could first ask this question was entitled to use a tone of limitless injury. "What you been doing? Where you going? Come on with us. Benson and I have got a little scheme."

The New York Kid pulled his arm from the grapple of the other. "I can't. I've got to take these sutlers to the circus. They stuck me for it shaking dice at Freddie's. I can't, I tell you."

The two did not at first attend to his remarks. "Come on! We've got a little scheme."

"I can't. They stuck me. I've got to take'm to the circus."

At this time it did not suit the men with the scheme to recognize these objections as important. "Oh, take'm some other time. Well, can't you take'm some other time? Let 'em go. Damn the circus. Get cold feet. What did you get stuck for? Get cold feet."

But despite their fighting, the New York Kid broke away from them. "I can't, I tell you. They stuck me." As he left them, they yelled with rage. "Well, meet us, now, do you hear? In the Casa Verde as soon as the circus quits! Hear?" They threw maledictions after him.

In the City of Mexico, a man goes to the circus without descending in any way to infant amusements because the Circo Teatro Orrin is one of the best in the world and too easily surpasses anything of the kind in the United States where it is merely a matter of a number of rings, if possible, and a great professional agreement to lie to the public. Moreover the American clown who in the Mexican arena prances and gabbles is the clown to whom writers refer as the delight of their childhood and lament that he is dead. At this circus the Kid was not debased by the sight of mournful prisoner elephants and caged animals forlorn and sickly. He sat in his box until late and laughed and swore when past laughing at the comic, foolish, wise clown.

When he returned to the Casa Verde there was no display of the 'Frisco Kid and Benson. Freddie was leaning upon the bar listening to four men terribly discuss a question that was not plain. There was a card-game in the corner, of course. Sounds of revelry pealed from the rear rooms.

When the Kid asked Freddie if he had seen his friend and Benson, Freddie looked bored. "Oh, yes, they were in here just a minute ago but I don't know where they went. They've got their skates on. Where've they been? Came in here rolling across the floor like two little gilt gods. They wobbled around for a time and then 'Frisco wanted me to send six bottles of wine around to Benson's rooms, but I didn't have anybody to send this time of night and so they got mad and went out. Where did they get their loads?"

In the first deep gloom of the street, the Kid paused a moment debating. But presently he heard quavering voices. "Oh, Kid! Kid!

Comere!" Peering, he recognized two vague figures against the opposite wall. He crossed the street and they said: "Hellokid."

"Say, where did you get it?" he demanded sternly. "You Indians better go home. What did you want to get scragged for?" His face was luminous with virtue.

As they swung to and fro, they made angry denials. "We ain' load'! We ain' load'. Big chump. Comonangetadrink." The sober youth turned then to his friend. "Hadn't you better go home, Kid? Come on, it's late. You'd better break away."

The 'Frisco Kid wagged his head decisively. "Got take Benson home first. He'll be wallowing 'round in a minute. Don't mind me. I'm all right."

"Cer'ly, he's all right," said Benson arousing from deep thought. "He's all right. But better take'm home, though. That's ri-right. He's load'. But he's all right. No need go home any more'n you. But better take'm home. He's load'." He looked at his companion with compassion. "Kid, you're load'."

The sober Kid spoke abruptly to his friend from San Francisco. "Kid, pull yourself together, now. Don't fool. We've got to brace this ass of a Benson all the way home. Get hold of his other arm."

The 'Frisco Kid immediately obeyed his comrade without a word or a glower. He seized Benson and came to attention like a soldier. Later, indeed, he meekly ventured: "Can't we take cab?" But when the New York Kid snapped out that there were no convenient cabs he subsided to an impassive silence. He seemed to be reflecting upon his state without astonishment, dismay or any particular emotion. He submitted himself woodenly to the direction of his friend.

Benson had protested when they had grasped his arms. "Washa doing?" he said in a new and guttural voice. "Washa doing? I ain' load'. Comonangetadrink. I——"

"Oh, come along, you idiot," said the New York Kid. The 'Frisco Kid merely presented the mien of a stoic to the appeal of Benson and in silence dragged away at one of his arms. Benson's feet came from that particular spot on the pavement with the reluctance of roots and also with the ultimate suddenness of roots. The three of them lurched out into the street in the abandon of tumbling chimneys. Benson was meanwhile noisily challenging the others to produce any reasons for his being taken home. His toes clashed into the kerb when they reached the other side of the *calle* and for a moment the Kids hauled him along with the points of his shoes scraping musically on the pavement. He balked formidably as they were about to pass the Casa Verde. "No! No! Leshavanothdrink! Anothdrink! One-more!"

But the 'Frisco Kid obeyed the voice of his partner in a manner that was blind but absolute and they scummed Benson on past the door. Locked together the three swung into a dark street. The sober Kid's flank was continually careering ahead of the other wing. He harshly admonished the 'Frisco child and the latter promptly improved in the same manner of unthinking complete obedience. Benson began to recite the tale of a love affair, a tale that didn't even have a middle. Occasionally the New York Kid swore. They toppled on their way like three comedians playing at it on the stage.

At midnight a little Mexican street burrowing among the walls of the city is as dark as a whale's throat at deep sea. Upon this occasion heavy clouds hung over the capital and the sky was a pall. The projecting balconies could make no shadows.

"Shay," said Benson breaking away from his escort suddenly, "what want gome for? I ain' load'. You got reg'lar spool-fact'ry in your head—you N' York Kid there. Thish oth' Kid, he's mos' proper, mos' proper shober. He's drunk but—but he's shober."

"Ah, shut up, Benson," said the New York Kid. "Come along now. We can't stay here all night." Benson refused to be cor-ralled but spread his legs and twirled like a dervish, meanwhile under the evident impression that he was conducting himself most handsomely. It was not long before he gained the opinion that he was laughing at the others. "Eight purple dogsh—dogs! Eight purple dogs. Thas what Kid'll see in the morn'. Look ou' for 'em. They——"

As Benson, describing the canine phenomena, swung wildly across the sidewalk, it chanced that three other pedestrians were passing in shadowy rank. Benson's shoulder jostled one of them.

A Mexican wheeled upon the instant. His hand flashed to his hip. There was a moment of silence during which Benson's voice was not heard raised in apology. Then an indescribable comment, one burning word, came from between the Mexican's teeth.

Benson, rolling about in a semi-detached manner, stared vacantly at the Mexican who thrust his lean yellow face forward while his fingers played nervously at his hip. The New York Kid could not follow Spanish well but he understood when the Mexican breathed softly: "Does the señor want fight?"

Benson simply gazed in gentle surprise. The woman next to him at dinner had said something inventive. His tailor had presented his bill. Something had occurred which was mildly out of the ordinary and his surcharged brain refused to cope with it. He displayed only the agitation of a smoker temporarily without a light.

The New York Kid had almost instantly grasped Benson's arm and was about to jerk him away when the other Kid who up to this time had been an automaton suddenly projected himself forward, thrust the rubber Benson aside and said: "Yes!"

There was no sound nor light in the world. The wall at the left happened to be of the common prison-like construction—no door, no window, no opening at all. Humanity was enclosed and asleep. Into the mouth of the sober Kid came a wretched bitter taste as if it had filled with blood. He was transfixed as if he was already seeing the lightning ripples on the knife-blade.

But the Mexican's hand did not move at that time. His face went still further forward and he whispered: "So?" The sober Kid saw this face as if he and it were alone in space—a yellow mask smiling in eager cruelty, in satisfaction, and above all it was lit with sinister decision. As for the features they were reminiscent of an unplaced, a forgotten type which really resembled with precision those of a man who had shaved him three times in Boston in 1888. But the expression burned his mind as sealing-wax burns the palm and fascinated, stupefied, he actually watched the progress of the man's thought toward the point where a knife would be wrenched from its sheath. The emotion, a sort of mechanical fury, a breeze made by electric fans, a rage made by vanity, smote the dark countenance in wave after wave.

Then the New York Kid took a sudden step forward. His hand was also at his hip. He was gripping there a revolver of robust size. He recalled that upon its black handle was stamped a hunting scene in which a sportsman in fine leggings and a peaked cap was taking aim at a stag less than one eighth of an inch away.

His pace forward caused instant movement of the Mexicans. One immediately took two steps to face him squarely. There was a general adjustment, pair and pair. This opponent of the New York Kid was a tall man and quite stout. His sombrero was drawn low over his eyes. His serape was flung on his left shoulder. His back was bended in the supposed manner of a Spanish grandee. This concave gentleman cut a fine and terrible figure. The lad, moved by the spirits of his modest and perpendicular ancestors, had time to feel his blood roar at sight of the pose.

He was aware that the third Mexican was over on the left fronting Benson and he was aware that Benson was leaning against the wall sleepily and peacefully eyeing the convention. So it happened that these six men stood, side fronting side, five of them with their right hands at their hips and with their bodies lifted nervously while the central pair exchanged a crescendo of provocations. The meaning of their words rose and rose. They were travelling in a straight line toward collision.

The New York Kid contemplated his Spanish grandee. He drew his revolver upward until the hammer was surely free of the holster. He waited immovable and watchful while the garrulous 'Frisco Kid expended two and a half lexicons on the middle Mexican.

The Eastern lad suddenly decided that he was going to be killed. His mind leaped forward and studied the aftermath. The story would be a marvel of brevity when first it reached the far New York home, written in a careful hand on a bit of cheap paper topped and footed and backed by the printed fortifications of the cable company. But they are often as stones flung into mirrors, these bits of paper upon which are laconically written all the most terrible chronicles of the times. He witnessed the uprising of his mother and sister and the invincible calm of his hard-mouthed old father who would probably shut himself in his library and smoke alone. Then his father would come and they would bring him here and say: "This is the place." Then, very likely, each would remove his hat. They would stand quietly with their hats in their hands for a decent minute. He pitied his old financing father, unyielding and millioned, a man who commonly spoke twenty-two words a year to his beloved son. The Kid understood it at this time. If his fate was not impregnable, he might have turned out to be a man and have been liked by his father.

The other Kid would mourn his death. He would be preternaturally correct for some weeks and recite the tale without swearing. But it would not bore him. For the sake of his dead comrade he would be glad to be preternaturally correct and to recite the tale without swearing.

These views were perfectly stereopticon, flashing in and away from his thought with an inconceivable rapidity until after all they were simply one quick dismal impression. And now here is the unreal real: into this Kid's nostrils, at the expectant moment of slaughter, had come the scent of new-mown hay, a fragrance from a field of prostrate grass, a fragrance which contained the sunshine, the bees, the peace of meadows and the wonder of a distant crooning stream. It had no right to be supreme but it was supreme and he breathed it as he waited for pain and a sight of the unknown.

But in the same instant, it may be, his thought flew to the 'Frisco Kid and it came upon him like a flicker of lightning that the 'Frisco Kid was not going to be there to perform, for instance, the extraordinary office of respectable mourner. The other Kid's head was muddled, his hand was unsteady, his agility was gone. This other Kid was facing the determined and most ferocious gentleman of the enemy. The New York Kid became convinced that his friend was lost. There was going to be a screaming murder. He was so certain of it that he wanted to shield his eyes from sight of the leaping arm and the knife. It was sickening, utterly sickening. The New York Kid might have been taking his first sea-voyage. A combination of honorable manhood and inability prevented him from running away.

He suddenly knew that it was possible to draw his own revolver and by a swift manoeuver face down all three Mexicans. If he was quick enough he would probably be victor. If any hitch occurred in the draw he would undoubtedly be dead with his friends. It was a new game; he had never been obliged to face a situation of this kind in the Beacon Club in New York. In this test, the lungs of the Kid still continued to perform their duty.

"Oh, five white mice of chance,
  Shirts of wool and corduroy pants,
  Gold and wine, women and sin,
  All for you if you let me come in—
  Into the house of chance."

He thought of the weight and size of his revolver and dismay pierced him. He feared that in his hands it would be as unwieldy as a sewing-machine for this quick work. He imagined, too, that some singular providence might cause him to lose his grip as he raised his weapon. Or it might get fatally entangled in the tails of his coat. Some of the eels of despair lay wet and cold against his back.

But at the supreme moment the revolver came forth as if it were greased and it arose like a feather. This somnolent machine, after months of repose, was finally looking at the breasts of men.

Perhaps in this one series of movements, the Kid had unconsciously used nervous force sufficient to raise a bale of hay. Before he comprehended it he was standing behind his revolver glaring over the barrel at the Mexicans menacing first one and then another. His finger was tremoring on the trigger. The revolver gleamed in the darkness with a fine silver light.

The fulsome grandee sprang backward with a low cry. The man who had been facing the 'Frisco Kid took a quick step away. The beautiful array of Mexicans was suddenly disorganized.

The cry and the backward steps revealed something of great importance to the New York Kid. He had never dreamed that he did not have a complete monopoly of all possible trepidations. The cry of the grandee was that of a man who suddenly sees a poisonous snake. Thus the Kid was able to understand swiftly that they were all human beings. They were unanimous in not wishing for too bloody combat. There was a sudden expression of the equality. He had vaguely believed that they were not going to evince much consideration for his dramatic developement as an active factor. They even might be exasperated into an on-slaught by it. Instead, they had respected his movement with a respect as great even as an ejaculation of fear and backward steps. Upon the instant he pounced forward and began to swear, unreeling great English oaths as thick as ropes and lashing the faces of the Mexicans with them. He was bursting with rage because these men had not previously confided to him that they were vulnerable. The whole thing had been an absurd imposi-tion. He had been seduced into respectful alarm by the concave attitude of the grandee. And after all there had been an equality of emotion, an equality: he was furious. He wanted to take the serape of the grandee and swaddle him in it.

The Mexicans slunk back, their eyes burning wistfully. The Kid took aim first at one and then at another. After they had achieved a certain distance they paused and drew up in a rank. They then resumed some of their old splendor of manner. A voice hailed him in a tone of cynical bravado as if it had come from between high lips of smiling mockery. "Well, señor, it is finished?"

The Kid scowled into the darkness, his revolver drooping at his side. After a moment he answered: "I am willing." He found it strange that he should be able to speak after this silence of years.

"Good night, señor."

"Good night."

When he turned to look at the 'Frisco Kid he found him in his original position, his hand upon his hip. He was blinking in perplexity at the point from whence the Mexicans had vanished.

"Well," said the sober Kid crossly, "are you ready to go home now?"

The 'Frisco Kid said: "Where they gone?" His voice was undis-turbed but inquisitive.

Benson suddenly propelled himself from his dreamful position against the wall. "Frishco Kid's all right. He's drunk's fool and he's all right. But you New York Kid, you're shober." He passed into a state of profound investigation. "Kid shober 'cause didn't go with us. Didn't go with us 'cause went to damn circus. Went

to damn circus 'cause lose shakin' dice. Lose shakin' dice 'cause
—what make lose shakin' dice, Kid?"

The New York Kid eyed the senile youth. "I don't know. The
five white mice, maybe."

Benson puzzled so over this reply that he had to be held erect
by his friends. Finally the 'Frisco Kid said: "Let's go home."

Nothing had happened.

A MAN AND SOME OTHERS

I

DARK mesquit spread from horizon to horizon. There was no house or horseman from which a mind could evolve a city or a crowd. The world was declared to be a desert and unpeopled. Sometimes, however, on days when no heat-mist arose, a blue shape, dim, of the substance of a specter's veil, appeared in the southwest, and a pondering sheep-herder might remember that there were mountains.

In the silence of these plains the sudden and childish banging of a tin pan could have made an iron-nerved man leap into the air. The sky was ever flawless; the manœuvering of clouds was an unknown pageant; but at times a sheep-herder could see, miles away, the long, white streamers of dust rising from the feet of another's flock, and the interest became intense.

Bill was arduously cooking his dinner, bending over the fire, and toiling like a blacksmith. A movement, a flash of strange color, perhaps, off in the bushes, caused him suddenly to turn his head. Presently he arose, and, shading his eyes with his hand, stood motionless and gazing. He perceived at last a Mexican sheep-herder winding through the brush toward his camp.

"Hello!" shouted Bill.

The Mexican made no answer, but came steadily forward until he was within some twenty yards. There he paused, and, folding his arms, drew himself up in the manner affected by the villain in the play. His serape muffled the lower part of his face, and his great sombrero shaded his brow. Being unexpected and also silent, he had something of the quality of an apparition; moreover, it was clearly his intention to be mysterious and devilish.

The American's pipe, sticking carelessly in the corner of his mouth, was twisted until the wrong side was uppermost, and he held his frying-pan poised in the air. He surveyed with evident surprise this apparition in the mesquit. "Hello, José!" he said; "what's the matter?"

The Mexican spoke with the solemnity of funeral tollings: "Beel, you mus' geet off range. We want you geet off range. We no like. Un'erstan'? We no like."

"What you talking about?" said Bill. "No like what?"

"We no like you here. Un'erstan'? Too mooch. You mus' geet out. We no like. Un'erstan'?"

"Understand? No; I don't know what the blazes you're gittin' at." Bill's eyes wavered in bewilderment, and his jaw fell. "I must git out? I must git off the range? What you givin' us?"

The Mexican unfolded his serape with his small yellow hand. Upon his face was then to be seen a smile that was gently, almost caressingly murderous. "Beel," he said, "geet out!"

Bill's arm dropped until the frying-pan was at his knee. Finally he turned again toward the fire. "Go on, you dog-gone little yaller rat!" he said over his shoulder. "You fellers can't chase me off this range. I got as much right here as anybody."

"Beel," answered the other in a vibrant tone, thrusting his head forward and moving one foot, "you geet out or we keel you."

"Who will?" said Bill.

"I—and the others." The Mexican tapped his breast gracefully.

Bill reflected for a time, and then he said: "You ain't got no manner of license to warn me off'n this range, and I won't move a rod. Understand? I've got rights, and I suppose if I don't see 'em through, no one is likely to give me a good hand and help me lick you fellers, since I'm the only white man in half a day's ride. Now, look; if you fellers try to rush this camp, I'm goin' to plug about fifty per cent of the gentlemen present, sure. I'm goin' in for trouble, an' I'll git a lot of you. 'Nuther thing: if I was a fine valuable caballero like you, I'd stay in the rear till the shootin' was done, because I'm goin' to make a particular p'int of shootin' you through the chest." He grinned affably, and made a gesture of dismissal.

As for the Mexican, he waved his hands in a consummate expression of indifference. "Oh, all right," he said. Then, in a tone of deep menace and glee, he added: "We will keel you eef you no geet. They have decide'."

"They have, have they?" said Bill. "Well, you tell them to go to the devil!"

II

Bill had been a mine-owner in Wyoming, a great man, an aristocrat, one who possessed unlimited credit in the saloons down the gulch. He had the social weight that could interrupt a lynching or advise a bad man of the particular merits of a remote geographical point. However, the fates exploded the toy balloon with which they had amused Bill, and on the evening of the same day he was a professional gambler with ill fortune dealing him unspeakable irritation in the shape of three big cards whenever another fellow stood pat. It is well here to inform the world that Bill considered his calamities of life all dwarfs in comparison with the excitement of one particular evening, when three kings came to him with criminal regularity against a man who always filled a straight. Later he became a cow-boy, more weirdly abandoned than if he had never been an aristocrat. By this time all that remained of his former splendor was his pride, or his vanity, which was one thing which need not have remained. He killed the foreman of the ranch over an inconsequent matter as to which of them was a liar, and the midnight train carried him eastward. He became a brakeman on the Union Pacific, and really gained high honors in the hobo war that for many years has devastated the beautiful railroads of our country. A creature of ill fortune himself, he practised all the ordinary cruelties upon these other creatures of ill fortune. He was of so fierce a mien that tramps usually surrendered at once whatever coin or tobacco they had in their possession; and if afterward he kicked them from the train, it was only because this was a recognized treachery of the war upon the hoboes. In a famous battle fought in Nebraska in 1879, he would have achieved a lasting distinction if it had not been for a deserter from the United States army. He was at the head of a heroic and sweeping charge, which really broke the power of the hoboes in that county for three months; he had already worsted four tramps with his own coupling-stick, when a stone thrown by the ex-third baseman of F Troop's nine laid him flat on the prairie, and later enforced a stay in the hospital in Omaha. After his recovery he engaged with other railroads, and shuffled cars in countless yards. An order to strike came upon him in Michigan, and afterward the vengeance of the railroad pursued him until he assumed a name. This mask is like the darkness in which the burglar chooses to move. It destroys many of the healthy fears. It is a small thing, but it eats that which we call our conscience. The conductor of No. 419 stood in the caboose within two feet of Bill's nose, and called him a liar. Bill requested him to use a milder term. He had not bored the foreman of Tin Can Ranch with any such request, but had killed him with expedition. The conductor seemed to insist, and so Bill let the matter drop.

He became the bouncer of a saloon on the Bowery in New York. Here most of his fights were as successful as had been his brushes with the hoboes in the West. He gained the complete admiration of the four clean bartenders who stood behind the great and glittering bar. He was an honored man. He nearly killed Bad Hennessy, who, as a matter of fact, had more reputation than ability, and his fame moved up the Bowery and down the Bowery.

But let a man adopt fighting as his business, and the thought grows constantly within him that it is his business to fight. These phrases became mixed in Bill's mind precisely as they are here mixed; and let a man get this idea in his mind, and defeat begins to move toward him over the unknown ways of circumstances. One summer night three sailors from the U.S.S. *Seattle* sat in the saloon drinking and attending to other people's affairs in an amiable fashion. Bill was a proud man since he had thrashed so many citizens, and it suddenly occurred to him that the loud talk of the sailors was very offensive. So he swaggered upon their attention, and warned them that the saloon was the flowery abode of peace and gentle silence. They glanced at him in surprise, and without a moment's pause consigned him to a worse place than any stoker of them knew. Whereupon he flung one of them through the side door before the others could prevent it. On the sidewalk there was a short struggle, with many hoarse epithets in the air, and then Bill slid into the saloon again. A frown of false rage was upon his brow, and he strutted like a savage king. He took a long yellow night-stick from behind the lunch-counter, and started importantly toward the main doors to see that the incensed seamen did not again enter.

The ways of sailormen are without speech, and, together in the street, the three sailors exchanged no word, but they moved at once. Landsmen would have required two years of discussion to gain such unanimity. In silence, and immediately, they seized a long piece of scantling that lay handily. With one forward to guide the battering-ram, and with two behind him to furnish the power, they made a beautiful curve, and came down like the Assyrians on the front door of that saloon.

Strange and still strange are the laws of fate. Bill, with his kingly frown and his long night-stick, appeared at precisely that moment in the doorway. He stood like a statue of victory; his pride was at its zenith; and in the same second this atrocious piece of scantling punched him in the bulwarks of his stomach, and he vanished like a mist. Opinions differed as to where the end of the scantling landed him, but it was ultimately clear that it landed him in southwestern Texas, where he became a sheep-herder.

The sailors charged three times upon the plate-glass front of the saloon, and when they had finished, it looked as if it had been the victim of a rural fire company's success in saving it from the flames. As the proprietor of the place surveyed the ruins, he remarked that Bill was a very zealous guardian of property. As the ambulance surgeon surveyed Bill, he remarked that the wound was really an excavation.

III

As his Mexican friend tripped blithely away, Bill turned with a thoughtful face to his frying-pan and his fire. After dinner he drew his revolver from its scarred old holster, and examined every part of it. It was the revolver that had dealt death to the foreman, and it had also been in free fights in which it had dealt death to several or none. Bill loved it because its allegiance was more than that of man, horse, or dog. It questioned neither social nor moral position; it obeyed alike the saint and the assassin. It was the claw of the eagle, the tooth of the lion, the poison of the snake; and when he swept it from its holster, this minion smote where he listed, even to the battering of a far penny. Wherefore it was his dearest possession, and was not to be exchanged in southwestern Texas for a handful of rubies, nor even the shame and homage of the conductor of No. 419.

During the afternoon he moved through his monotony of work and leisure with the same air of deep meditation. The smoke of his supper-time fire was curling across the shadowy sea of mesquit when the instinct of the plainsman warned him that the stillness, the desolation, was again invaded. He saw a motionless horseman in black outline against the pallid sky. The silhouette displayed serape and sombrero, and even the Mexican spurs as large as pies. When this black figure began to move toward the camp, Bill's hand dropped to his revolver.

The horseman approached until Bill was enabled to see pronounced American features, and a skin too red to grow on a Mexican face. Bill released his grip on his revolver.

"Hello!" called the horseman.

"Hello!" answered Bill.

The horseman cantered forward. "Good evening," he said, as he again drew rein.

"Good evenin'," answered Bill, without committing himself by too much courtesy.

For a moment the two men scanned each other in a way that is not ill-mannered on the plains, where one is in danger of meeting horse-thieves or tourists.

Bill saw a type which did not belong in the mesquit. The young fellow had invested in some Mexican trappings of an expensive kind. Bill's eyes searched the outfit for some sign of craft, but there was none. Even with his local regalia, it was clear that the young man was of a far, black Northern city. He had discarded the enormous stirrups of his Mexican saddle; he used the small English stirrup, and his feet were thrust forward until the steel tightly gripped his ankles. As Bill's eyes traveled over the stranger, they lighted suddenly upon the stirrups and the thrust feet, and immediately he smiled in a friendly way. No dark purpose could dwell in the innocent heart of a man who rode thus on the plains.

As for the stranger, he saw a tattered individual with a tangle of hair and beard, and with a complexion turned brick-color from the sun and whisky. He saw a pair of eyes that at first looked at him as the wolf looks at the wolf, and then became childlike, almost timid, in their glance. Here was evidently a man who had often stormed the iron walls of the city of success, and who now sometimes valued himself as the rabbit values his prowess.

The stranger smiled genially, and sprang from his horse. "Well, sir, I suppose you will let me camp here with you to-night?"

"Eh?" said Bill.

"I suppose you will let me camp here with you to-night?"

Bill for a time seemed too astonished for words. "Well," —he answered, scowling in inhospitable annoyance—"well, I don't believe this here is a good place to camp to-night, mister."

The stranger turned quickly from his saddle-girth.

"What?" he said in surprise. "You don't want me here? You don't want me to camp here?"

Bill's feet scuffled awkwardly, and he looked steadily at a cactus-plant. "Well, you see, mister," he said, "I'd like your company well enough, but—you see, some of these here greasers are goin' to chase me off the range to-night; and while I might like a man's company all right, I couldn't let him in for no such game when he ain't got nothin' to do with the trouble."

"Going to chase you off the range?" cried the stranger.

"Well, they said they were goin' to do it," said Bill.

"And—great heavens! will they kill you, do you think?"

"Don't know. Can't tell till afterwards. You see, they take some feller that's alone like me, and then they rush his camp when he ain't quite ready for 'em, and ginerally plug 'im with a sawed-off shot-gun load before he has a chance to git at 'em. They lay around and wait for their chance, and it comes soon enough. Of course a feller alone like me has got to let up watching some time. Maybe they ketch 'im asleep. Maybe the feller gits tired waiting, and goes out in broad day, and kills two or three just to make the whole crowd pile on him and settle the thing. I heard of a case like that once. It's awful hard on a man's mind—to git a gang after him."

"And so they're going to rush your camp to-night?" cried the stranger. "How do you know? Who told you?"

"Feller come and told me."

"And what are you going to do? Fight?"

"Don't see nothin' else to do," answered Bill, gloomily, still staring at the cactus-plant.

There was a silence. Finally the stranger burst out in an amazed cry. "Well, I never heard of such a thing in my life! How many of them are there?"

"Eight," answered Bill. "And now look-a-here; you ain't got no manner of business foolin' around here just now, and you might better lope off before dark. I don't ask no help in this here row. I know your happening along here just now don't give me no call on you, and you better hit the trail."

"Well, why in the name of wonder don't you go get the sheriff?" cried the stranger.

"Oh, h——!" said Bill.

IV

Long, smoldering clouds spread in the western sky, and to the east silver mists lay on the purple gloom of the wilderness.

Finally, when the great moon climbed the heavens and cast its ghastly radiance upon the bushes, it made a new and more brilliant crimson of the camp-fire, where the flames capered merrily through its mesquit branches, filling the silence with the fire chorus, an ancient melody which surely bears a message of the inconsequence of individual tragedy—a message that is in the boom of the sea, the sliver of the wind through the grass-blades, the silken clash of hemlock boughs.

No figures moved in the rosy space of the camp, and the search of the moonbeams failed to disclose a living thing in the bushes. There was no owl-faced clock to chant the weariness of the long silence that brooded upon the plain.

The dew gave the darkness under the mesquit a velvet quality that made air seem nearer to water, and no eye could have seen through it the black things that moved like monster lizards toward the camp. The branches, the leaves, that are fain to cry out when death approaches in the wilds, were frustrated by these uncanny bodies gliding with the finesse of the escaping serpent. They crept forward to the last point where assuredly no frantic attempt of the fire could discover them, and there they paused to locate the prey. A romance relates the tale of the black cell hidden deep in the earth, where, upon entering, one sees only the little eyes of snakes fixing him in menaces. If a man could have approached a certain spot in the bushes, he would not have found it romantically necessary to have his hair rise. There would have been a sufficient expression of horror in the feeling of the death-hand at the nape of his neck and in his rubber knee-joints.

Two of these bodies finally moved toward each other until for each there grew out of the darkness a face placidly smiling with tender dreams of assassination. "The fool is asleep by the fire, God be praised!" The lips of the other widened in a grin of affectionate appreciation of the fool and his plight. There was some signaling in the gloom, and then began a series of subtle rustlings, interjected often with pauses, during which no sound arose but the sound of faint breathing.

A bush stood like a rock in the stream of firelight, sending its long shadow backward. With painful caution the little company traveled along this shadow, and finally arrived at the rear of the bush. Through its branches they surveyed for a moment of comfortable satisfaction a form in a gray blanket extended on the ground near the fire. The smile of joyful anticipation fled quickly, to give place to a quiet air of business. Two men lifted shot-guns with much of the barrels gone, and sighting these weapons through the branches, pulled trigger together.

The noise of the explosions roared over the lonely mesquit as if these guns wished to inform the entire world; and as the gray smoke fled, the dodging company back of the bush saw the blanketed form twitching. Whereupon they burst out in chorus in a laugh, and arose as merry as a lot of banqueters. They gleefully gestured congratulations, and strode bravely into the light of the fire.

Then suddenly a new laugh rang from some unknown spot in the darkness. It was a fearsome laugh of ridicule, hatred, ferocity. It might have been demoniac. It smote them motionless in their gleeful prowl, as the stern voice from the sky smites the legendary malefactor. They might have been a weird group in wax, the light of the dying fire on their yellow faces, and shining athwart their eyes turned toward the darkness whence might come the unknown and the terrible.

The thing in the gray blanket no longer twitched; but if the knives in their hands had been thrust toward it, each knife was now drawn back, and its owner's elbow was thrown upward, as if he expected death from the clouds.

This laugh had so chained their reason that for a moment they had no wit to flee. They were prisoners to their terror. Then suddenly the belated decision arrived, and with bubbling cries they turned to run; but at that instant there was a long flash of red in the darkness, and with the report one of the men shouted a bitter shout, spun once, and tumbled headlong. The thick bushes failed to impede the rout of the others.

The silence returned to the wilderness. The tired flames faintly illumined the blanketed thing and the flung corse of the marauder, and sang the fire chorus, the ancient melody which bears the message of the inconsequence of human tragedy.

V

"Now you are worse off than ever," said the young man, dry-voiced and awed.

"No, I ain't," said Bill, rebelliously. "I'm one ahead."

After reflection, the stranger remarked, "Well, there's seven more."

They were cautiously and slowly approaching the camp. The sun was flaring its first warming rays over the gray wilderness. Upreared twigs, prominent branches, shone with golden light, while the shadows under the mesquit were heavily blue.

Suddenly the stranger uttered a frightened cry. He had arrived at a point whence he had, through openings in the thicket, a clear view of a dead face.

"Gosh!" said Bill, who at the next instant had seen the thing; "I thought at first it was that there José. That would have been queer, after what I told 'im yesterday."

They continued their way, the stranger wincing in his walk, and Bill exhibiting considerable curiosity.

The yellow beams of the new sun were touching the grim hues of the dead Mexican's face, and creating there an inhuman effect, which made his countenance more like a mask of dulled brass. One hand, grown curiously thinner, had been flung out regardlessly to a cactus bush.

Bill walked forward and stood looking respectfully at the body. "I know that feller; his name is Miguel. He——"

The stranger's nerves might have been in that condition when there is no backbone to the body, only a long groove. "Good heavens!" he exclaimed, much agitated; "don't speak that way!"

"What way?" said Bill. "I only said his name was Miguel."

After a pause the stranger said:

"Oh, I know; but——" He waved his hand. "Lower your voice, or something. I don't know. This part of the business rattles me, don't you see?"

"Oh, all right," replied Bill, bowing to the other's mysterious mood. But in a moment he burst out violently and loud in the most extraordinary profanity, the oaths winging from him as the sparks go from the funnel.

He had been examining the contents of the bundled gray blanket, and he had brought forth, among other things, his frying-pan. It was now only a rim with a handle; the Mexican volley had centered upon it. A Mexican shot-gun of the abbreviated description is ordinarily loaded with flat-irons, stove-lids, lead pipe, old horseshoes, sections of chain, window weights, railroad sleepers and spikes, dumb-bells, and any other junk which may be at hand. When one of these loads encounters a man vitally, it is likely to make an impression upon him, and a cooking-utensil may be supposed to subside before such an assault of curiosities.

Bill held high his desecrated frying-pan, turning it this way and that way. He swore until he happened to note the absence of the stranger. A moment later he saw him leading his horse from the bushes. In silence and sullenly the young man went about saddling the animal. Bill said, "Well, goin' to pull out?"

The stranger's hands fumbled uncertainly at the throat-latch. Once he exclaimed irritably, blaming the buckle for the trembling of his fingers. Once he turned to look at the dead face with the light of the morning sun upon it. At last he cried, "Oh, I know the whole thing was all square enough—couldn't be squarer—but—somehow or other, that man there takes the heart out of me." He turned his troubled face for another look. "He seems to be all the time calling me a—he makes me feel like a murderer."

"But," said Bill, puzzling, "you didn't shoot him, mister; I shot him."

"I know; but I feel that way, somehow. I can't get rid of it."

Bill considered for a time; then he said diffidently, "Mister, you're a' eddycated man, ain't you?"

"What?"

"You're what they call a'—a' eddycated man, ain't you?"

The young man, perplexed, evidently had a question upon his lips, when there was a roar of guns, bright flashes, and in the air such hooting and whistling as would come from a swift flock of steam-boilers. The stranger's horse gave a mighty, convulsive spring, snorting wildly in its sudden anguish, fell upon its knees, scrambled afoot again, and was away in the uncanny death run known to men who have seen the finish of brave horses.

"This comes from discussin' things," cried Bill, angrily.

He had thrown himself flat on the ground facing the thicket whence had come the firing. He could see the smoke winding over the bush-tops. He lifted his revolver, and the weapon came slowly up from the ground and poised like the glittering crest of a snake. Somewhere on his face there was a kind of smile, cynical, wicked, deadly, of a ferocity which at the same time had brought a deep flush to his face, and had caused two upright lines to glow in his eyes.

"Hello, José!" he called, amiable for satire's sake. "Got your old blunderbusses loaded up again yet?"

The stillness had returned to the plain. The sun's brilliant rays swept over the sea of mesquit, painting the far mists of the west with faint rosy light, and high in the air some great bird fled toward the south.

"You come out here," called Bill, again addressing the landscape, "and I'll give you some shootin' lessons. That ain't the way to shoot." Receiving no reply, he began to invent epithets and yell them at the thicket. He was something of a master of insult, and, moreover, he dived into his memory to bring forth imprecations tarnished with age, unused since fluent Bowery days. The occupation amused him, and sometimes he laughed so that it was uncomfortable for his chest to be against the ground.

Finally the stranger, prostrate near him, said wearily, "Oh, they've gone."

"Don't you believe it," replied Bill, sobering swiftly. "They're there yet—every man of 'em."

"How do you know?"

"Because I do. They won't shake us so soon. Don't put your head up, or they'll get you, sure."

Bill's eyes, meanwhile, had not wavered from their scrutiny of the thicket in front. "They're there, all right; don't you forget it. Now you listen." So he called out: "José! Ojo,. José! Speak up, *hombre*! I want have talk. Speak up, you yaller cuss, you!"

Whereupon a mocking voice from off in the bushes said, "Señor?"

"There," said Bill to his ally; "didn't I tell you? The whole batch." Again he lifted his voice. "José—look—ain't you gittin' kinder tired? You better go home, you fellers, and git some rest."

The answer was a sudden furious chatter of Spanish, eloquent with hatred, calling down upon Bill all the calamities which life holds. It was as if some one had suddenly enraged a cageful of wildcats. The spirits of all the revenges which they had imagined were loosened at this time, and filled the air.

"They're in a holler," said Bill, chuckling, "or there'd be shootin'."

Presently he began to grow angry. His hidden enemies called him nine kinds of coward, a man who could fight only in the dark, a baby who would run from the shadows of such noble Mexican gentlemen, a dog that sneaked. They described the affair of the previous night, and informed him of the base advan-

tage he had taken of their friend. In fact, they in all sincerity
endowed him with every quality which he no less earnestly
believed them to possess. One could have seen the phrases bite
him as he lay there on the ground fingering his revolver.

VI

It is sometimes taught that men do the furious and desperate
thing from an emotion that is as even and placid as the thoughts
of a village clergyman on Sunday afternoon. Usually, however, it
is to be believed that a panther is at the time born in the heart,
and that the subject does not resemble a man picking mulber-
ries.

"B' G——!" said Bill, speaking as from a throat filled with dust,
"I'll go after 'em in a minute."

"Don't you budge an inch!" cried the stranger, sternly. "Don't
you budge!"

"Well," said Bill, glaring at the bushes—"well——"

"Put your head down!" suddenly screamed the stranger, in
white alarm. As the guns roared, Bill uttered a loud grunt, and
for a moment leaned panting on his elbow, while his arm shook
like a twig. Then he upreared like a great and bloody spirit of
vengeance, his face lighted with the blaze of his last passion.
The Mexicans came swiftly and in silence.

The lightning action of the next few moments was of the
fabric of dreams to the stranger. The muscular struggle may not
be real to the drowning man. His mind may be fixed on the far,
straight shadows back of the stars, and the terror of them. And
so the fight, and his part in it, had to the stranger only the
quality of a picture half drawn. The rush of feet, the spatter of
shots, the cries, the swollen faces seen like masks on the smoke,
resembled a happening of the night.

And yet afterward certain lines, forms, lived out so strongly
from the incoherence that they were always in his memory.

He killed a man, and the thought went swiftly by him, like the
feather on the gale, that it was easy to kill a man.

Moreover, he suddenly felt for Bill, this grimy sheep-herder,
some deep form of idolatry. Bill was dying, and the dignity of

last defeat, the superiority of him who stands in his grave, was in the pose of the lost sheep-herder.

The stranger sat on the ground idly mopping the sweat and powder-stain from his brow. He wore the gentle idiot smile of an aged beggar as he watched three Mexicans limping and staggering in the distance. He noted at this time that one who still possessed a serape had from it none of the grandeur of the cloaked Spaniard, but that against the sky the silhouette resembled a cornucopia of childhood's Christmas.

They turned to look at him, and he lifted his weary arm to menace them with his revolver. They stood for a moment banded together, and hooted curses at him.

Finally he arose, and, walking some paces, stooped to loosen Bill's gray hands from a throat. Swaying as if slightly drunk, he stood looking down into the still face.

Struck suddenly with a thought, he went about with dulled eyes on the ground, until he plucked his gaudy blanket from where it lay dirty from trampling feet. He dusted it carefully, and then returned and laid it over Bill's form. There he again stood motionless, his mouth just agape and the same stupid glance in his eyes, when all at once he made a gesture of fright and looked wildly about him.

He had almost reached the thicket when he stopped, smitten with alarm. A body contorted, with one arm stiff in the air, lay in his path. Slowly and warily he moved around it, and in a moment the bushes, nodding and whispering, their leaf-faces turned toward the scene behind him, swung and swung again into stillness and the peace of the wilderness.

THE OPEN BOAT

A TALE INTENDED TO BE AFTER THE FACT.
BEING THE EXPERIENCE OF FOUR MEN
FROM THE SUNK STEAMER COMMODORE

I

NONE of them knew the color of the sky. Their eyes glanced level, and were fastened upon the waves that swept toward them. These waves were of the hue of slate, save for the tops, which were of foaming white, and all of the men knew the colors of the sea. The horizon narrowed and widened, and dipped and rose, and at all times its edge was jagged with waves that seemed thrust up in points like rocks.

Many a man ought to have a bath-tub larger than the boat which here rode upon the sea. These waves were most wrongfully and barbarously abrupt and tall, and each froth-top was a problem in small boat navigation.

The cook squatted in the bottom and looked with both eyes at the six inches of gunwale which separated him from the ocean. His sleeves were rolled over his fat forearms, and the two flaps of his unbuttoned vest dangled as he bent to bail out the boat. Often he said: "Gawd! That was a narrow clip." As he remarked it he invariably gazed eastward over the broken sea.

The oiler, steering with one of the two oars in the boat, sometimes raised himself suddenly to keep clear of water that swirled in over the stern. It was a thin little oar and it seemed often ready to snap.

The correspondent, pulling at the other oar, watched the waves and wondered why he was there.

The injured captain, lying in the bow, was at this time buried in that profound dejection and indifference which comes, temporarily at least, to even the bravest and most enduring when, willy nilly, the firm fails, the army loses, the ship goes down. The mind of the master of a vessel is rooted deep in the timbers of her, though he command for a day or a decade, and this captain had on him the stern impression of a scene in the grays of dawn of seven turned faces, and later a stump of a top-mast with a white ball on it that slashed to and fro at the waves, went low and lower, and down. Thereafter there was something strange in his voice. Although steady, it was deep with mourning, and of a quality beyond oration or tears.

"Keep'er a little more south, Billie," said he.

" 'A little more south,' sir," said the oiler in the stern.

A seat in this boat was not unlike a seat upon a bucking broncho, and, by the same token, a broncho is not much smaller. The craft pranced and reared, and plunged like an animal. As each wave came, and she rose for it, she seemed like a horse making at a fence outrageously high. The manner of her scramble over these walls of water is a mystic thing, and, moreover, at the top of them were ordinarily these problems in white water, the foam racing down from the summit of each wave, requiring a new leap, and a leap from the air. Then, after scornfully bumping a crest, she would slide, and race, and splash down a long incline and arrive bobbing and nodding in front of the next menace.

A singular disadvantage of the sea lies in the fact that after successfully surmounting one wave you discover that there is another behind it just as important and just as nervously anxious to do something effective in the way of swamping boats. In a ten-foot dingey one can get an idea of the resources of the sea in the line of waves that is not probable to the average experience, which is never at sea in a dingey. As each slaty wall of water approached, it shut all else from the view of the men in the boat, and it was not difficult to imagine that this particular wave was the final outburst of the ocean, the last effort of the grim water. There was a terrible grace in the move of the waves, and they came in silence, save for the snarling of the crests.

In the wan light, the faces of the men must have been gray. Their eyes must have glinted in strange ways as they gazed steadily astern. Viewed from a balcony, the whole thing would doubtlessly have been weirdly picturesque. But the men in the boat had no time to see it, and if they had had leisure there were other things to occupy their minds. The sun swung steadily up the sky, and they knew it was broad day because the color of the sea changed from slate to emerald-green, streaked with amber lights, and the foam was like tumbling snow. The process of the breaking day was unknown to them. They were aware only of this effect upon the color of the waves that rolled toward them.

In disjointed sentences the cook and the correspondent argued as to the difference between a life-saving station and a house of refuge. The cook had said: "There's a house of refuge just north of the Mosquito Inlet Light, and as soon as they see us, they'll come off in their boat and pick us up."

"As soon as who see us?" said the correspondent.

"The crew," said the cook.

"Houses of refuge don't have crews," said the correspondent. "As I understand them, they are only places where clothes and grub are stored for the benefit of shipwrecked people. They don't carry crews."

"Oh, yes, they do," said the cook.

"No, they don't," said the correspondent.

"Well, we're not there yet, anyhow," said the oiler, in the stern.

"Well," said the cook, "perhaps it's not a house of refuge that I'm thinking of as being near Mosquito Inlet Light. Perhaps it's a life-saving station."

"We're not there yet," said the oiler, in the stern.

II

As the boat bounced from the top of each wave, the wind tore through the hair of the hatless men, and as the craft plopped her stern down again the spray slashed past them. The crest of each of these waves was a hill, from the top of which the men surveyed, for a moment, a broad tumultuous expanse, shining and wind-riven. It was probably splendid. It was probably glorious, this play of the free sea, wild with lights of emerald and white and amber.

"Bully good thing it's an on-shore wind," said the cook. "If not, where would we be? Wouldn't have a show."

"That's right," said the correspondent.

The busy oiler nodded his assent.

Then the captain, in the bow, chuckled in a way that expressed humor, contempt, tragedy, all in one. "Do you think we've got much of a show, now, boys?" said he.

Whereupon the three were silent, save for a trifle of hemming and hawing. To express any particular optimism at this time they felt to be childish and stupid, but they all doubtless possessed this sense of the situation in their mind. A young man thinks doggedly at such times. On the other hand, the ethics of their condition was decidedly against any open suggestion of hopelessness. So they were silent.

"Oh, well," said the captain, soothing his children, "we'll get ashore all right."

But there was that in his tone which made them think, so the oiler quoth: "Yes! If this wind holds!"

The cook was bailing. "Yes! If we don't catch hell in the surf."

Canton flannel gulls flew near and far. Sometimes they sat down on the sea, near patches of brown sea-weed that rolled over the waves with a movement like carpets on a line in a gale. The birds sat comfortably in groups, and they were envied by some in the dingey, for the wrath of the sea was no more to them than it was to a covey of prairie chickens a thousand miles inland. Often they came very close and stared at the men with black bead-like eyes. At these times they were uncanny and sinister in their unblinking scrutiny, and the men hooted angrily at them, telling them to be gone. One came, and evidently decided to alight on the top of the captain's head. The bird flew parallel to the boat and did not circle, but made short sidelong jumps in the air in chicken-fashion. His black eyes were wistfully fixed upon the captain's head. "Ugly brute," said the oiler to the bird. "You look as if you were made with a jack-knife." The cook and the correspondent swore darkly at the creature. The captain naturally wished to knock it away with the end of the heavy painter, but he did not dare do it, because anything resembling an emphatic gesture would have capsized this freighted boat, and so with his open hand, the captain gently and carefully waved the gull away. After it had been discouraged from the pursuit the captain breathed easier on account of his hair, and others breathed easier because the bird struck their minds at this time as being somehow grewsome and ominous.

In the meantime the oiler and the correspondent rowed. And also they rowed.

They sat together in the same seat, and each rowed an oar. Then the oiler took both oars; then the correspondent took both oars; then the oiler; then the correspondent. They rowed and they rowed. The very ticklish part of the business was when the time came for the reclining one in the stern to take his turn at the oars. By the very last star of truth, it is easier to steal eggs from under a hen than it was to change seats in the dingey. First the man in the stern slid his hand along the thwart and moved with care, as if he were of Sèvres. Then the man in the rowing seat slid his hand along the other thwart. It was all done with the most extraordinary care. As the two sidled past each other, the whole party kept watchful eyes on the coming wave, and the captain cried: "Look out now! Steady there!"

The brown mats of sea-weed that appeared from time to time were like islands, bits of earth. They were travelling, apparently, neither one way nor the other. They were, to all intents, stationary. They informed the men in the boat that it was making progress slowly toward the land.

The captain, rearing cautiously in the bow, after the dingey soared on a great swell, said that he had seen the light-house at Mosquito Inlet. Presently the cook remarked that he had seen it. The correspondent was at the oars, then, and for some reason he too wished to look at the light-house, but his back was toward the far shore and the waves were important, and for some time he could not seize an opportunity to turn his head. But at last there came a wave more gentle than the others, and when at the crest of it he swiftly scoured the western horizon.

"See it?" said the captain.

"No," said the correspondent, slowly, "I didn't see anything."

"Look again," said the captain. He pointed. "It's exactly in that direction."

At the top of another wave, the correspondent did as he was bid, and this time his eyes chanced on a small still thing on the edge of the swaying horizon. It was precisely like the point of a pin. It took an anxious eye to find a light-house so tiny.

"Think we'll make it, Captain?"

"If this wind holds and the boat don't swamp, we can't do much else," said the captain.

The little boat, lifted by each towering sea, and splashed viciously by the crests, made progress that in the absence of sea-weed was not apparent to those in her. She seemed just a wee thing wallowing, miraculously, top-up, at the mercy of five oceans. Occasionally, a great spread of water, like white flames, swarmed into her.

"Bail her, cook," said the captain, serenely.

"All right, Captain," said the cheerful cook.

III

It would be difficult to describe the subtle brotherhood of men that was here established on the seas. No one said that it was so. No one mentioned it. But it dwelt in the boat, and each man felt it warm him. They were a captain, an oiler, a cook, and a correspondent, and they were friends, friends in a more curiously iron-bound degree than may be common. The hurt captain, lying against the water-jar in the bow, spoke always in a low voice and calmly, but he could never command a more ready and swiftly obedient crew than the motley three of the dingey. It was more than a mere recognition of what was best for the common safety. There was surely in it a quality that was personal and heartfelt. And after this devotion to the commander of the boat there was this comradeship that the correspondent, for instance, who had been taught to be cynical of men, knew even at the time was the best experience of his life. But no one said that it was so. No one mentioned it.

"I wish we had a sail," remarked the captain. "We might try my overcoat on the end of an oar and give you two boys a chance to rest." So the cook and the correspondent held the mast and spread wide the overcoat. The oiler steered, and the little boat made good way with her new rig. Sometimes the oiler had to scull sharply to keep a sea from breaking into the boat, but otherwise sailing was a success.

Meanwhile the light-house had been growing slowly larger. It had now almost assumed color, and appeared like a little gray shadow on the sky. The man at the oars could not be prevented from turning his head rather often to try for a glimpse of this little gray shadow.

At last, from the top of each wave the men in the tossing boat could see land. Even as the light-house was an upright shadow on the sky, this land seemed but a long black shadow on the sea. It certainly was thinner than paper. "We must be about opposite New Smyrna," said the cook, who had coasted this shore often in schooners. "Captain, by the way, I believe they abandoned that life-saving station there about a year ago."

"Did they?" said the captain.

The wind slowly died away. The cook and the correspondent were not now obliged to slave in order to hold high the oar. But the waves continued their old impetuous swooping at the dingey, and the little craft, no longer under way, struggled woundily over them. The oiler or the correspondent took the oars again.

Shipwrecks are *apropos* of nothing. If men could only train for them and have them occur when the men had reached pink condition, there would be less drowning at sea. Of the four in the dingey none had slept any time worth mentioning for two days and two nights previous to embarking in the dingey, and in the excitement of clambering about the deck of a foundering ship they had also forgotten to eat heartily.

For these reasons, and for others, neither the oiler nor the correspondent was fond of rowing at this time. The correspondent wondered ingenuously how in the name of all that was sane could there be people who thought it amusing to row a boat. It was not an amusement; it was a diabolical punishment, and even a genius of mental aberrations could never conclude that it was anything but a horror to the muscles and a crime against the back. He mentioned to the boat in general how the amusement of rowing struck him, and the weary-faced oiler smiled in full sympathy. Previously to the foundering, by the way, the oiler had worked double-watch in the engine-room of the ship.

"Take her easy, now, boys," said the captain. "Don't spend yourselves. If we have to run a surf you'll need all your strength, because we'll sure have to swim for it. Take your time."

Slowly the land arose from the sea. From a black line it became a line of black and a line of white—trees and sand. Finally, the captain said that he could make out a house on the shore. "That's the house of refuge, sure," said the cook. "They'll see us before long, and come out after us."

The distant light-house reared high. "The keeper ought to be able to make us out now, if he's looking through a glass," said the captain. "He'll notify the life-saving people."

"None of those other boats could have got ashore to give word of the wreck," said the oiler, in a low voice. "Else the life-boat would be out hunting us."

Slowly and beautifully the land loomed out of the sea. The wind came again. It had veered from the northeast to the southeast. Finally, a new sound struck the ears of the men in the boat. It was the low thunder of the surf on the shore. "We'll never be able to make the light-house now," said the captain. "Swing her head a little more north, Billie."

" 'A little more north,' sir," said the oiler.

Whereupon the little boat turned her nose once more down the wind, and all but the oarsman watched the shore grow. Under the influence of this expansion doubt and direful apprehension was leaving the minds of the men. The management of the boat was still most absorbing, but it could not prevent a quiet cheerfulness. In an hour, perhaps, they would be ashore.

Their back-bones had become thoroughly used to balancing in the boat and they now rode this wild colt of a dingey like circus men. The correspondent thought that he had been drenched to the skin, but happening to feel in the top pocket of his coat, he found therein eight cigars. Four of them were soaked with sea-water; four were perfectly scatheless. After a search, somebody produced three dry matches, and thereupon the four waifs rode impudently in their little boat, and with an assurance of an impending rescue shining in their eyes, puffed at the big cigars and judged well and ill of all men. Everybody took a drink of water.

IV

"Cook," remarked the captain, "there don't seem to be any signs of life about your house of refuge."

"No," replied the cook. "Funny they don't see us!"

A broad stretch of lowly coast lay before the eyes of the men. It was of dunes topped with dark vegetation. The roar of the surf was plain, and sometimes they could see the white lip of a wave as it spun up the beach. A tiny house was blocked out black upon the sky. Southward, the slim light-house lifted its little gray length.

Tide, wind, and waves were swinging the dingey northward. "Funny they don't see us," said the men.

The surf's roar was here dulled, but its tone was, nevertheless, thunderous and mighty. As the boat swam over the great rollers, the men sat listening to this roar. "We'll swamp sure," said everybody.

It is fair to say here that there was not a life-saving station within twenty miles in either direction, but the men did not know this fact and in consequence they made dark and opprobrious remarks concerning the eyesight of the nation's life-savers. Four scowling men sat in the dingey and surpassed records in the invention of epithets.

"Funny they don't see us."

The light-heartedness of a former time had completely faded. To their sharpened minds it was easy to conjure pictures of all kinds of incompetency and blindness and, indeed, cowardice. There was the shore of the populous land, and it was bitter and bitter to them that from it came no sign.

"Well," said the captain, ultimately, "I suppose we'll have to make a try for ourselves. If we stay out here too long, we'll none of us have strength left to swim after the boat swamps."

And so the oiler, who was at the oars, turned the boat straight for the shore. There was a sudden tightening of muscles. There was some thinking.

"If we don't all get ashore—" said the captain. "If we don't all get ashore, I suppose you fellows know where to send news of my finish?"

They then briefly exchanged some addresses and admonitions. As for the reflections of the men, there was a great deal of rage in them. Perchance they might be formulated thus: "If I am going to be drowned—if I am going to be drowned—if I am going to be drowned, why, in the name of the seven mad gods who rule the sea, was I allowed to come thus far and contemplate sand and trees? Was I brought here merely to have my nose dragged away as I was about to nibble the sacred cheese of life? It is preposterous. If this old ninny-woman, Fate, cannot do better than this, she should be deprived of the management of men's fortunes. She is an old hen who knows not her intention. If she has decided to drown me, why did she not do it in the beginning and save me all this trouble. The whole affair is absurd. . . . But, no, she cannot mean to drown me. She dare not drown me. She cannot drown me. Not after all this work." Afterward the man might have had an impulse to shake his fist at the clouds. "Just you drown me, now, and then hear what I call you!"

The billows that came at this time were more formidable. They seemed always just about to break and roll over the little boat in a turmoil of foam. There was a preparatory and long growl in the speech of them. No mind unused to the sea would have concluded that the dingey could ascend these sheer heights in time. The shore was still afar. The oiler was a wily surfman. "Boys," he said, swiftly, "she won't live three minutes more and we're too far out to swim. Shall I take her to sea again, Captain?"

"Yes! Go ahead!" said the captain.

This oiler, by a series of quick miracles, and fast and steady oarsmanship, turned the boat in the middle of the surf and took her safely to sea again.

There was a considerable silence as the boat bumped over the furrowed sea to deeper water. Then somebody in gloom spoke. "Well, anyhow, they must have seen us from the shore by now."

The gulls went in slanting flight up the wind toward the gray desolate east. A squall, marked by dingy clouds, and clouds brick-red, like smoke from a burning building, appeared from the southeast.

"What do you think of those life-saving people? Ain't they peaches?"

"Funny they haven't seen us."

"Maybe they think we're out here for sport! Maybe they think we're fishin'. Maybe they think we're damned fools."

It was a long afternoon. A changed tide tried to force them southward, but wind and wave said northward. Far ahead, where coast-line, sea, and sky formed their mighty angle, there were little dots which seemed to indicate a city on the shore.

"St. Augustine?"

The captain shook his head. "Too near Mosquito Inlet."

And the oiler rowed, and then the correspondent rowed. Then the oiler rowed. It was a weary business. The human back can become the seat of more aches and pains than are registered in books for the composite anatomy of a regiment. It is a limited area, but it can become the theatre of innumerable muscular conflicts, tangles, wrenches, knots, and other comforts.

"Did you ever like to row, Billie?" asked the correspondent.

"No," said the oiler. "Hang it."

When one exchanged the rowing-seat for a place in the bottom of the boat, he suffered a bodily depression that caused him to be careless of everything save an obligation to wiggle one finger. There was cold sea-water swashing to and fro in the boat, and he lay in it. His head, pillowed on a thwart, was within an inch of the swirl of a wave crest, and sometimes a particularly obstreperous sea came in-board and drenched him once more. But these matters did not annoy him. It is almost certain that if the boat had capsized he would have tumbled comfortably out upon the ocean as if he felt sure that it was a great soft mattress.

"Look! There's a man on the shore!"

"Where?"

"There! See 'im? See 'im?"

"Yes, sure! He's walking along."

"Now he's stopped. Look! He's facing us!"

"He's waving at us!"

"So he is! By thunder!"

"Ah, now, we're all right! Now we're all right! There'll be a boat out here for us in half an hour."

"He's going on. He's running. He's going up to that house there."

The remote beach seemed lower than the sea, and it required a searching glance to discern the little black figure. The captain saw a floating stick and they rowed to it. A bath-towel was by some weird chance in the boat, and, tying this on the stick, the captain waved it. The oarsman did not dare turn his head, so he was obliged to ask questions.

"What's he doing now?"

"He's standing still again. He's looking, I think. . . . There he goes again. Toward the house. . . . Now he's stopped again."

"Is he waving at us?"

"No, not now! he was, though."

"Look! There comes another man!"

"He's running."

"Look at him go, would you."

"Why, he's on a bicycle. Now he's met the other man. They're both waving at us. Look!"

"There comes something up the beach."

"What the devil is that thing?"

"Why, it looks like a boat."

"Why, certainly it's a boat."

"No, it's on wheels."

"Yes, so it is. Well, that must be the life-boat. They drag them along shore on a wagon."

"That's the life-boat, sure."

"No, by——, it's—it's an omnibus."

"I tell you it's a life-boat."

"It is not! It's an omnibus. I can see it plain. See? One of those big hotel omnibuses."

"By thunder, you're right. It's an omnibus, sure as fate. What do you suppose they are doing with an omnibus? Maybe they are going around collecting the life-crew, hey?"

"That's it, likely. Look! There's a fellow waving a little black flag. He's standing on the steps of the omnibus. There come those other two fellows. Now they're all talking together. Look at the fellow with the flag. Maybe he ain't waving it!"

"That ain't a flag, is it? That's his coat. Why, certainly, that's his coat."

"So it is. It's his coat. He's taken it off and is waving it around his head. But would you look at him swing it!"

"Oh, say, there isn't any life-saving station there. That's just a winter resort hotel omnibus that has brought over some of the boarders to see us drown."

"What's that idiot with the coat mean? What's he signaling, anyhow?"

"It looks as if he were trying to tell us to go north. There must be a life-saving station up there."

"No! He thinks we're fishing. Just giving us a merry hand. See? Ah, there, Willie."

"Well, I wish I could make something out of those signals. What do you suppose he means?"

"He don't mean anything. He's just playing."

"Well, if he'd just signal us to try the surf again, or to go to sea and wait, or go north, or go south, or go to hell—there would be some reason in it. But look at him. He just stands there and keeps his coat revolving like a wheel. The ass!"

"There come more people."

"Now there's quite a mob. Look! Isn't that a boat?"

"Where? Oh, I see where you mean. No, that's no boat."

"That fellow is still waving his coat."

"He must think we like to see him do that. Why don't he quit it. It don't mean anything."

"I don't know. I think he is trying to make us go north. It must be that there's a life-saving station there somewhere."

"Say, he ain't tired yet. Look at 'im wave."

"Wonder how long he can keep that up. He's been revolving his coat ever since he caught sight of us. He's an idiot. Why aren't they getting men to bring a boat out. A fishing boat—one of those big yawls—could come out here all right. Why don't he do something?"

"Oh, it's all right, now."

"They'll have a boat out here for us in less than no time, now that they've seen us."

A faint yellow tone came into the sky over the low land. The shadows on the sea slowly deepened. The wind bore coldness with it, and the men began to shiver.

"Holy smoke!" said one, allowing his voice to express his impious mood, "if we keep on monkeying out here! If we've got to flounder out here all night!"

"Oh, we'll never have to stay here all night! Don't you worry. They've seen us now, and it won't be long before they'll come chasing out after us."

The shore grew dusky. The man waving a coat blended gradually into this gloom, and it swallowed in the same manner the omnibus and the group of people. The spray, when it dashed uproariously over the side, made the voyagers shrink and swear like men who were being branded.

"I'd like to catch the chump who waved the coat. I feel like soaking him one, just for luck."

"Why? What did he do?"

"Oh, nothing, but then he seemed so damned cheerful."

In the meantime the oiler rowed, and then the correspondent rowed, and then the oiler rowed. Gray-faced and bowed forward, they mechanically, turn by turn, plied the leaden oars. The form of the light-house had vanished from the southern horizon, but finally a pale star appeared, just lifting from the sea. The streaked saffron in the west passed before the all-merging darkness, and the sea to the east was black. The land had vanished, and was expressed only by the low and drear thunder of the surf.

"If I am going to be drowned—if I am going to be drowned—if I am going to be drowned, why, in the name of the seven mad gods who rule the sea, was I allowed to come thus far and contemplate sand and trees? Was I brought here merely to have my nose dragged away as I was about to nibble the sacred cheese of life?"

The patient captain, drooped over the water-jar, was sometimes obliged to speak to the oarsman.

"Keep her head up! Keep her head up!"

" 'Keep her head up,' sir." The voices were weary and low.

This was surely a quiet evening. All save the oarsman lay heavily and listlessly in the boat's bottom. As for him, his eyes were just capable of noting the tall black waves that swept forward in a most sinister silence, save for an occasional subdued growl of a crest.

The cook's head was on a thwart, and he looked without interest at the water under his nose. He was deep in other scenes. Finally he spoke. "Billie," he murmured, dreamfully, "what kind of pie do you like best?"

V

"Pie," said the oiler and the correspondent, agitatedly. "Don't talk about those things, blast you!"

"Well," said the cook, "I was just thinking about ham sandwiches, and——"

A night on the sea in an open boat is a long night. As darkness settled finally, the shine of the light, lifting from the sea in the south, changed to full gold. On the northern horizon a new light appeared, a small bluish gleam on the edge of the waters. These two lights were the furniture of the world. Otherwise there was nothing but waves.

Two men huddled in the stern, and distances were so magnificent in the dingey that the rower was enabled to keep his feet partly warmed by thrusting them under his companions. Their legs indeed extended far under the rowing-seat until they touched the feet of the captain forward. Sometimes, despite the efforts of the tired oarsman, a wave came piling into the boat, an icy wave of the night, and the chilling water soaked them anew. They would twist their bodies for a moment and groan, and sleep the dead sleep once more, while the water in the boat gurgled about them as the craft rocked.

The plan of the oiler and the correspondent was for one to row until he lost the ability, and then arouse the other from his sea-water couch in the bottom of the boat.

The oiler plied the oars until his head drooped forward, and the overpowering sleep blinded him. And he rowed yet afterward. Then he touched a man in the bottom of the boat, and called his name. "Will you spell me for a little while?" he said, meekly.

"Sure, Billie," said the correspondent, awakening and dragging himself to a sitting position. They exchanged places carefully, and the oiler, cuddling down in the sea-water at the cook's side, seemed to go to sleep instantly.

The particular violence of the sea had ceased. The waves came without snarling. The obligation of the man at the oars was to keep the boat headed so that the tilt of the rollers would not capsize her, and to preserve her from filling when the crests rushed past. The black waves were silent and hard to be seen in the darkness. Often one was almost upon the boat before the oarsman was aware.

In a low voice the correspondent addressed the captain. He was not sure that the captain was awake, although this iron man seemed to be always awake. "Captain, shall I keep her making for that light north, sir?"

The same steady voice answered him. "Yes. Keep it about two points off the port bow."

The cook had tied a life-belt around himself in order to get even the warmth which this clumsy cork contrivance could donate, and he seemed almost stove-like when a rower, whose teeth invariably chattered wildly as soon as he ceased his labor, dropped down to sleep.

The correspondent, as he rowed, looked down at the two men sleeping under foot. The cook's arm was around the oiler's shoulders, and, with their fragmentary clothing and haggard faces, they were the babes of the sea, a grotesque rendering of the old babes in the wood.

Later he must have grown stupid at his work, for suddenly there was a growling of water, and a crest came with a roar and a swash into the boat, and it was a wonder that it did not set the cook afloat in his life-belt. The cook continued to sleep, but the oiler sat up, blinking his eyes and shaking with the new cold.

"Oh, I'm awful sorry, Billie," said the correspondent, contritely.

"That's all right, old boy," said the oiler, and lay down again and was asleep.

Presently it seemed that even the captain dozed, and the correspondent thought that he was the one man afloat on all the oceans. The wind had a voice as it came over the waves, and it was sadder than the end.

There was a long, loud swishing astern of the boat, and a gleaming trail of phosphorescence, like blue flame, was furrowed on the black waters. It might have been made by a monstrous knife.

Then there came a stillness, while the correspondent breathed with the open mouth and looked at the sea.

Suddenly there was another swish and another long flash of

bluish light, and this time it was alongside the boat, and might almost have been reached with an oar. The correspondent saw an enormous fin speed like a shadow through the water, hurling the crystalline spray and leaving the long glowing trail.

The correspondent looked over his shoulder at the captain. His face was hidden, and he seemed to be asleep. He looked at the babes of the sea. They certainly were asleep. So, being bereft of sympathy, he leaned a little way to one side and swore softly into the sea.

But the thing did not then leave the vicinity of the boat. Ahead or astern, on one side or the other, at intervals long or short, fled the long sparkling streak, and there was to be heard the whiroo of the dark fin. The speed and power of the thing was greatly to be admired. It cut the water like a gigantic and keen projectile.

The presence of this biding thing did not affect the man with the same horror that it would if he had been a picnicker. He simply looked at the sea dully and swore in an undertone.

Nevertheless, it is true that he did not wish to be alone with the thing. He wished one of his companions to awaken by chance and keep him company with it. But the captain hung motionless over the water-jar and the oiler and the cook in the bottom of the boat were plunged in slumber.

VI

"If I am going to be drowned—if I am going to be drowned—if I am going to be drowned, why, in the name of the seven mad gods who rule the sea, was I allowed to come thus far and contemplate sand and trees?"

During this dismal night, it may be remarked that a man would conclude that it was really the intention of the seven mad gods to drown him, despite the abominable injustice of it. For it was certainly an abominable injustice to drown a man who had worked so hard, so hard. The man felt it would be a crime most unnatural. Other people had drowned at sea since galleys swarmed with painted sails, but still——

When it occurs to a man that nature does not regard him as important, and that she feels she would not maim the universe by disposing of him, he at first wishes to throw bricks at the temple, and he hates deeply the fact that there are no bricks and no temples. Any visible expression of nature would surely be pelleted with his jeers.

Then, if there be no tangible thing to hoot he feels, perhaps, the desire to confront a personification and indulge in pleas, bowed to one knee, and with hands supplicant, saying: "Yes, but I love myself."

A high cold star on a winter's night is the word he feels that she says to him. Thereafter he knows the pathos of his situation.

The men in the dingey had not discussed these matters, but each had, no doubt, reflected upon them in silence and according to his mind. There was seldom any expression upon their faces save the general one of complete weariness. Speech was devoted to the business of the boat.

To chime the notes of his emotion, a verse mysteriously entered the correspondent's head. He had even forgotten that he had forgotten this verse, but it suddenly was in his mind.

> A soldier of the Legion lay dying in Algiers,
> There was lack of woman's nursing, there was dearth
>   of woman's tears;
> But a comrade stood beside him, and he took that
>   comrade's hand,
> And he said: "I never more shall see my own, my
>   native land."

In his childhood, the correspondent had been made acquainted with the fact that a soldier of the Legion lay dying in Algiers, but he had never regarded it as important. Myriads of his school-fellows had informed him of the soldier's plight, but the dinning had naturally ended by making him perfectly indifferent. He had never considered it his affair that a soldier of the Legion lay dying in Algiers, nor had it appeared to him as a matter for sorrow. It was less to him than the breaking of a pencil's point.

Now, however, it quaintly came to him as a human, living thing. It was no longer merely a picture of a few throes in the breast of a poet, meanwhile drinking tea and warming his feet at the grate; it was an actuality—stern, mournful, and fine.

The correspondent plainly saw the soldier. He lay on the sand with his feet out straight and still. While his pale left hand was upon his chest in an attempt to thwart the going of his life, the blood came between his fingers. In the far Algerian distance, a city of low square forms was set against a sky that was faint with the last sunset hues. The correspondent, plying the oars and dreaming of the slow and slower movements of the lips of the soldier, was moved by a profound and perfectly impersonal comprehension. He was sorry for the soldier of the Legion who lay dying in Algiers.

The thing which had followed the boat and waited had evidently grown bored at the delay. There was no longer to be heard the slash of the cut-water, and there was no longer the flame of the long trail. The light in the north still glimmered, but it was apparently no nearer to the boat. Sometimes the boom of the surf rang in the correspondent's ears, and he turned the craft seaward then and rowed harder. Southward, some one had evidently built a watch-fire on the beach. It was too low and too far to be seen, but it made a shimmering, roseate reflection upon the bluff back of it, and this could be discerned from the boat. The wind came stronger, and sometimes a wave suddenly raged out like a mountain-cat and there was to be seen the sheen and sparkle of a broken crest.

The captain, in the bow, moved on his water-jar and sat erect. "Pretty long night," he observed to the correspondent. He looked at the shore. "Those life-saving people take their time."

"Did you see that shark playing around?"

"Yes, I saw him. He was a big fellow, all right."

"Wish I had known you were awake."

Later the correspondent spoke into the bottom of the boat.

"Billie!" There was a slow and gradual disentanglement. "Billie, will you spell me?"

"Sure," said the oiler.

As soon as the correspondent touched the cold comfortable sea-water in the bottom of the boat, and had huddled close to the cook's life-belt he was deep in sleep, despite the fact that his teeth played all the popular airs. This sleep was so good to him that it was but a moment before he heard a voice call his name in a tone that demonstrated the last stages of exhaustion. "Will you spell me?"

"Sure, Billie."

The light in the north had mysteriously vanished, but the correspondent took his course from the wide-awake captain.

Later in the night they took the boat farther out to sea, and the captain directed the cook to take one oar at the stern and keep the boat facing the seas. He was to call out if he should hear the thunder of the surf. This plan enabled the oiler and the correspondent to get respite together. "We'll give those boys a chance to get into shape again," said the captain. They curled down and, after a few preliminary chatterings and trembles, slept once more the dead sleep. Neither knew they had bequeathed to the cook the company of another shark, or perhaps the same shark.

As the boat caroused on the waves, spray occasionally bumped over the side and gave them a fresh soaking, but this had no power to break their repose. The ominous slash of the wind and the water affected them as it would have affected mummies.

"Boys," said the cook, with the notes of every reluctance in his voice, "she's drifted in pretty close. I guess one of you had better take her to sea again." The correspondent, aroused, heard the crash of the toppled crests.

As he was rowing, the captain gave him some whiskey and water, and this steadied the chills out of him. "If I ever get ashore and anybody shows me even a photograph of an oar——"

At last there was a short conversation.

"Billie. . . . Billie, will you spell me?"

"Sure," said the oiler.

VII

When the correspondent again opened his eyes, the sea and the sky were each of the gray hue of the dawning. Later, carmine and gold was painted upon the waters. The morning appeared finally, in its splendor, with a sky of pure blue, and the sunlight flamed on the tips of the waves.

On the distant dunes were set many little black cottages, and a tall white wind-mill reared above them. No man, nor dog, nor bicycle appeared on the beach. The cottages might have formed a deserted village.

The voyagers scanned the shore. A conference was held in the boat. "Well," said the captain, "if no help is coming, we might better try a run through the surf right away. If we stay out here much longer we will be too weak to do anything for ourselves at all." The others silently acquiesced in this reasoning. The boat was headed for the beach. The correspondent wondered if none ever ascended the tall wind-tower, and if then they never looked seaward. This tower was a giant, standing with its back to the plight of the ants. It represented in a degree, to the correspondent, the serenity of nature amid the struggles of the individual —nature in the wind, and nature in the vision of men. She did not seem cruel to him then, nor beneficent, nor treacherous, nor wise. But she was indifferent, flatly indifferent. It is, perhaps, plausible that a man in this situation, impressed with the uncon-cern of the universe, should see the innumerable flaws of his life and have them taste wickedly in his mind and wish for another chance. A distinction between right and wrong seems absurdly clear to him, then, in this new ignorance of the grave-edge, and he understands that if he were given another opportunity he would mend his conduct and his words, and be better and brighter during an introduction, or at a tea.

"Now, boys," said the captain, "she is going to swamp sure. All we can do is to work her in as far as possible, and then when she swamps, pile out and scramble for the beach. Keep cool now, and don't jump until she swamps sure."

The oiler took the oars. Over his shoulders he scanned the surf. "Captain," he said, "I think I'd better bring her about, and keep her head-on to the seas and back her in."

"All right, Billie," said the captain. "Back her in." The oiler swung the boat then and, seated in the stern, the cook and the correspondent were obliged to look over their shoulders to con-template the lonely and indifferent shore.

The monstrous inshore rollers heaved the boat high until the men were again enabled to see the white sheets of water scud-ding up the slanted beach. "We won't get in very close," said the captain. Each time a man could wrest his attention from the rollers, he turned his glance toward the shore, and in the expression of the eyes during this contemplation there was a singular quality. The correspondent, observing the others, knew that they were not afraid, but the full meaning of their glances was shrouded.

As for himself, he was too tired to grapple fundamentally with the fact. He tried to coerce his mind into thinking of it, but the mind was dominated at this time by the muscles, and the muscles said they did not care. It merely occurred to him that if he should drown it would be a shame.

There were no hurried words, no pallor, no plain agitation. The men simply looked at the shore. "Now, remember to get well clear of the boat when you jump," said the captain.

Seaward the crest of a roller suddenly fell with a thunderous crash, and the long white comber came roaring down upon the boat.

"Steady now," said the captain. The men were silent. They turned their eyes from the shore to the comber and waited. The boat slid up the incline, leaped at the furious top, bounced over it, and swung down the long back of the wave. Some water had been shipped and the cook bailed it out.

But the next crest crashed also. The tumbling boiling flood of white water caught the boat and whirled it almost perpendicular. Water swarmed in from all sides. The correspondent had his hands on the gunwale at this time, and when the water entered at that place he swiftly withdrew his fingers, as if he objected to wetting them.

The little boat, drunken with this weight of water, reeled and snuggled deeper into the sea.

"Bail her out, cook! Bail her out," said the captain.

"All right, Captain," said the cook.

"Now, boys, the next one will do for us, sure," said the oiler. "Mind to jump clear of the boat."

The third wave moved forward, huge, furious, implacable. It fairly swallowed the dingey, and almost simultaneously the men tumbled into the sea. A piece of life-belt had lain in the bottom of the boat, and as the correspondent went overboard he held this to his chest with his left hand.

The January water was icy, and he reflected immediately that it was colder than he had expected to find it off the coast of Florida. This appeared to his dazed mind as a fact important enough to be noted at the time. The coldness of the water was sad; it was tragic. This fact was somehow so mixed and confused with his opinion of his own situation that it seemed almost a proper reason for tears. The water was cold.

When he came to the surface he was conscious of little but the noisy water. Afterward he saw his companions in the sea. The oiler was ahead in the race. He was swimming strongly and rapidly. Off to the correspondent's left, the cook's great white and corked back bulged out of the water, and in the rear the captain was hanging with his one good hand to the keel of the overturned dingey.

There is a certain immovable quality to a shore, and the correspondent wondered at it amid the confusion of the sea.

It seemed also very attractive, but the correspondent knew that it was a long journey, and he paddled leisurely. The piece of life-preserver lay under him, and sometimes he whirled down the incline of a wave as if he were on a hand-sled.

But finally he arrived at a place in the sea where travel was beset with difficulty. He did not pause swimming to inquire what manner of current had caught him, but there his progress ceased. The shore was set before him like a bit of scenery on a stage, and he looked at it and understood with his eyes each detail of it.

As the cook passed, much farther to the left, the captain was calling to him, "Turn over on your back, cook! Turn over on your back and use the oar."

"All right, sir." The cook turned on his back, and, paddling with an oar, went ahead as if he were a canoe.

Presently the boat also passed to the left of the correspondent with the captain clinging with one hand to the keel. He would have appeared like a man raising himself to look over a board fence, if it were not for the extraordinary gymnastics of the boat. The correspondent marvelled that the captain could still hold to it.

They passed on, nearer to shore—the oiler, the cook, the captain—and following them went the water-jar, bouncing gayly over the seas.

The correspondent remained in the grip of this strange new enemy—a current. The shore, with its white slope of sand and its green bluff, topped with little silent cottages, was spread like a picture before him. It was very near to him then, but he was impressed as one who in a gallery looks at a scene from Brittany or Holland.

He thought: "I am going to drown? Can it be possible? Can it be possible? Can it be possible?" Perhaps an individual must consider his own death to be the final phenomenon of nature.

But later a wave perhaps whirled him out of this small deadly current, for he found suddenly that he could again make progress toward the shore. Later still, he was aware that the captain, clinging with one hand to the keel of the dingey, had his face turned away from the shore and toward him, and was calling his name. "Come to the boat! Come to the boat!"

In his struggle to reach the captain and the boat, he reflected that when one gets properly wearied, drowning must really be a comfortable arrangement, a cessation of hostilities accompanied by a large degree of relief, and he was glad of it, for the main thing in his mind for some moments had been horror of the temporary agony. He did not wish to be hurt.

Presently he saw a man running along the shore. He was undressing with most remarkable speed. Coat, trousers, shirt, everything flew magically off him.

"Come to the boat," called the captain.

"All right, Captain." As the correspondent paddled, he saw the captain let himself down to bottom and leave the boat. Then the correspondent performed his one little marvel of the voyage. A large wave caught him and flung him with ease and supreme speed completely over the boat and far beyond it. It struck him even then as an event in gymnastics, and a true miracle of the sea. An overturned boat in the surf is not a plaything to a swimming man.

The correspondent arrived in water that reached only to his waist, but his condition did not enable him to stand for more than a moment. Each wave knocked him into a heap, and the under-tow pulled at him.

Then he saw the man who had been running and undressing, and undressing and running, come bounding into the water. He dragged ashore the cook, and then waded toward the captain, but the captain waved him away, and sent him to the correspondent. He was naked, naked as a tree in winter, but a halo was about his head, and he shone like a saint. He gave a strong pull, and a long drag, and a bully heave at the correspondent's hand. The correspondent, schooled in the minor formulæ, said: "Thanks, old man." But suddenly the man cried: "What's that?" He pointed a swift finger. The correspondent said: "Go."

In the shallows, face downward, lay the oiler. His forehead touched sand that was periodically, between each wave, clear of the sea.

The correspondent did not know all that transpired afterward. When he achieved safe ground he fell, striking the sand with each particular part of his body. It was as if he had dropped from a roof, but the thud was grateful to him.

It seems that instantly the beach was populated with men with blankets, clothes, and flasks, and women with coffee-pots and all the remedies sacred to their minds. The welcome of the land to the men from the sea was warm and generous, but a still and dripping shape was carried slowly up the beach, and the land's welcome for it could only be the different and sinister hospitality of the grave.

When it came night, the white waves paced to and fro in the moonlight, and the wind brought the sound of the great sea's voice to the men on shore, and they felt that they could then be interpreters.

FLANAGAN
AND HIS SHORT FILIBUSTERING ADVENTURE

I

"I HAVE got twenty men at me back who will fight to the death," said the warrior to the old filibuster.

"And they can be blowed, for all me," replied the old filibuster. "Common as sparrows. Cheap as cigarettes. Show me twenty men with steel clamps on their mouths, with holes in their heads where memory ought to be, and I want 'em. But twenty brave men merely? I'd rather have twenty brave onions."

Thereupon the warrior removed sadly, feeling that no salaams were paid to valor in these days of mechanical excellence.

Valor, in truth, is no bad thing to have when filibustering, but many medals are to be won by the man who knows not the meaning of pow-wow, before or afterward. Twenty brave men with tongues hung lightly may make trouble rise from the ground like smoke from grass because of their subsequent fiery pride, whereas twenty cow-eyed villains who accept unrighteous and far-compelling kicks as they do the rain of heaven may halo the ultimate history of an expedition with gold and plentifully bedeck their names, winning forty years of gratitude from patriots, simply by remaining silent. As for the cause, it may be only that they have no friends or other credulous furniture.

If it were not for the curse of the swinging tongue it is surely to be said that the filibustering industry, flourishing now in the United States, would be pie. Under correct conditions, it is merely a matter of dealing with some little detectives whose skill at search is rated by those who pay them at a value of twelve or twenty dollars each week. It is nearly axiomatic that normally a twelve-dollar-per-week detective cannot defeat a one-hundred-thousand-dollar filibustering excursion. Against the criminal the detective represents the commonwealth; but in this other case he represents his desire to show cause why his salary should be paid. He represents himself merely, and he counts no more than a grocer's clerk.

But the pride of the successful filibuster often smites him and his cause like an ax, and men who have not confided in their mothers go prone with him. It can make the dome of the Capitol tremble and incite the Senators to overturning benches. It can increase the salaries of detectives who could not detect the location of a pain in the chest. It is a wonderful thing, this pride.

Filibustering was once such a simple game. It was managed blandly by gentle captains and smooth and undisturbed gentlemen who at other times dealt in the law, soap, medicine, and bananas. It was a great pity that the little cote of doves in Washington was obliged to rustle officially, and naval men were kept from their berths at night, and sundry custom-house people got wiggings, all because the returned adventurer pow-wowed in his pride. A yellow and red banner would have been long since smothered in a shame of defeat if a contract to filibuster had been let to some admirable organization like one of our trusts.

And yet the game is not obsolete. It is still played by the wise and the silent, men whose names are not display-typed and blathered from one end of the country to the other.

There is in mind now a man who knew one side of a fence from the other side when he looked sharply. They were hunting for captains then to command the first vessels of what has since become a famous little fleet. One was recommended to this man, and he said: "Send him down to my office and I'll look him over." He was an attorney, and he liked to lean back in his chair, twirl a paper-knife, and let the other fellow talk.

The seafaring man came and stood and appeared confounded. The attorney asked the terrible first question of the filibuster to the applicant. He said: "Why do you want to go?"

The captain reflected, changed his attitude three times, and decided ultimately that he didn't know. He seemed greatly ashamed. The attorney, looking at him, saw that he had eyes that resembled a lambkin's eyes.

"Glory?" said the attorney at last.

"No-o," said the captain.

"Pay?"

"No-o. Not that, so much."

"Think they'll give you a land grant when they win out?"

"No. Never thought."

"No glory. No immense pay. No land grant. What are you going for, then?"

"Well, I don't know," said the captain, with his glance on the floor and shifting his position again. "I don't know. I guess it's just for fun, mostly." The attorney asked him out to have a drink.

When he stood on the bridge of his outgoing steamer, the attorney saw him again. His shore meekness and uncertainty were gone. He was clear-eyed and strong, aroused like a mastiff at night. He took his cigar out of his mouth and yelled some sudden language at the deck.

This steamer had about her a quality of unholy mediæval disrepair which is usually accounted the principal prerogative of the United States revenue marine. There is many a seaworthy ice-house if she was a good ship. She swashed through the seas as genially as an old wooden clock, burying her head under waves that came only like children at play, and on board it cost a ducking to go from anywhere to anywhere.

The captain had commanded vessels that shore people thought were liners, but when a man gets the ant of desire-to-see-what-it's-like stirring in his heart, he will wallow out to sea in a pail. The thing surpasses a man's love for his sweetheart. The great tank-steamer *Thunder Voice* had long been Flanagan's sweetheart, but he was far happier off Hatteras, watching this wretched little portmanteau boom down the slant of a wave.

The crew scraped acquaintance one with another gradually. Each man came ultimately to ask his neighbor what particular turn of ill-fortune or inherited deviltry caused him to try this voyage. When one frank, bold man saw another frank, bold man aboard, he smiled, and they became friends. There was not a mind on board the ship that was not fastened to the dangers of the coast of Cuba and taking wonder at this prospect and delight in it. Still, in jovial moments they termed each other accursed idiots.

At first there was some trouble in the engine-room, where there were many steel animals, for the most part painted red and in other places very shiny, bewildering, complex, incomprehensible to anyone who don't care, usually thumping, thumping, thumping with the monotony of a snore.

It seems that this engine was as whimsical as a gas-meter. The chief engineer was a fine old fellow with a grey moustache, but the engine told him that it didn't intend to budge until it felt better. He came to the bridge and said: "The blamed old thing has laid down on us, sir."

"Who was on duty?" roared the captain.

"The second, sir."

"Why didn't he call you?"

"Don't know, sir." Later the stokers had occasion to thank the stars that they were not second engineers.

The *Foundling* was soundly thrashed by the waves for loitering while the captain and the engineers fought the obstinate machinery. During this wait on the sea, the first gloom came to the faces of the company. The ocean is wide, and a ship is a small place for the feet, and an ill ship is worriment. Even when she was again under way, the gloom was still upon the crew. From time to time men went to the engine-room doors and, looking down, wanted to ask questions of the chief engineer, who slowly prowled to and fro and watched with careful eye his red-painted mysteries. No man wished to have a companion know that he was anxious, and so questions were caught at the lips. Perhaps none commented save the first mate, who remarked to the captain: "Wonder what the bally old thing will do, sir, when we're chased by a Spanish cruiser?"

The captain merely grinned. Later he looked over the side and said to himself with scorn: "Sixteen knots! Sixteen knots! Sixteen hinges on the inner gates of Hades! Sixteen knots! Seven is her gait, and nine if you crack her up to it."

There may never be a captain whose crew can't sniff his misgivings. They scent it as a herd scents the menace far through the trees and over the ridges. A captain that does not know that he is on a foundering ship sometimes can take his men to tea and buttered toast twelve minutes before the disaster; but let him fret for a moment in the loneliness of his cabin, and in no time it affects the liver of a distant and sensitive seaman. Even as Flanagan reflected on the *Foundling*, viewing her as a filibuster, word arrived that a winter of discontent had come to the stoke-room.

The captain knew that it requires sky to give a man courage. He sent for a stoker and talked to him on the bridge. The man, standing under the sky, instantly and shamefacedly denied all knowledge of the business. Nevertheless a jaw had presently to be broken by a fist because the *Foundling* could only steam nine knots and because the stoke-room has no sky, no wind, no bright horizon.

When the *Foundling* was somewhere off Savannah a blow came from the northeast, and the steamer, headed southeast, rolled like a boiling potato. The first mate was a fine officer, and so a wave crashed him into the deck-house and broke his arm. The cook was a good cook, and so the heave of the ship flung him heels over head with a pot of boiling water and caused him to lose interest in everything save his legs. "By the piper," said Flanagan to himself, "this filibustering is no trick with cards."

Later there was more trouble in the stoke-room. All the stokers participated save the one with a broken jaw, who had become discouraged. The captain had an excellent chest development. When he went aft, roaring, it was plain that a man could beat carpets with a voice like that one.

II

One night the *Foundling* was off the southern coast of Florida and running at half speed toward the shore. The captain was on the bridge. "Four flashes at intervals of one minute," he said to himself, gazing steadfastly toward the beach. Suddenly a yellow eye opened in the black face of the night and looked at the *Foundling* and closed again. The captain studied his watch and the shore. Three times more the eye opened and looked at the *Foundling* and closed again. The captain called to the vague figures on the deck below him. "Answer it." The flash of a light from the bow of the steamer displayed for a moment in golden color the crests of the inriding waves.

The *Foundling* lay to and waited. The long swells rolled her gracefully, and her two stub masts reaching into the darkness swung with the solemnity of batons timing a dirge. When the ship had left Boston she had been as encrusted with ice as a Dakota stage-driver's beard; but now the gentle wind of Florida softly swayed the lock on the forehead of the coatless Flanagan, and he lit a new cigar without troubling to make a shield of his hands.

Finally a dark boat came plashing over the waves. As it came very near, the captain leaned forward and perceived that the men in her rowed like seamstresses, and at the same time a voice hailed him in bad English. "It's a dead sure connection," said he to himself.

At sea, to load two hundred thousand rounds of rifle ammunition, seven hundred and fifty rifles, two rapid-fire field guns with a hundred shells, forty bundles of machetes, and a hundred pounds of dynamite, from yawls and by men who are not born stevedores, and in a heavy ground swell and with the searchlight of a United States cruiser sometimes flashing like lightning in the sky to the southward, is no business for a Sunday-school class. When at last the *Foundling* was steaming for the open over the grey sea at dawn, there was not a man of the forty come aboard from the Florida shore, nor of the fifteen sailed from Boston, who was not glad, standing with his hair matted to his forehead with sweat, smiling at the broad wake of the *Foundling* and the dim streak on the horizon which was Florida.

But there is a point of the compass in these waters which men call the northeast. When the strong winds come from that direction they kick up a turmoil that is not good for a *Foundling* stuffed with coal and war-stores. In the gale which came, this ship was no more than a drunken soldier.

The Cuban leader, standing on the bridge with the captain, was presently informed that of his men thirty-nine out of a possible thirty-nine were seasick. And in truth they were seasick. There are degrees in this complaint, but that matter was waived between them. They were all sick to the limits. They strewed the deck in every posture of human anguish; and when the *Foundling* ducked and water came sluicing down from the bows, they let it sluice. They were satisfied if they could keep their heads clear of the wash; and if they could not keep their heads clear of the wash, they didn't care. Presently the *Foundling* swung her course to the southeast, and the waves pounded her broadside. The patriots were all ordered below decks, and there they howled and measured their misery one against another. All day the *Foundling* plopped and floundered over a blazing bright meadow of an ocean whereon the white foam was like flowers.

The captain on the bridge mused and studied the bare horizon. "Hell!" said he to himself, and the word was more in amazement than in indignation or sorrow. "Thirty-nine seasick passengers, the mate with a broken arm, a stoker with a broken jaw, the cook with a pair of scalded legs, and an engine likely to be taken with all these diseases, if not more. If I get back to a home port with a spoke of the wheel gripped in my hands, it'll be fair luck."

There is a kind of corn whisky bred in Florida which the natives declare is potent in the proportion of seven fights to a drink. Some of the Cuban volunteers had had the forethought to bring a small quantity of this whisky aboard with them, and being now in the fire-room and seasick, and feeling that they would not care to drink liquor for two or three years to come, they gracefully tendered their portions to the stokers. The stokers accepted these gifts without avidity, but with a certain earnestness of manner.

As they were stokers and toiling, the whirl of emotion was delayed, but it arrived ultimately and with emphasis. One stoker called another stoker a weird name, and the latter, righteously inflamed at it, smote his mate with an iron shovel, and the man fell headlong over a heap of coal which crashed gently while piece after piece rattled down upon the deck.

A third stoker was providentially enraged at the scene, and assailed the second stoker. They fought for some moments, while the seasick Cubans sprawled on the deck watched with languid rolling glances the ferocity of this scuffle. One was so indifferent to the strategic importance of the space he occupied that he was kicked in the shins.

When the second engineer came to separate the combatants, he was sincere in his efforts, and he came near to disabling them for life.

The captain said, "I'll go down there and——" But the leader

of the Cubans restrained him. "No, no," he cried, "you must not. We must treat them like children, very gently, all the time, you see, or else when we get back to a United States port they will—what you call—spring? Yes—spring the whole business. We must—jolly them. You see?"

"You mean," said the captain thoughtfully, "they are likely to get mad and give the expedition dead away when we reach port again unless we blarney them now?"

"Yes, yes," cried the Cuban leader, "unless we are so very gentle with them they will make many troubles afterward for us in the newspapers and then in court."

"Well, but I won't have my crew——" began the captain.

"But you must," interrupted the Cuban. "You must. It is the only thing. You are like the captain of a pirate ship. You see? Only you can't throw them overboard like him. You see?"

"Hum," said the captain, "this here filibustering business has got a lot to it when you come to look it over."

He called the fighting stokers to the bridge, and the three came meek and considerably battered. He was lecturing them soundly but sensibly, when he suddenly tripped a sentence and cried: "Here! Where's that other fellow? How does it come he wasn't in the fight?"

The row of stokers cried at once eagerly: "He's hurt, sir. He's got a broken jaw, sir."

"So he has. So he has," murmured the captain, much embarrassed.

And because of all these affairs the *Foundling* steamed toward Cuba with its crew in a sling, if one may be allowed to speak in that way.

III

At night the *Foundling* approached the coast like a thief. Her lights were muffled so that from the deck the sea shone with its own radiance, like the faint shimmer of some kinds of silk. The men on deck spoke in whispers, and even down in the fire-room the hidden stokers working before the blood-red furnace doors used no words and walked tip-toe. The stars were out in the blue-velvet sky, and their light with the soft shine of the sea caused the coast to appear black as the side of a coffin. The surf boomed in low thunder on the distant beach.

The *Foundling's* engines ceased their thumping for a time. She glided quietly forward until a bell chimed faintly in the engine-room. Then she paused with a flourish of phosphorescent waters.

"Give the signal," said the captain. Three times a flash of light went from the bow. There was a moment of waiting. Then an eye like the one on the coast of Florida opened and closed, opened and closed, opened and closed. The Cubans, grouped in a great shadow on deck, burst into a low chatter of delight. A hiss from their leader silenced them.

"Well?" said the captain.

"All right," said the leader.

At the giving of the word it was not apparent that anyone on board of the *Foundling* had ever been seasick. The boats were lowered swiftly, too swiftly. Boxes of cartridges were dragged from the hold and passed over the side with a rapidity that made men in the boats exclaim against it. They were being bombarded. When a boat headed for shore its rowers pulled like madmen. The captain paced slowly to and fro on the bridge. In the engine-room the engineers stood at their station, and in the stoke-hole the firemen fidgeted silently around the furnace doors.

On the bridge Flanagan reflected. "Oh, I don't know," he observed, "this filibustering business isn't so bad. Pretty soon I'll be off to sea again with nothing to do but some big lying when I get into port."

In one of the boats returning from shore came twelve Cuban officers, the greater number of them convalescing from wounds, while two or three of them had been ordered to America on commissions from the insurgents. The captain welcomed them, and assured them of a speedy and safe voyage.

Presently he went again to the bridge and scanned the horizon. The sea was lonely like the spaces amid the suns. The captain grinned and softly smote his chest. "It's dead easy," said he.

It was near the end of the cargo, and the men were breathing like spent horses, although their elation grew with each moment, when suddenly a voice spoke from the sky. It was not a loud voice, but the quality of it brought every man on deck to full stop and motionless, as if they had all been changed to wax. "Captain," said the man at the masthead, "there's a light to the west'ard, sir. Think it's a steamer, sir."

There was a still moment until the captain called: "Well, keep your eye on it now." Speaking to the deck, he said: "Go ahead with your unloading."

The second engineer went to the galley to borrow a tin cup. "Hear the news, second?" asked the cook. "Steamer coming up from the west'ard."

"Gee!" said the second engineer. In the engine-room he said to the chief: "Steamer coming up to the west'ard, sir." The chief engineer began to test various little machines with which his domain was decorated. Finally he addressed the stoke-room. "Boys, I want you to look sharp now. There's a steamer coming up to the west'ard."

"All right, sir," said the stoke-room.

From time to time the captain hailed the masthead. "How is she now?"

"Seems to be coming down on us pretty fast, sir."

The Cuban leader came anxiously to the captain. "Do you think we can save all the cargo? It is rather delicate business. No?"

"Go ahead," said Flanagan. "Fire away. I'll wait for you."

There continued the hurried shuffling of feet on deck and the low cries of the men unloading the cargo. In the engine-room the chief and his assistant were staring at the gong. In the stoke-room the firemen breathed through their teeth. A shovel slipped from where it leaned against the side and banged on the floor. The stokers started and looked around quickly.

Climbing to the rail and holding on to a stay, the captain gazed westward. A light had raised out of the deep. After watching this light for a time he called to the Cuban leader, "Well, as soon as you're ready now, we might as well be skipping out."

Finally the Cuban leader told him: "Well, this is the last load. As soon as the boats come back you can be off."

"Shan't wait for all the boats," said the captain. "That fellow is too close." As the second boat came aboard, the *Foundling* turned, and like a black shadow stole seaward to cross the bows of the oncoming steamer. "Waited about ten minutes too long," said the captain to himself.

Suddenly the light in the west vanished. "Hum," said Flanagan, "he's up to some meanness." Everyone outside of the engine-rooms was set on watch. The *Foundling*, going at full speed into the northeast, slashed a wonderful trail of blue silver on the dark bosom of the sea.

A man on deck cried out hurriedly, "There she is, sir." Many eyes searched the western gloom, and one after another the glances of the men found a tiny black shadow on the deep with a line of white beneath it. "He couldn't be heading better if he had a line to us," said Flanagan.

There was a thin flash of red in the darkness. It was long and keen like a crimson rapier. A short, sharp report sounded, and then a shot whined swiftly in the air and blipped into the sea. The captain had been about to take a bite of plug tobacco at the beginning of this incident, and his arm was raised. He remained like a frozen figure while the shot whined, and then, as it blipped into the sea, his hand went to his mouth and he bit the plug. He looked wide-eyed at the shadow with its line of white.

The senior Cuban officer came hurriedly to the bridge. "It is no good to surrender," he cried; "they would only shoot or hang all of us."

There was another thin red flash and a report. A loud whirring noise passed over the ship.

"I'm not going to surrender," said the captain, hanging with both hands to the rail. He appeared like a man whose traditions of peace are clinched in his heart. He was as astonished as if his hat had turned into a dog. Presently he wheeled quickly and said: "What kind of a gun is that?"

"It is a one-pounder," cried the Cuban officer. "The boat is one of those little gunboats made from a yacht. You see?"

"Well, if it's only a yawl, he'll sink us in five more minutes," said Flanagan. For a moment he looked helplessly off at the horizon. His under jaw hung low. But, a moment later, something touched him like a stiletto point of inspiration. He leaped to the pilot-house and roared at the man at the wheel. The *Foundling* sheered suddenly to starboard, made a clumsy turn, and Flanagan was bellowing through the tube to the engine-room before anybody discovered that the old basket was heading straight for the Spanish gunboat. The ship lunged forward like a draught-horse on the gallop.

This strange manœuver by the *Foundling* first dealt conster-nation on board. Men instinctively crouched on the instant, and then swore their supreme oath, which was unheard by their own ears.

Later, the manœuver of the *Foundling* dealt consternation on board of the gunboat. She had been going victoriously forward, dim-eyed from the fury of her pursuit. Then this tall threatening shape had suddenly loomed over her like a giant apparition.

The people on board the *Foundling* heard panic shouts, hoarse orders. The little gunboat was paralyzed with astonishment.

Suddenly Flanagan yelled with rage and sprang for the wheel. The helmsman had turned his eyes away. As the captain whirled the wheel far to starboard he heard a crunch as the *Found-ling*, lifted on a wave, smashed her shoulder against the gun-boat, and he saw shooting past a little launch sort of a thing with men on her that ran this way and that way. The Cuban officers, joined by the cook and a seaman, emptied their revolvers into the surprised terror of the seas.

There was naturally no pursuit. Under comfortable speed the *Foundling* stood to the northward.

The captain went to his berth chuckling. "There, by God," he said. "There, now!"

IV

When Flanagan came again on deck, the first mate, his arm in a sling, walked the bridge. Flanagan was smiling a wide smile. The bridge of the *Foundling* was dipping afar and then afar. With each lunge of the little steamer the water seethed and boomed alongside and the spray dashed high and swiftly.

"Well," said Flanagan, inflating himself, "we've had a great deal of a time, and we've come through it all right, and thank heaven it is all over."

The sky in the northeast was of a dull brick-red in tone,

shaded here and there by black masses that billowed out in some fashion from the flat heavens.

"Look there," said the mate.

"Hum," said the captain. "Looks like a blow, don't it?"

Later the surface of the water rippled and flickered in the preliminary wind. The sea had become the color of lead. The swashing sound of the waves on the sides of the *Foundling* was now provided with some manner of ominous significance. The men's shouts were hoarse.

A squall struck the *Foundling* on her starboard quarter, and she leaned under the force of it as if she were never to return to the even keel. "I'll be glad when we get in," said the mate. "I'm going to quit then. I've got enough."

"Hell!" said the beaming Flanagan.

The steamer crawled on into the northwest. The white water sweeping out from her deadened the chug-chug-chug of the tired old engines.

Once, when the boat careened, she laid her shoulder flat on the sea and rested in that manner. The mate, looking down the bridge, which slanted more than a coal-chute, whistled softly to himself. Slowly, heavily, the *Foundling* arose to meet another sea.

At night waves thundered mightily on the bows of the steamer, and water lit with the beautiful phosphorescent glamour went boiling and howling along the deck.

By good fortune the chief engineer crawled safely, but utterly drenched, to the galley for coffee. "Well, how goes it, chief?" said the cook, standing with his fat arms folded in order to prove that he could balance himself under any condition.

The engineer shook his head dejectedly. "This old biscuit-box will never see port again. Why, she'll fall to pieces."

Finally at night the captain said: "Launch the boats." The Cubans hovered about him. "Is the ship going to sink?" The captain addressed them politely. "Gentlemen, we are in trouble, but all I ask of you is that you do just what I tell you, and no harm will come to anybody."

The mate directed the lowering of the first boat, and the men performed this task with all decency, like people at the side of a grave.

A young oiler came to the captain. "The chief sends word, sir, that the water is almost up to the fires."

"Keep at it as long as you can."

"Keep at it as long as we can, sir."

Flanagan took the senior Cuban officer to the rail, and, as the steamer sheered high on a great sea, showed him a yellow dot on the horizon. It was smaller than a needle when its point is toward you.

"There," said the captain. The wind-driven spray was lashing his face. "That's Jupiter Light on the Florida coast. Put your men in the boat we've just launched, and the mate will take you to that light."

Afterward Flanagan turned to the chief engineer. "We can never beach her," said the old man. "The stokers have got to quit in a minute." Tears were in his eyes.

The *Foundling* was a wounded thing. She lay on the water with gasping engines, and each wave resembled her death blow.

Now the way of a good ship on the sea is finer than swordplay. But this is when she is alive. If a time comes that the ship dies, then her way is the way of a floating old glove, and she has that much vim, spirit, buoyancy. At this time many men on the *Foundling* suddenly came to know that they were clinging to a corpse.

The captain went to the stoke-room, and what he saw as he swung down the companion suddenly turned him hesitant and dumb. He had served the sea for many years, but this fire-room said something to him which he had not heard in his other voyages. Water was swirling to and fro with the roll of the ship, fuming greasily around half-strangled machinery that still attempted to perform its duty. Steam arose from the water, and through its clouds shone the red glare of the dying fires. As for the stokers, death might have been with silence in this room. One lay in his berth, his hands under his head, staring moodily at the wall. One sat near the foot of the companion, his face hidden in his arms. One leaned against the side, and gazed at the snarling water as it rose and its mad eddies among the machinery. In the unholy red light and grey mist of this stifling dim inferno they were strange figures with their silence and their immobility. The wretched *Foundling* groaned deeply as she lifted, and groaned deeply as she sank into the trough, while hurried waves then thundered over her with the noise of land-slides. The terrified machinery was making gestures.

But Flanagan took control of himself suddenly, and then he stirred the fire-room. The stillness had been so unearthly that he was not altogether inapprehensive of strange and grim deeds when he charged into them, but precisely as they had submitted to the sea so they submitted to Flanagan. For a moment they rolled their eyes like hurt cows, but they obeyed the Voice. The situation simply required a Voice.

When the captain returned to the deck the hue of this fire-room was in his mind, and then he understood doom and its weight and complexion.

When finally the *Foundling* sank she shifted and settled as calmly as an animal curls down in the bush grass. Away over the waves two bobbing boats paused to witness this quiet death. It was a slow manœuver, altogether without the pageantry of up-roar, but it flashed pallor into the faces of all men who saw it, and they groaned when they said: "There she goes!" Suddenly the captain whirled and knocked his head on the gunwale. He sobbed for a time, and then he sobbed and swore also.

There was a dance at the Imperial Inn. During the evening some irresponsible young men came from the beach bringing the statement that several boatloads of people had been perceived off shore. It was a charming dance, and none cared to take time to believe this tale. The fountain in the courtyard plashed softly, and couple after couple paraded through the aisles of palms where lamps with red shades threw a rose light upon the gleam-ing leaves. High on some balcony a mocking-bird called into the evening. The band played its waltzes slumberously, and its music to the people among the palms came faintly and like the melodies in dreams.

Sometimes a woman said: "Oh, it is not really true, is it, that there was a wreck out at sea?"

A man usually said: "No, of course not."

At last, however, a youth came violently from the beach. He was triumphant in manner. "They're out there," he cried. "A whole boatload!" He received eager attention, and he told all that he supposed. His news destroyed the dance. After a time the band was playing beautifully to space. The guests had donned wraps and hurried to the beach. One little girl cried: "Oh, mamma, may I go too?" Being refused permission, she pouted.

As they came from the shelter of the great hotel, the wind was blowing swiftly from the sea, and at intervals a breaker shone livid. The women shuddered, and their bending companions seized opportunity to draw the cloaks closer. The sand of the beach was wet, and dainty slippers made imprints in it clear and deep.

"Oh, dear," said a girl, "supposin' they were out there drowning while we were dancing!"

"Oh, nonsense!" said her younger brother; "that don't happen."

"Well, it might, you know, Roger. How can you tell?"

A man who was not her brother gazed at her then with profound admiration. Later she complained of the damp sand, and drawing back her skirts, looked ruefully at her little feet.

A mother's son was venturing too near to the water in his interest and excitement. Occasionally she cautioned and reproached him from the background.

Save for the white glare of the breakers, the sea was a great wind-crossed void. From the throng of charming women floated the perfume of many flowers. Later there floated to them a body with a calm face of an Irish type. The expedition of the *Foundling* will never be historic.

THE BRIDE COMES TO YELLOW SKY

I

THE great Pullman was whirling onward with such dignity of motion that a glance from the window seemed simply to prove that the plains of Texas were pouring eastward. Vast flats of green grass, dull-hued spaces of mesquite and cactus, little groups of frame houses, woods of light and tender trees, all were sweeping into the east, sweeping over the horizon, a precipice.

A newly married pair had boarded this coach at San Antonio. The man's face was reddened from many days in the wind and sun, and a direct result of his new black clothes was that his brick-colored hands were constantly performing in a most conscious fashion. From time to time he looked down respectfully at his attire. He sat with a hand on each knee, like a man waiting in a barber's shop. The glances he devoted to other passengers were furtive and shy.

The bride was not pretty, nor was she very young. She wore a dress of blue cashmere, with small reservations of velvet here and there and with steel buttons abounding. She continually twisted her head to regard her puff sleeves, very stiff, straight, and high. They embarrassed her. It was quite apparent that she had cooked, and that she expected to cook, dutifully. The blushes caused by the careless scrutiny of some passengers as she had entered the car were strange to see upon this plain, under-class countenance, which was drawn in placid, almost emotionless lines.

They were evidently very happy. "Ever been in a parlor-car before?" he asked, smiling with delight.

"No," she answered. "I never was. It's fine, ain't it?"

"Great! And then after a while we'll go forward to the diner and get a big lay-out. Finest meal in the world. Charge a dollar."

"Oh, do they?" cried the bride. "Charge a dollar? Why, that's too much—for us—ain't it, Jack?"

"Not this trip, anyhow," he answered bravely. "We're going to go the whole thing."

Later, he explained to her about the trains. "You see, it's a thousand miles from one end of Texas to the other, and this train runs right across it and never stops but four times." He had the pride of an owner. He pointed out to her the dazzling fittings of the coach, and in truth her eyes opened wider as she contemplated the sea-green figured velvet, the shining brass, silver, and glass, the wood that gleamed as darkly brilliant as the surface of a pool of oil. At one end a bronze figure sturdily held a support for a separated chamber, and at convenient places on the ceiling were frescoes in olive and silver.

To the minds of the pair, their surroundings reflected the glory of their marriage that morning in San Antonio. This was the environment of their new estate, and the man's face in particular beamed with an elation that made him appear ridiculous to the negro porter. This individual at times surveyed them from afar with an amused and superior grin. On other occasions he bullied them with skill in ways that did not make it exactly plain to them that they were being bullied. He subtly used all the manners of the most unconquerable kind of snobbery. He oppressed them, but of this oppression they had small knowledge, and they speedily forgot that infrequently a number of travelers covered them with stares of derisive enjoyment. Historically there was supposed to be something infinitely humorous in their situation.

"We are due in Yellow Sky at 3.42," he said, looking tenderly into her eyes.

"Oh, are we?" she said, as if she had not been aware of it. To evince surprise at her husband's statement was part of her wifely amiability. She took from a pocket a little silver watch, and as she held it before her and stared at it with a frown of attention, the new husband's face shone.

"I bought it in San Anton' from a friend of mine," he told her gleefully.

"It's seventeen minutes past twelve," she said, looking up at him with a kind of shy and clumsy coquetry. A passenger, noting this play, grew excessively sardonic, and winked at himself in one of the numerous mirrors.

At last they went to the dining-car. Two rows of negro waiters in glowing white suits surveyed their entrance with the interest and also the equanimity of men who had been forewarned. The pair fell to the lot of a waiter who happened to feel pleasure in steering them through their meal. He viewed them with the manner of a fatherly pilot, his countenance radiant with benevolence. The patronage entwined with the ordinary deference was not plain to them. And yet as they returned to their coach they showed in their faces a sense of escape.

To the left, miles down a long purple slope, was a little ribbon of mist where moved the keening Rio Grande. The train was approaching it at an angle, and the apex was Yellow Sky. Presently it was apparent that as the distance from Yellow Sky grew shorter, the husband became commensurately restless. His brick-red hands were more insistent in their prominence. Occasionally he was even rather absent-minded and far-away when the bride leaned forward and addressed him.

As a matter of truth, Jack Potter was beginning to find the shadow of a deed weigh upon him like a leaden slab. He, the town marshal of Yellow Sky, a man known, liked, and feared in his corner, a prominent person, had gone to San Antonio to meet a girl he believed he loved, and there, after the usual prayers, had actually induced her to marry him, without consulting Yellow Sky for any part of the transaction. He was now bringing his bride before an innocent and unsuspecting community.

Of course, people in Yellow Sky married as it pleased them in accordance with a general custom; but such was Potter's thought of his duty to his friends, or of their idea of his duty, or of an unspoken form which does not control men in these matters, that he felt he was heinous. He had committed an extraordinary crime. Face to face with this girl in San Antonio, and spurred by his sharp impulse, he had gone headlong over all the social hedges. At San Antonio he was like a man hidden in the dark. A knife to sever any friendly duty, any form, was easy to his hand in that remote city. But the hour of Yellow Sky, the hour of daylight, was approaching.

He knew full well that his marriage was an important thing to his town. It could only be exceeded by the burning of the new hotel. His friends would not forgive him. Frequently he had reflected on the advisability of telling them by telegraph, but a new cowardice had been upon him. He feared to do it. And now the train was hurrying him toward a scene of amazement, glee, reproach. He glanced out of the window at the line of haze swinging slowly in toward the train.

Yellow Sky had a kind of brass band which played painfully to the delight of the populace. He laughed without heart as he thought of it. If the citizens could dream of his prospective arrival with his bride, they would parade the band at the station and escort them, amid cheers and laughing congratulations, to his adobe home.

He resolved that he would use all the devices of speed and plains-craft in making the journey from the station to his house. Once within that safe citadel, he could issue some sort of a vocal bulletin, and then not go among the citizens until they had time to wear off a little of their enthusiasm.

The bride looked anxiously at him. "What's worrying you, Jack?"

He laughed again. "I'm not worrying, girl. I'm only thinking of Yellow Sky."

, She flushed in comprehension.

A sense of mutual guilt invaded their minds and developed a finer tenderness. They looked at each other with eyes softly aglow. But Potter often laughed the same nervous laugh. The flush upon the bride's face seemed quite permanent.

The traitor to the feelings of Yellow Sky narrowly watched the speeding landscape. "We're nearly there," he said.

Presently the porter came and announced the proximity of Potter's home. He held a brush in his hand and, with all his airy superiority gone, he brushed Potter's new clothes as the latter slowly turned this way and that way. Potter fumbled out a coin and gave it to the porter as he had seen others do. It was a heavy and muscle-bound business, as that of a man shoeing his first horse.

The porter took their bag, and as the train began to slow they moved forward to the hooded platform of the car. Presently the two engines and their long string of coaches rushed into the station of Yellow Sky.

"They have to take water here," said Potter, from a constricted throat and in mournful cadence as one announcing death. Before the train stopped his eye had swept the length of the platform, and he was glad and astonished to see there was none upon it but the station-agent, who, with a slightly hurried and anxious air, was walking toward the water-tanks. When the train had halted, the porter alighted first and placed in position a little temporary step.

"Come on, girl," said Potter hoarsely. As he helped her down they each laughed on a false note. He took the bag from the negro, and bade his wife cling to his arm. As they slunk rapidly away, his hang-dog glance perceived that they were unloading the two trunks, and also that the station-agent far ahead near the baggage-car had turned and was running toward him, making gestures. He laughed, and groaned as he laughed, when he noted the first effect of his marital bliss upon Yellow Sky. He gripped his wife's arm firmly to his side, and they fled. Behind them the porter stood chuckling fatuously.

II

The California Express on the Southern Railway was due at Yellow Sky in twenty-one minutes. There were six men at the bar of the Weary Gentleman saloon. One was a drummer who talked a great deal and rapidly; three were Texans who did not care to talk at that time; and two were Mexican sheep-herders who did not talk as a general practice in the Weary Gentleman saloon. The bar-keeper's dog lay on the board-walk that crossed in front of the door. His head was on his paws, and he glanced drowsily here and there with the constant vigilance of a dog that is kicked on occasion. Across the sandy street were some vivid green grass plots, so wonderful in appearance amid the sands that burned near them in a blazing sun that they caused a doubt in the mind. They exactly resembled the grass mats used to represent lawns on the stage. At the cooler end of the railway station a man without a coat sat in a tilted chair and smoked his pipe. The fresh-cut bank of the Rio Grande circled near the town, and there could be seen beyond it a great plum-colored plain of mesquite.

Save for the busy drummer and his companions in the saloon, Yellow Sky was dozing. The new-comer leaned gracefully upon the bar, and recited many tales with the confidence of a bard who has come upon a new field.

"——and at the moment that the old man fell down stairs with the bureau in his arms, the old woman was coming up with two scuttles of coal, and, of course——"

The drummer's tale was interrupted by a young man who suddenly appeared in the open door. He cried: "Scratchy Wilson's drunk, and has turned loose with both hands." The two Mexicans at once set down their glasses and faded out of the rear entrance of the saloon.

The drummer, innocent and jocular, answered: "All right, old man. S'pose he has. Come in and have a drink, anyhow."

But the information had made such an obvious cleft in every skull in the room that the drummer was obliged to see its importance. All had become instantly morose. "Say," said he, mystified, "what is this?" His three companions made the introductory gesture of eloquent speech, but the young man at the door forestalled them.

"It means, my friend," he answered, as he came into the saloon, "that for the next two hours this town won't be a health resort."

The bar-keeper went to the door and locked and barred it. Reaching out of the window, he pulled in heavy wooden shutters and barred them. Immediately a solemn, chapel-like gloom was upon the place. The drummer was looking from one to another.

"But say," he cried, "what is this, anyhow? You don't mean there is going to be a gun-fight?"

"Don't know whether there'll be a fight or not," answered one man grimly. "But there'll be some shootin'—some good shootin'."

The young man who had warned them waved his hand. "Oh, there'll be a fight fast enough, if anyone wants it. Anybody can get a fight out there in the street. There's a fight just waiting."

The drummer seemed to be swayed between the interest of a foreigner and a perception of personal danger.

"What did you say his name was?" he asked.

"Scratchy Wilson," they answered in chorus.

"And will he kill anybody? What are you going to do? Does this happen often? Does he rampage around like this once a week or so? Can he break in that door?"

"No, he can't break down that door," replied the bar-keeper. "He's tried it three times. But when he comes you'd better lay down on the floor, stranger. He's dead sure to shoot at it, and a bullet may come through."

Thereafter the drummer kept a strict eye upon the door. The time had not yet been called for him to hug the floor, but as a minor precaution he sidled near to the wall. "Will he kill anybody?" he said again.

The men laughed low and scornfully at the question.

"He's out to shoot, and he's out for trouble. Don't see any good in experimentin' with him."

"But what do you do in a case like this? What do you do?"

A man responded: "Why, he and Jack Potter——"

But, in chorus, the other men interrupted: "Jack Potter's in San Anton'."

"Well, who is he? What's he got to do with it?"

"Oh, he's the town marshal. He goes out and fights Scratchy when he gets on one of these tears."

"Wow," said the drummer, mopping his brow. "Nice job he's got."

The voices had toned away to mere whisperings. The drummer wished to ask further questions which were born of an increasing anxiety and bewilderment; but when he attempted them, the men merely looked at him in irritation and motioned him to remain silent. A tense waiting hush was upon them. In the deep shadows of the room their eyes shone as they listened for sounds from the street. One man made three gestures at the bar-keeper, and the latter, moving like a ghost, handed him a glass and a bottle. The man poured a full glass of whisky, and set down the bottle noiselessly. He gulped the whisky in a swallow, and turned again toward the door in immovable silence.

The drummer saw that the bar-keeper, without a sound, had taken a Winchester from beneath the bar. Later he saw this individual beckoning to him, so he tiptoed across the room.

"You better come with me back of the bar."

"No, thanks," said the drummer, perspiring. "I'd rather be where I can make a break for the back door."

Whereupon the man of bottles made a kindly but peremptory gesture. The drummer obeyed it, and finding himself seated on a box with his head below the level of the bar, balm was laid upon his soul at sight of various zinc and copper fittings that bore a resemblance to armor-plate. The bar-keeper took a seat comfortably upon an adjacent box.

"You see," he whispered, "this here Scratchy Wilson is a wonder with a gun—a perfect wonder—and when he goes on the war trail, we hunt our holes—naturally. He's about the last one of the old gang that used to hang out along the river here. He's a terror when he's drunk. When he's sober he's all right—kind of simple—wouldn't hurt a fly—nicest fellow in town. But when he's drunk—whoo!"

There were periods of stillness. "I wish Jack Potter was back from San Anton'," said the bar-keeper. "He shot Wilson up once —in the leg—and he would sail in and pull out the kinks in this thing."

Presently they heard from a distance the sound of a shot, followed by three wild yowls. It instantly removed a bond from the men in the darkened saloon. There was a shuffling of feet. They looked at each other. "Here he comes," they said.

III

A man in a maroon-colored flannel shirt, which had been purchased for purposes of decoration and made, principally, by some Jewish women on the east side of New York, rounded a corner and walked into the middle of the main street of Yellow Sky. In either hand the man held a long, heavy blue-black revolver. Often he yelled, and these cries rang through a semblance of a deserted village, shrilly flying over the roofs in a volume that seemed to have no relation to the ordinary vocal strength of a

man. It was as if the surrounding stillness formed the arch of a
tomb over him. These cries of ferocious challenge rang against
walls of silence. And his boots had red tops with gilded imprints,
of the kind beloved in winter by little sledding boys on the
hillsides of New England.

The man's face flamed in a rage begot of whisky. His eyes,
rolling and yet keen for ambush, hunted the still door-ways and
windows. He walked with the creeping movement of the midnight cat. As it occurred to him, he roared menacing information.
The long revolvers in his hands were as easy as straws; they were
moved with an electric swiftness. The little fingers of each hand
played sometimes in a musician's way. Plain from the low collar
of the shirt, the cords of his neck straightened and sank, straightened and sank, as passion moved him. The only sounds were his
terrible invitations. The calm adobes preserved their demeanor at
the passing of this small thing in the middle of the street.

There was no offer of fight; no offer of fight. The man called
to the sky. There were no attractions. He bellowed and fumed
and swayed his revolvers here and everywhere.

The dog of the bar-keeper of the Weary Gentleman saloon had
not appreciated the advance of events. He yet lay dozing in front
of his master's door. At sight of the dog, the man paused and
raised his revolver humorously. At sight of the man, the dog
sprang up and walked diagonally away, with a sullen head and
growling. The man yelled, and the dog broke into a gallop. As it
was about to enter an alley, there was a loud noise, a whistling,
and something spat the ground directly before it. The dog
screamed, and, wheeling in terror, galloped headlong in a new
direction. Again there was a noise, a whistling, and sand was
kicked viciously before it. Fear-stricken, the dog turned and
flurried like an animal in a pen. The man stood laughing, his
weapons at his hips.

Ultimately the man was attracted by the closed door of the
Weary Gentleman saloon. He went to it, and hammering with a
revolver, demanded drink.

The door remaining imperturbable, he picked a bit of paper
from the walk and nailed it to the framework with a knife. He
then turned his back contemptuously upon this popular resort,
and walking to the opposite side of the street, and spinning there

on his heel quickly and lithely, fired at the bit of paper. He missed it by a half inch. He swore at himself, and went away. Later, he comfortably fusilladed the windows of his most intimate friend. The man was playing with this town. It was a toy for him.

But still there was no offer of fight. The name of Jack Potter, his ancient antagonist, entered his mind, and he concluded that it would be a glad thing if he should go to Potter's house and by bombardment induce him to come out and fight. He moved in the direction of his desire, chanting Apache scalp-music.

When he arrived at it, Potter's house presented the same still, calm front as had the other adobes. Taking up a strategic position, the man howled a challenge. But this house regarded him as might a great stone god. It gave no sign. After a decent wait, the man howled further challenges, mingling with them wonderful epithets.

Presently there came the spectacle of a man churning himself into deepest rage over the immobility of a house. He fumed at it as the winter wind attacks a prairie cabin in the North. To the distance there should have gone the sound of a tumult like the fighting of two hundred Mexicans. As necessity bade him, he paused for breath or to reload his revolvers.

IV

Potter and his bride walked sheepishly and with speed. Sometimes they laughed together shamefacedly and low.

"Next corner, dear," he said finally.

They put forth the efforts of a pair walking bowed against a strong wind. Potter was about to raise a finger to point the first appearance of the new home when, as they circled the corner, they came face to face with a man in a maroon-colored shirt who was feverishly pushing cartridges into a large revolver. Upon the instant the man dropped this revolver to the ground, and, like lightning, whipped another from its holster. The second weapon was aimed at the bridegroom's chest.

There was a silence. Potter's mouth seemed to be merely a

grave for his tongue. He exhibited an instinct to at once loosen his arm from the woman's grip, and he dropped the bag to the sand. As for the bride, her face had gone as yellow as old cloth. She was a slave to hideous rites gazing at the apparitional snake.

The two men faced each other at a distance of three paces. He of the revolver smiled with a new and quiet ferocity. "Tried to sneak up on me," he said. "Tried to sneak up on me!" His eyes grew more baleful. As Potter made a slight movement, the man thrust his revolver venomously forward. "No, don't you do it, Jack Potter. Don't you move a finger toward a gun just yet. Don't you move an eyelash. The time has come for me to settle with you, and I'm goin' to do it my own way and loaf along with no interferin'. So if you don't want a gun bent on you, just mind what I tell you."

Potter looked at his enemy. "I ain't got a gun on me, Scratchy," he said. "Honest, I ain't." He was stiffening and steadying, but yet somewhere at the back of his mind a vision of the Pullman floated, the sea-green figured velvet, the shining brass, silver, and glass, the wood that gleamed as darkly brilliant as the surface of a pool of oil—all the glory of the marriage, the environment of the new estate. "You know I fight when it comes to fighting, Scratchy Wilson, but I ain't got a gun on me. You'll have to do all the shootin' yourself."

His enemy's face went livid. He stepped forward and lashed his weapon to and fro before Potter's chest. "Don't you tell me you ain't got no gun on you, you whelp. Don't tell me no lie like that. There ain't a man in Texas ever seen you without no gun. Don't take me for no kid." His eyes blazed with light, and his throat worked like a pump.

"I ain't takin' you for no kid," answered Potter. His heels had not moved an inch backward. "I'm takin' you for a —— fool. I tell you I ain't got a gun, and I ain't. If you're goin' to shoot me up, you better begin now. You'll never get a chance like this again."

So much enforced reasoning had told on Wilson's rage. He was calmer. "If you ain't got a gun, why ain't you got a gun?" he sneered. "Been to Sunday-school?"

"I ain't got a gun because I've just come from San Anton' with my wife. I'm married," said Potter. "And if I'd thought there was going to be any galoots like you prowling around when I brought my wife home, I'd had a gun, and don't you forget it."

"Married!" said Scratchy, not at all comprehending.

"Yes, married. I'm married," said Potter distinctly.

"Married?" said Scratchy. Seemingly for the first time he saw the drooping drowning woman at the other man's side. "No!" he said. He was like a creature allowed a glimpse of another world. He moved a pace backward, and his arm with the revolver dropped to his side. "Is this—is this the lady?" he asked.

"Yes, this is the lady," answered Potter.

There was another period of silence.

"Well," said Wilson at last, slowly, "I s'pose it's all off now."

"It's all off if you say so, Scratchy. You know I didn't make the trouble." Potter lifted his valise.

"Well, I 'low it's off, Jack," said Wilson. He was looking at the ground. "Married!" He was not a student of chivalry; it was merely that in the presence of this foreign condition he was a simple child of the earlier plains. He picked up his starboard revolver, and placing both weapons in their holsters, he went away. His feet made funnel-shaped tracks in the heavy sand.

DEATH AND THE CHILD

I

THE peasants who were streaming down the mountain trail had in their sharp terror evidently lost their ability to count. The cattle and the huge round bundles seemed to suffice to the minds of the crowd if there were now two in each case where there had been three. This brown stream poured on with a constant wastage of goods and beasts. A goat fell behind to scout the dried grass, and its owner, howling, flogging his donkeys, passed far ahead. A colt, suddenly frightened, made a stumbling charge up the hill-side. The expenditure was always profligate and always unnamed, unnoted. It was as if fear was a river, and this horde had simply been caught in the torrent, man tumbling over beast, beast over man, as helpless in it as the logs that fall and shoulder grindingly through the gorges of a lumber country. It was a freshet that might sear the face of the tall quiet mountain; it might draw a livid line across the land, this downpour of fear with a thousand homes adrift in the current—men, women, babes, animals. From it there arose a constant babble of tongues, shrill, broken, and sometimes choking as from men drowning. Many made gestures, painting their agonies on the air with fingers that twirled swiftly.

The blue bay with its pointed ships, and the white town lay below them, distant, flat, serene. There was upon this vista a peace that a bird knows when high in air it surveys the world, a great calm thing rolling noiselessly toward the end of the mystery. Here on the height one felt the existence of the universe scornfully defining the pain in ten thousand minds. The sky was an arch of stolid sapphire. Even to the mountains raising their mighty shapes from the valley, this headlong rush of the fugitives was too minute. The sea, the sky, and the hills combined in their grandeur to term this misery inconsequent. Then, too, it sometimes happened that a face seen as it passed on the flood reflected curiously the spirit of them all, and still more. One saw then a woman of the opinion of the vaults above the clouds. When a child cried it cried always because of some adjacent misfortune, some discomfort of a pack-saddle or rudeness of an encircling arm. In the dismal melody of this flight there were often sounding chords of apathy. Into these preoccupied countenances one felt that needles could be thrust without purchasing a scream. The trail wound here and there as the sheep had willed in the making of it.

Although this throng seemed to prove that the whole of humanity was fleeing in one direction—with every tie severed that binds us to the soil—a young man was walking rapidly up the mountain, hastening to a side of the path from time to time to avoid some particularly wide rush of people and cattle. He looked at everything in agitation and pity. Frequently he called admonitions to maniacal fugitives, and at other moments he exchanged strange stares with the imperturbable ones. They seemed to him to wear merely the expressions of so many boulders rolling down the hill. He exhibited wonder and awe with his pitying glances.

Turning once toward the rear, he saw a man in the uniform of a lieutenant of infantry marching the same way. He waited then, subconsciously elate at a prospect of being able to make into words the emotion which heretofore had only been expressed in the flash of eyes and sensitive movements of his flexible mouth. He spoke to the officer in rapid French, waving his arms wildly, and often pointing with a dramatic finger. "Ah, this is too cruel, too cruel, too cruel. Is it not? I did not think it would be as bad as this. I did not think—God's mercy—I did not think at all. And yet I am a Greek. Or at least my father was a Greek. I did not come here to fight. I am really a correspondent, you see? I was to write for an Italian paper. I have been educated in Italy. I have spent nearly all my life in Italy. At the schools and universities. I knew nothing of war! I was a student—a student. I came here merely because my father was a Greek, and for his sake I thought of Greece—I loved Greece. But I did not dream——"

He paused, breathing heavily. His eyes glistened from that soft overflow which comes on occasion to the glance of a young woman. Eager, passionate, profoundly moved, his first words while facing the procession of fugitives had been an active definition of his own dimension, his personal relation to men, geography, life. Throughout he had preserved the fiery dignity of a tragedian.

The officer's manner at once deferred to this outburst. "Yes," he said, polite but mournful, "these poor people! These poor people! I do not know what is to become of these poor people."

The young man declaimed again. "I had no dream—I had no dream that it would be like this! This is too cruel! Too cruel! Now I want to be a soldier. Now I want to fight. Now I want to do battle for the land of my father." He made a sweeping gesture into the northwest.

The officer was also a young man, but he was very bronzed and steady. Above his high military collar of crimson cloth with one silver star upon it, appeared a profile stern, quiet, and confident, respecting fate, fearing only opinion. His clothes were covered with dust; the only bright spot was the flame of the crimson collar. At the violent cries of his companion he smiled as if to himself, meanwhile keeping his eyes fixed in a glance ahead.

From a land toward which their faces were bent came a continuous boom of artillery fire. It was sounding in regular measures like the beating of a colossal clock—a clock that was counting the seconds in the lives of the stars, and men had time to die between the ticks. Solemn, oracular, inexorable, the great seconds tolled over the hills as if God fronted this dial rimmed by the horizon. The soldier and the correspondent found themselves silent. The latter in particular was sunk in a great mournfulness, as if he had resolved willy-nilly to swing to the bottom of the abyss where dwell secrets of this kind, and had learned beforehand that all to be met there was cruelty and hopelessness. A strap of his bright new leather leggings came unfastened, and he bowed over it slowly, impressively, as one bending over the grave of a child.

Then suddenly, the reverberations mingled until one could not separate an explosion from another, and into the hubbub came the drawling sound of a leisurely musketry fire. Instantly, for some reason of cadence, the noise was irritating, silly, infantile. This uproar was childish. It forced the nerves to object, to protest against this racket which was as idle as the din of a lad with a drum.

The lieutenant lifted his finger and pointed. He spoke in vexed tones, as if he held the other man personally responsible for the noise. "Well, there!" he said. "If you wish for war you now have an opportunity magnificent."

The correspondent raised himself upon his toes. He tapped his chest with gloomy pride. "Yes! There is war! There is the war I wish to enter. I fling myself in. I am a Greek, a Greek, you understand. I wish to fight for my country. You know the way. Lead me. I offer myself." Struck with a sudden thought, he brought a case from his pocket, and extracting a card handed it to the officer with a bow. "My name is Peza," he said simply.

A strange smile passed over the soldier's face. There was pity and pride—the vanity of experience—and contempt in it. "Very well," he said, returning the bow. "If my company is in the middle of the fight I shall be glad for the honor of your companionship. If my company is not in the middle of the fight, I will make other arrangements for you."

Peza bowed once more, very stiffly, and correctly spoke his thanks. On the edge of what he took to be a great venture toward death, he discovered that he was annoyed at something in the lieutenant's tone. Things immediately assumed new and extraordinary proportions. The battle, the great carnival of woe, was sunk at once to an equation with a vexation by a stranger. He wanted to ask the lieutenant what was his meaning. He bowed again majestically; the lieutenant bowed. They flung a shadow of manners, of capering tinsel ceremony across a land that groaned, and it satisfied something within themselves completely.

In the meantime the river of fleeing villagers had changed to simply a last dropping of belated creatures, who fled past stammering and flinging their hands high. The two men had come to the top of the great hill. Before them was a green plain as level as an inland sea. It swept northward, and merged finally into a length of silvery mist. Upon the near part of this plain, and upon two grey treeless mountains at the sides of it, were little black lines from which floated slanting sheets of smoke. It was not a battle to the nerves. One could survey it with equanimity, as if it were a tea-table; but upon Peza's mind it struck a loud clanging blow. It was war. Edified, aghast, triumphant, he paused suddenly, his lips apart. He remembered the pageants of carnage that had marched through the dreams of his childhood. Love he knew that he had confronted, alone, isolated, wondering, an individual, an atom taking the hand of a titanic principle. But like the faintest breeze on his forehead, he felt here the vibration from the hearts of forty thousand men.

The lieutenant's nostrils were moving. "I must go at once," he said. "I must go at once."

"I will go with you wherever you go," shouted Peza loudly.

A primitive track wound down the side of the mountain, and in their rush they bounded from here to there, choosing risks which in the ordinary caution of man would surely have seemed of remarkable danger. The ardor of the correspondent surpassed the full energy of the soldier. Several times he turned and shouted: "Come on! Come on!"

At the foot of the path they came to a wide road which extended toward the battle in a yellow and straight line. Some men were trudging wearily to the rear. They were without rifles; their clumsy uniforms were dirty and all awry. They turned eyes dully aglow with fever upon the pair striding toward the battle. Others were bandaged with the triangular kerchief upon which one could still see through blood-stains the little explanatory pictures illustrating the ways to bind various wounds. "Fig. 1." —"Fig. 2."—"Fig. 7." Mingled with the pacing soldiers were peasants, indifferent, capable of smiling, gibbering about the battle, which was to them an ulterior drama. A man was leading a string of three donkeys to the rear, and at intervals he was accosted by wounded or fevered soldiers, from whom he defended his animals with ape-like cries and mad gesticulation. After much chattering they usually subsided gloomily, and allowed him to go with his sleek little beasts unburdened. Finally he encountered a soldier who walked slowly with the assistance of a staff. His head was bound with a wide bandage, grimy from blood and mud. He made application to the peasant, and immediately they were involved in a hideous Levantine discussion. The peasant whined and clamored, sometimes spitting like a kitten. The wounded soldier jawed on thunderously, his great hands stretched in claw-like graspings over the peasant's head. Once he raised his staff and made threat with it. Then suddenly the row was at an end. The other sick men saw their comrade mount the leading donkey and at once begin to drum with his heels. None attempted to gain the backs of the remaining animals. They gazed after him dully. Finally they saw the caravan outlined for a moment against the sky. The soldier was still waving his arms passionately, having it out with the peasant.

Peza was alive with despair for these men who looked at him with such doleful, quiet eyes. "Ah, my God!" he cried to the lieutenant, "these poor souls! These poor souls!"

The officer faced about angrily. "If you are coming with me there is no time for this." Peza obeyed instantly and with a sudden meekness. In the moment some portion of egotism left him, and he modestly wondered if the universe took cognizance of him to an important degree. This theatre for slaughter, built by the inscrutable needs of the earth, was an enormous affair, and he reflected that the accidental destruction of an individual, Peza by name, would perhaps be nothing at all.

With the lieutenant, he was soon walking along behind a series of little crescent-shaped trenches, in which were soldiers tranquilly interested, gossiping with the hum of a tea-party. Although these men were not at this time under fire, he concluded that they were fabulously brave. Else they would not be so comfortable, so at home in their sticky brown trenches. They were certain to be heavily attacked before the day was old. The universities had not taught him to understand this attitude. At the passing of the young man in very nice tweed, with his new leggings, his new white helmet, his new field-glass case, his new revolver holster, the soiled soldiers turned with the same curiosity which a being in strange garb meets at the corners of streets. He might as well have been promenading a populous avenue. The soldiers volubly discussed his identity.

To Peza there was something awful in the absolute familiarity of each tone, expression, gesture. These men, menaced with battle, displayed the curiosity of the café. Then, on the verge of his great encounter toward death, he found himself extremely embarrassed, composing his face with difficulty, wondering what to do with his hands, like a gawk at a levee.

He felt ridiculous, and also he felt awed, aghast, at these men who could turn their faces from the ominous front and debate his clothes, his business. There was an element which was new born into his theory of war. He was not averse to the brisk pace at which the lieutenant moved along the line.

The roar of fighting was always in Peza's ears. It came from some short hills ahead and to the left. The road curved suddenly and entered a wood. The trees stretched their luxuriant and graceful branches over grassy slopes. A breeze made all this verdure gently rustle and speak in long silken sighs. Absorbed in listening to the hurricane racket from the front, he still remembered that these trees were growing, the grass-blades were extending according to their process. He inhaled a deep breath of moisture and fragrance from the grove, a wet odor which expressed all the opulent fecundity of unmoved nature, marching on with her million plans for multiple life, multiple death.

Further on they came to a place where the Turkish shells were landing. There was a long hurtling sound in the air, and then one had sight of a shell. To Peza it was of the conical missiles which friendly officers had displayed to him on board warships. Curiously enough, too, this first shell smacked of the foundry, of men with smudged faces, of the blare of furnace fires. It brought machinery immediately into his mind. He thought that if he was killed there at that time it would be as romantic, to the old standards, as death by a bit of falling iron in a factory.

II

A child was playing on a mountain, and disregarding a battle that was waging on the plain. Behind him was the little cobbled hut of his fled parents. It was now occupied by a pearl-colored cow that stared out from the darkness, thoughtful and tender-eyed. The child ran to and fro, fumbling with sticks and making great machinations with pebbles. By a striking exercise of artistic license the sticks were ponies, cows, and dogs, and the pebbles were sheep. He was managing large agricultural and herding affairs. He was too intent on them to pay much heed to the fight four miles away, which at that distance resembled in sound the beating of surf upon rocks. However, there were occasions when some louder outbreak of that thunder stirred him from his serious occupation, and he turned then a questioning eye upon the battle, a small stick poised in his hand, interrupted in the act of sending his dog after his sheep. His tranquillity in regard to the death on the plain was as invincible as that of the mountain on which he stood.

It was evident that fear had swept the parents away from their home in a manner that could make them forget this child, the first-born. Nevertheless, the hut was cleaned bare. The cow had committed no impropriety in billeting herself at the domicile of her masters. This smoke-colored and odorous interior contained nothing as large as a humming-bird. Terror had operated on these runaway people in its sinister fashion, elevating details to enormous heights, causing a man to remember a button while he forgot a coat, overpowering every one with recollections of a broken coffee-cup, deluging them with fears for the safety of an old pipe, and causing them to forget their first-born. Meanwhile the child played soberly with his trinkets.

He was solitary; engrossed in his own pursuits, it was seldom that he lifted his head to inquire of the world why it made so much noise. The stick in his hand was much larger to him than was an army corps of the distance. It was too childish for the mind of the child. He was dealing with sticks.

The battle lines writhed at times in the agony of a sea-creature on the sands. These tentacles flung and waved in a supreme excitement of pain, and the struggles of the great outlined body brought it nearer and nearer to the child. Once he looked at the plain and saw some men running wildly across a field. He had seen people chasing obdurate beasts in such fashion, and it struck him immediately that it was a manly thing which he would incorporate in his game. Consequently he raced furiously at his stone sheep, flourishing a cudgel, crying the shepherd calls. He paused frequently to get a cue of manner from the soldiers fighting on the plain. He reproduced, to a degree, any movements which he accounted rational to his theory of sheep-herding, the business of men, the traditional and exalted living of his father.

III

It was as if Peza was a corpse walking on the bottom of the
sea, and finding there fields of grain, groves, weeds, the faces of
men, voices. War, a strange employment of the race, presented
to him a scene crowded with familiar objects which wore the
livery of their commonness placidly, undauntedly. He was smitten with keen astonishment; a spread of green grass lit with the
flames of poppies was too old for the company of this new ogre.
If he had been devoting the full lens of his mind to this phase, he
would have known he was amazed that the trees, the flowers, the
grass, all tender and peaceful nature had not taken to heels at
once upon the outbreak of battle. He venerated the immovable
poppies.

The road seemed to lead into the apex of an angle formed by
the two defensive lines of the Greeks. There was a straggle of
wounded men and of gunless and jaded men. These latter did
not seem to be frightened. They remained very cool, walking
with unhurried steps and busy in gossip. Peza tried to define
them. Perhaps during the fight they had reached the limit of
their mental storage, their capacity for excitement, for tragedy,
and had then simply come away. Peza remembered his visit to a
certain place of pictures, where he had found himself amid
heavenly skies and diabolic midnights—the sunshine beating
red upon desert sands, nude bodies flung to the shore in the
green moon-glow, ghastly and starving men clawing at a wall in
darkness, a girl at her bath with screened rays falling upon her
pearly shoulders, a dance, a funeral, a review, an execution, all
the strength of argus-eyed art; and he had whirled and whirled
amid this universe with cries of woe and joy, sin and beauty,
piercing his ears until he had been obliged to simply come away.
He remembered that as he had emerged he had lit a cigarette
with unction and advanced promptly to a café. A great hollow
quiet seemed to be upon the earth.

This was a different case, but in his thoughts he conceded the
same causes to many of these gunless wanderers. They too may
have dreamed at lightning speed until the capacity for it was

overwhelmed. As he watched them he again saw himself walking toward the café, puffing upon his cigarette. As if to reinforce his theory, a soldier stopped him with an eager but polite inquiry for a match. He watched the man light his little roll of tobacco and paper and begin to smoke ravenously.

Peza no longer was torn with sorrow at the sight of wounded men. Evidently he found that pity had a numerical limit, and when this was passed the emotion became another thing. Now, as he viewed them, he merely felt himself very lucky, and beseeched the continuance of his superior fortune. At the passing of these slouched and stained figures he now heard a reiteration of warning. A part of himself was appealing through the medium of these grim shapes. It was plucking at his sleeve and pointing, telling him to beware, and so it had come to pass that he cared for the implacable misery of these soldiers only as he would have cared for the harms of broken dolls. His whole vision was focussed upon his own chance.

The lieutenant suddenly halted. "Look," he said. "I find that my duty is in another direction. I must go another way. But if you wish to fight you have only to go forward, and any officer of the fighting line will give you opportunity." He raised his cap ceremoniously; Peza raised his new white helmet. The stranger to battles uttered thanks to his chaperon, the one who had presented him. They bowed punctiliously, staring at each other with civil eyes.

The lieutenant moved quietly away through a field. In an instant it flashed upon Peza's mind that this desertion was perfidious. He had been subjected to a criminal discourtesy. The officer had fetched him into the middle of the thing, and then left him to wander helplessly toward death. At one time he was upon the point of shouting at the officer.

In the vale there was an effect as if one was then beneath the battle. It was going on above somewhere. Alone, unguided, Peza felt like a man groping in a cellar. He reflected, too, that one should always see the beginning of a fight. It was too difficult to thus approach it when the affair was in full swing. The trees hid all movements of troops from him, and he thought he might be walking out to the very spot which chance had provided for the reception of a fool. He asked eager questions of passing soldiers. Some paid no heed to him; others shook their heads mournfully. They knew nothing save that war was hard work. If they talked at all it was in testimony of having fought well, savagely. They did not know if the army was going to advance, hold its ground, or retreat; they were weary.

A long pointed shell flashed through the air and struck near the base of a tree with a fierce upheaval, compounded of earth and flames. Looking back, Peza could see the shattered tree quivering from head to foot. Its whole being underwent a convulsive tremor which was an exhibition of pain and, furthermore, deep amazement. As he advanced through the vale the shells continued to hiss and hurtle in long low flights, and the bullets purred in the air. The missiles were flying into the breast of an astounded nature. The landscape, bewildered, agonized, was suffering a rain of infamous shots, and Peza imagined a million eyes gazing at him with the gaze of startled antelopes.

There was a resolute crashing of musketry from the tall hill on the left, and from directly in front there was a mingled din of artillery and musketry firing. Peza felt that his pride was playing a great trick in forcing him forward in this manner under conditions of strangeness, isolation, and ignorance. But he recalled the manner of the lieutenant, the smile on the hill-top among the flying peasants. Peza blushed and pulled the peak of his helmet down on his forehead. He strode onward firmly. Nevertheless, he hated the lieutenant, and he resolved that on some future occasion he would take much trouble to arrange a stinging social revenge upon that grinning jackanapes. It did not occur to him until later that he was now going to battle mainly because at a previous time a certain man had smiled.

IV

The road moved around the base of a little hill, and on this hill a battery of mountain guns was leisurely shelling something unseen. In the lee of the height the mules, contented under their heavy saddles, were quietly browsing the long grass. Peza ascended the hill by a slanting path. He felt his heart beat swiftly; once at the top of the hill he would be obliged to look this phenomenon in the face. He hurried, with a mysterious idea of preventing by this strategy the battle from making his appearance a signal for some tremendous renewal. This vague thought seemed logical at the time. Certainly this living thing had knowledge of his coming. He endowed it with the intelligence of a barbaric deity. And so he hurried; he wished to surprise war, this terrible emperor, when it was only growling on its throne. The ferocious and horrible sovereign was not to be allowed to make the arrival a pretext for some fit of smoky rage and blood. In this half-lull, Peza had distinctly the sense of stealing upon the battle unawares.

The soldiers watching the mules did not seem to be impressed by anything august. Two of them sat side by side and talked comfortably; another lay flat upon his back staring dreamily at the sky; another cursed a mule for certain refractions. Despite their uniforms, their bandoleers and rifles, they were dwelling in the peace of hostlers. However, the long shells were whooping from time to time over the brow of the hill, and swirling in almost straight lines toward the vale of trees, flowers, and grass. Peza, hearing and seeing the shells, and seeing the pensive guardians of the mules, felt reassured. They were accepting the condition of war as easily as an old sailor accepts the chair behind the counter of a tobacco-shop. Or it was merely that the farm-boy had gone to sea, and he had adjusted himself to the circumstances immediately, and with only the usual first misadventures in conduct. Peza was proud and ashamed that he was not of them, these stupid peasants, who, throughout the world, hold potentates on their thrones, make statesmen illustrious, provide generals with lasting victories, all with ignorance, indifference, or half-witted hatred, moving the world with the strength of their arms and getting their heads knocked together in the name of God, the king, or the Stock Exchange—immortal, dreaming, hopeless asses who surrender their reason to the care of a shining puppet, and persuade some toy to carry their lives in his purse. Peza mentally abased himself before them, and wished to stir them with furious kicks.

As his eyes ranged above the rim of the plateau, he saw a group of artillery officers talking busily. They turned at once and regarded his ascent. A moment later a row of infantry soldiers in a trench beyond the little guns all faced him. Peza bowed to the officers. He understood at the time that he had made a good and cool bow, and he wondered at it, for his breath was coming in gasps; he was stifling from sheer excitement. He felt like a tipsy man trying to conceal his muscular uncertainty from the people in the street. But the officers did not display any knowledge. They bowed. Behind them Peza saw the plain, glittering green, with three lines of black marked upon it heavily. The front of the first of these lines was frothy with smoke. To the left of this hill was a craggy mountain, from which came a continual dull rattle of musketry. Its summit was ringed with the white smoke. The black lines on the plain slowly moved. The shells that came from there passed overhead with the sound of great birds frantically flapping their wings. Peza thought of the first sight of the sea during a storm. He seemed to feel against his face the wind that races over the tops of cold and tumultuous billows.

He heard a voice afar off. "Sir, what would you?" He turned, and saw the dapper captain of the battery standing beside him. Only a moment had elapsed. "Pardon me, sir," said Peza, bowing again. The officer was evidently reserving his bows; he scanned the new-comer attentively. "Are you a correspondent?" he asked. Peza produced a card. "Yes, I came as a correspondent," he replied, "but now, sir, I have other thoughts. I wish to help. You see? I wish to help."

"What do you mean?" said the captain. "Are you a Greek? Do you wish to fight?"

"Yes, I am a Greek. I wish to fight." Peza's voice surprised him by coming from his lips in even and deliberate tones. He thought with gratification that he was behaving rather well. Another shell travelling from some unknown point on the plain whirled close and furiously in the air, pursuing an apparently horizontal course, as if it were never going to touch the earth. The dark shape swished across the sky.

"Ah," cried the captain, now smiling, "I am not sure that we will be able to accommodate you with a fierce affair here just at this time, but——" He walked gaily to and fro behind the guns with Peza, pointing out to him the lines of the Greeks, and describing his opinion of the general plan of defence. He wore the air of an amiable host. Other officers questioned Peza in regard to the politics of the war. The king, the ministry, Germany, England, Russia, all these huge words were continually upon their tongues. "And the people in Athens? Were they——" Amid this vivacious babble Peza, seated upon an ammunition box, kept his glance high, watching the appearance of shell after shell. These officers were like men who had been lost for days in the forest. They were thirsty for any scrap of news. Nevertheless, one of them would occasionally dispute their informant courteously. What would Servia have to say to that? No, no, France and Russia could never allow it. Peza was elated. The shells killed no one; war was not so bad. He was simply having coffee in the smoking-room of some embassy where reverberate the names of nations.

A rumor had passed along the motley line of privates in the trench. The new arrival with the clean white helmet was a famous English cavalry officer come to assist the army with his counsel. They stared at the figure of him, surrounded by officers. Peza, gaining sense of the glances and whispers, felt that his coming was an event.

Later, he resolved that he could with temerity do something finer. He contemplated the mountain where the Greek infantry was engaged, and announced leisurely to the captain of the battery that he thought presently of going in that direction and getting into the fight. He re-affirmed the sentiments of a patriot. The captain seemed surprised. "Oh, there will be fighting here at this knoll in a few minutes," he said orientally. "That will be sufficient? You had better stay with us. Besides, I have been ordered to resume fire." The officers all tried to dissuade him from departing. It was really not worth the trouble. The battery would begin again directly. Then it would be amusing for him.

Peza felt that he was wandering with his protestations of high patriotism through a desert of sensible men. These officers gave no heed to his exalted declarations. They seemed too jaded. They were fighting the men who were fighting them. Palaver of the particular kind had subsided before their intense preoccupation in war as a craft. Moreover, many men had talked in that manner, and only talked.

Peza believed at first that they were treating him delicately. They were considerate of his inexperience. War had turned out to be such a gentle business that Peza concluded he could scorn this idea. He bade them a heroic farewell despite their objections.

However, when he reflected upon their ways afterward, he saw dimly that they were actuated principally by some universal childish desire for a spectator of their fine things. They were going into action, and they wished to be seen at war, precise and fearless.

V

Climbing slowly to the high infantry position, Peza was amazed to meet a soldier whose jaw had been half shot away, and who was being helped down the sheep track by two tearful comrades. The man's breast was drenched with blood, and from a cloth which he held to the wound drops were splashing wildly upon the stones of the path. He gazed at Peza for a moment. It was a mystic gaze, which Peza withstood with difficulty. He was exchanging looks with a spectre; all aspect of the man was somehow gone from this victim. As Peza went on, one of the unwounded soldiers loudly shouted to him to return and assist in this tragic march. But even Peza's fingers revolted; he was afraid of the spectre; he would not have dared to touch it. He was surely craven in the movement of refusal he made to them. He scrambled hastily on up the path. He was running away.

At the top of the hill he came immediately upon a part of the line that was in action. Another battery of mountain guns was here firing at the streaks of black on the plain. There were trenches filled with men lining parts of the crest, and near the base were other trenches, all crashing away mightily. The plain stretched as far as the eye could see, and from where silver mist ended this emerald ocean of grass, a great ridge of snow-topped mountains poised against a fleckless blue sky. Two knolls, green and yellow with grain, sat on the prairie confronting the dark hills of the Greek position. Between them were the lines of the enemy. A row of trees, a village, a stretch of road, showed faintly on this great canvas, this tremendous picture; but men, the Turkish battalions, were emphasized startlingly upon it. The ranks of troops between the knolls and the Greek position were as black as ink. The first line, of course, was muffled in smoke, but at the rear of it battalions crawled up and to and fro plainer than beetles on a plate. Peza had never understood that masses of men were so declarative, so unmistakable, as if nature makes every arrangement to give information of the coming and the presence of destruction, the end, oblivion. The firing was full, complete, a roar of cataracts, and this pealing of connected volleys was adjusted to the grandeur of the far-off range of snowy mountains. Peza, breathless, pale, felt that he had been set upon a pillar and was surveying mankind, the world. In the meantime dust had got in his eye. He took his handkerchief and mechanically administered to it.

An officer with a double stripe of purple on his trousers paced in the rear of the battery of howitzers. He waved a little cane. Sometimes he paused in his promenade to study the field through his glasses. "A fine scene, sir," he cried airily, upon the approach of Peza. It was like a blow in the chest to the wide-eyed volunteer. It revealed to him a point of view. "Yes, sir, it is a fine scene," he answered. They spoke in French. "I am happy to be able to entertain monsieur with a little fine practice," continued the officer. "I am firing upon that mass of troops you see there a little to the right. They are probably forming for another attack." Peza smiled; here again appeared manners, manners erect by the side of death.

The right-flank gun of the battery thundered; there was a belch of fire and smoke; the shell flung swiftly and afar was known only to the ear in which rang a broadening hooting wake of sound. The howitzer had thrown itself backward convulsively, and lay with its wheels moving in the air as a squad of men rushed toward it. And later, it seemed as if each little gun had made the supreme effort of its being in each particular shot. They roared with voices far too loud, and the thunderous effort caused a gun to bound as in a dying convulsion. And then occasionally one was hurled with wheels in air. These shuddering howitzers presented an appearance of so many cowards always longing to bolt to the rear, but being implacably held up to their business by this throng of soldiers, who ran in squads to drag them up again to their obligation. The guns were herded and cajoled and bullied interminably. One by one, in relentless program, they were dragged forward to contribute a profound vibration of steel and wood, a flash and a roar, to the important happiness of man.

The adjacent infantry celebrated a good shot with smiles and an outburst of gleeful talk.

"Look, sir," cried an officer once to Peza. Thin smoke was drifting lazily before Peza, and, dodging impatiently, he brought his eyes to bear upon that part of the plain indicated by the officer's finger. The enemy's infantry was advancing to attack. From the black lines had come forth an inky mass, which was shaped much like a human tongue. It advanced slowly, casually, without apparent spirit, but with an insolent confidence that was like a proclamation of the inevitable.

The impetuous part was all played by the defensive side. Officers called, men plucked each other by the sleeve; there were shouts, motions; all eyes were turned upon the inky mass which was flowing toward the base of the hills, heavily, languorously, as oily and thick as one of the streams that ooze through a swamp.

Peza was chattering a question at every one. In the way, pushed aside, or in the way again, he continued to repeat it. "Can they take the position? Can they take the position? Can they take the position?" He was apparently addressing an assemblage of deaf men. Every eye was busy watching every hand. The soldiers did not even seem to see the interesting stranger in the white helmet who was crying out so feverishly.

Finally, however, the hurried captain of the battery espied him and heeded his question. "No, sir! No, sir! It is impossible," he shouted angrily. His manner seemed to denote that if he had had sufficient time he would have completely insulted Peza. The latter swallowed the crumb of news without regard to the coating of scorn, and, waving his hand in adieu, he began to run along the crest of the hill toward the part of the Greek line against which the attack was directed.

VI

Peza, as he ran along the crest of the mountain, believed that his action was receiving the wrathful attention of the hosts of the foe. To him then it was incredible foolhardiness thus to call to himself the stares of thousands of hateful eyes. He was like a lad induced by playmates to commit some indiscretion in a cathedral. He was abashed; perhaps he even blushed as he ran. It seemed to him that the whole solemn ceremony of war had paused during this commission. So he scrambled wildly over the rocks in his haste to end the embarrassing ordeal. When he came among the crowning rifle-pits filled with eager soldiers he wanted to yell with joy. None noticed him save a young officer of infantry, who said: "Sir, what do you want?" It was obvious that people had devoted some attention to their own affairs.

Peza asserted, in Greek, that he wished above everything to battle for the fatherland. The officer nodded; with a smile he pointed to some dead men covered with blankets, from which were thrust upturned dusty shoes.

"Yes, I know, I know," cried Peza. He thought the officer was poetically alluding to the danger.

"No," said the officer at once. "I mean cartridges—a bandoleer. Take a bandoleer from one of them."

Peza went cautiously toward a body. He moved a hand toward the corner of a blanket. There he hesitated, stuck, as if his arm had turned to plaster. Hearing a rustle behind him, he spun quickly. Three soldiers of the close rank in the trench were regarding him. The officer came again and tapped him on the shoulder. "Have you any tobacco?" Peza looked at him in bewilderment. His hand was still extended toward the blanket which covered the dead soldier. "Yes," he said, "I have some tobacco." He gave the officer his pouch. As if in compensation, the other directed a soldier to strip the bandoleer from the corpse. Peza, having crossed the long cartridge-belt on his breast, felt that the dead man had flung his two arms around him.

A soldier with a polite nod and smile gave Peza a rifle, a relic of another dead man. Thus, he felt, besides the clutch of a corpse about his neck, that the rifle was as unhumanly horrible as a snake that lives in a tomb. He heard at his ear something that was in effect like the voices of those two dead men, their low voices speaking to him of bloody death, mutilation. The bandoleer gripped him tighter; he wished to raise his hands to his throat like a man who is choking. The rifle was clammy; upon his palms he felt the movement of the sluggish currents of a serpent's life; it was crawling and frightful.

All about him were these peasants, with their interested countenances, gibbering of the fight. From time to time a soldier cried out in semi-humorous lamentations descriptive of his thirst. One bearded man sat munching a great bit of hard bread. Fat, greasy, squat, he was like an idol made of tallow. Peza felt dimly that there was a distinction between this man and a young student who could write sonnets and play the piano quite well. This old blockhead was cooly gnawing at the bread, while he, Peza, was being throttled by a dead man's arms.

He looked behind him, and saw that a head by some chance had been uncovered from its blanket. Two liquid-like eyes were staring into his face. The head was turned a little sideways as if to get better opportunity for the scrutiny. Peza could feel himself blanch; he was being drawn and drawn by these dead men slowly, firmly down as to some mystic chamber under the earth where they could walk, dreadful figures, swollen and blood-marked. He was bidden; they had commanded him; he was going, going, going.

When the man in the new white helmet bolted for the rear, many of the soldiers in the trench thought that he had been struck. But those who had been nearest to him knew better. Otherwise they would have heard the silken, sliding, tender noise of the bullet and the thud of its impact. They bawled after him curses, and also outbursts of self-congratulation and vanity. Despite the prominence of the cowardly part, they were enabled to see in this exhibition a fine comment upon their own fortitude. The other soldiers thought that Peza had been wounded somewhere in the neck, because as he ran he was tearing madly at the bandoleer, the dead man's arms. The soldier with the bread paused in his eating and cynically remarked upon the speed of the runaway.

An officer's voice was suddenly heard calling out the calculation of the distance to the enemy, the readjustment of the sights. There was a stirring rattle along the line. The men turned their eyes to the front. Other trenches beneath them to the right were already heavily in action. The smoke was lifting toward the blue sky. The soldier with the bread placed it carefully on a bit of paper beside him as he turned to kneel in the trench.

VII

In the late afternoon, the child ceased his play on the mountain with his flocks and his dogs. Part of the battle had whirled very near to the base of his hill, and the noise was great. Sometimes he could see fantastic smoky shapes which resembled the curious figures in foam which one sees on the slant of a rough sea. The plain, indeed, was etched in white circles and whirligigs like the slope of a colossal wave. The child took seat on a stone and contemplated the fight. He was beginning to be astonished; he had never before seen cattle herded with such uproar. Lines of flame flashed out here and there. It was mystery.

Finally, without any preliminary indication, he began to weep. If the men struggling on the plain had had time and greater vision, they could have seen this strange tiny figure seated on a boulder, surveying them while the tears streamed. It was as simple as some powerful symbol.

As the magic clear light of day amid the mountains dimmed the distances, and the plain shone as a pallid blue cloth marked by the red threads of the firing, the child arose and moved off to the unwelcoming door of his home. He called softly for his mother, and complained of his hunger in the familiar formulæ. The pearl-colored cow, grinding her jaws thoughtfully, stared at him with her large eyes. The peaceful gloom of evening was slowly draping the hills.

The child heard a rattle of loose stones on the hill-side, and facing the sound, saw a moment later a man drag himself up to the crest of the hill and fall panting. Forgetting his mother and his hunger, filled with calm interest, the child walked forward and stood over the heaving form. His eyes, too, were now large and inscrutably wise and sad, like those of the animal in the house.

After a silence, he spoke inquiringly. "Are you a man?"

Peza rolled over quickly and gazed up into the fearless cherubic countenance. He did not attempt to reply. He breathed as if life was about to leave his body. He was covered with dust; his face had been cut in some way, and his cheek was ribboned with blood. All the spick of his former appearance had vanished in a general dishevelment, in which he resembled a creature that had been flung to and fro, up and down, by cliffs and prairies during an earthquake. He rolled his eye glassily at the child.

They remained thus until the child repeated his words. "Are you a man?"

Peza gasped in the manner of a fish. Palsied, windless, and abject, he confronted the primitive courage, the sovereign child, the brother of the mountains, the sky and the sea, and he knew that the definition of his misery could be written on a wee grass-blade.

THE BLUE HOTEL

I

THE Palace Hotel at Fort Romper was painted a light blue, a shade that is on the legs of a kind of heron, causing the bird to declare its position against any background. The Palace Hotel, then, was always screaming and howling in a way that made the dazzling winter landscape of Nebraska seem only a gray swampish hush. It stood alone on the prairie, and when the snow was falling the town two hundred yards away was not visible. But when the traveler alighted at the railway station he was obliged to pass the Palace Hotel before he could come upon the company of low clap-board houses which composed Fort Romper, and it was not to be thought that any traveler could pass the Palace Hotel without looking at it. Pat Scully, the proprietor, had proved himself a master of strategy when he chose his paints. It is true that on clear days, when the great trans-continental expresses, long lines of swaying Pullmans, swept through Fort Romper, passengers were overcome at the sight, and the cult that knows the brown-reds and the subdivisions of the dark greens of the East expressed shame, pity, horror, in a laugh. But to the citizens of this prairie town, and to the people who would naturally stop there, Pat Scully had performed a feat. With this opulence and splendor, these creeds, classes, egotisms, that streamed through Romper on the rails day after day, they had no color in common.

As if the displayed delights of such a blue hotel were not sufficiently enticing, it was Scully's habit to go every morning and evening to meet the leisurely trains that stopped at Romper and work his seductions upon any man that he might see wavering, gripsack in hand.

One morning, when a snow-crusted engine dragged its long string of freight cars and its one passenger coach to the station, Scully performed the marvel of catching three men. One was a shaky and quick-eyed Swede, with a great shining cheap valise; one was a tall bronzed cowboy, who was on his way to a ranch near the Dakota line; one was a little silent man from the East, who didn't look it, and didn't announce it. Scully practically made them prisoners. He was so nimble and merry and kindly that each probably felt it would be the height of brutality to try to escape. They trudged off over the creaking board sidewalks in the wake of the eager little Irishman. He wore a heavy fur cap squeezed tightly down on his head. It caused his two red ears to stick out stiffly, as if they were made of tin.

At last, Scully, elaborately, with boisterous hospitality, conducted them through the portals of the blue hotel. The room which they entered was small. It seemed to be merely a proper temple for an enormous stove, which, in the center, was humming with god-like violence. At various points on its surface the iron had become luminous and glowed yellow from the heat. Beside the stove Scully's son Johnnie was playing High-Five with an old farmer who had whiskers both gray and sandy. They were quarreling. Frequently the old farmer turned his face toward a box of sawdust—colored brown from tobacco juice—that was behind the stove, and spat with an air of great impatience and irritation. With a loud flourish of words Scully destroyed the game of cards, and bustled his son upstairs with part of the baggage of the new guests. He himself conducted them to three basins of the coldest water in the world. The cowboy and the Easterner burnished themselves fiery red with this water, until it seemed to be some kind of a metal polish. The Swede, however, merely dipped his fingers gingerly and with trepidation. It was notable that throughout this series of small ceremonies the three travelers were made to feel that Scully was very benevolent. He was conferring great favors upon them. He handed the towel from one to the other with an air of philanthropic impulse.

Afterward they went to the first room, and, sitting about the stove, listened to Scully's officious clamor at his daughters, who were preparing the midday meal. They reflected in the silence of experienced men who tread carefully amid new people. Nevertheless, the old farmer, stationary, invincible in his chair near the warmest part of the stove, turned his face from the sawdust box frequently and addressed a glowing commonplace to the strangers. Usually he was answered in short but adequate sentences by either the cowboy or the Easterner. The Swede said nothing. He seemed to be occupied in making furtive estimates of each man in the room. One might have thought that he had the sense of silly suspicion which comes to guilt. He resembled a badly frightened man.

Later, at dinner, he spoke a little, addressing his conversation entirely to Scully. He volunteered that he had come from New York, where for ten years he had worked as a tailor. These facts seemed to strike Scully as fascinating, and afterward he volunteered that he had lived at Romper for fourteen years. The Swede asked about the crops and the price of labor. He seemed barely to listen to Scully's extended replies. His eyes continued to rove from man to man.

Finally, with a laugh and a wink, he said that some of these Western communities were very dangerous; and after his statement he straightened his legs under the table, tilted his head, and laughed again, loudly. It was plain that the demonstration had no meaning to the others. They looked at him wondering and in silence.

II

As the men trooped heavily back into the front room, the two little windows presented views of a turmoiling sea of snow. The huge arms of the wind were making attempts—mighty, circular, futile—to embrace the flakes as they sped. A gate-post like a still man with a blanched face stood aghast amid this profligate fury. In a hearty voice Scully announced the presence of a blizzard. The guests of the blue hotel, lighting their pipes, assented with grunts of lazy masculine contentment. No island of the sea could be exempt in the degree of this little room with its humming stove. Johnnie, son of Scully, in a tone which defined his opinion of his ability as a card-player, challenged the old farmer of both gray and sandy whiskers to a game of High-Five. The farmer agreed with a contemptuous and bitter scoff. They sat close to the stove, and squared their knees under a wide board. The cowboy and the Easterner watched the game with interest. The

Swede remained near the window, aloof, but with a countenance that showed signs of an inexplicable excitement.

The play of Johnnie and the gray-beard was suddenly ended by another quarrel. The old man arose while casting a look of heated scorn at his adversary. He slowly buttoned his coat, and then stalked with fabulous dignity from the room. In the discreet silence of all other men the Swede laughed. His laughter rang somehow childish. Men by this time had begun to look at him askance, as if they wished to inquire what ailed him.

A new game was formed jocosely. The cowboy volunteered to become the partner of Johnnie, and they all then turned to ask the Swede to throw in his lot with the little Easterner. He asked some questions about the game, and learning that it wore many names, and that he had played it when it was under an alias, he accepted the invitation. He strode toward the men nervously, as if he expected to be assaulted. Finally, seated, he gazed from face to face and laughed shrilly. This laugh was so strange that the Easterner looked up quickly, the cowboy sat intent and with his mouth open, and Johnnie paused, holding the cards with still fingers.

Afterward there was a short silence. Then Johnnie said: "Well, let's get at it. Come on now!" They pulled their chairs forward until their knees were bunched under the board. They began to play, and their interest in the game caused the others to forget the manner of the Swede.

The cowboy was a board-whacker. Each time that he held superior cards he whanged them, one by one, with exceeding force, down upon the improvised table, and took the tricks with a glowing air of prowess and pride that sent thrills of indignation into the hearts of his opponents. A game with a board-whacker in it is sure to become intense. The countenances of the Easterner and the Swede were miserable whenever the cowboy thundered down his aces and kings, while Johnnie, his eyes gleaming with joy, chuckled and chuckled.

Because of the absorbing play none considered the strange ways of the Swede. They paid strict heed to the game. Finally, during a lull caused by a new deal, the Swede suddenly addressed Johnnie: "I suppose there have been a good many men killed in this room." The jaws of the others dropped and they looked at him.

"What in hell are you talking about?" said Johnnie.

The Swede laughed again his blatant laugh, full of a kind of false courage and defiance. "Oh, you know what I mean all right," he answered.

"I'm a liar if I do!" Johnnie protested. The card was halted, and the men stared at the Swede. Johnnie evidently felt that as the son of the proprietor he should make a direct inquiry. "Now, what might you be drivin' at, mister?" he asked. The Swede winked at him. It was a wink full of cunning. His fingers shook on the edge of the board. "Oh, maybe you think I have been to nowheres. Maybe you think I'm a tenderfoot?"

"I don't know nothin' about you," answered Johnnie, "and I don't give a damn where you've been. All I got to say is that I don't know what you're driving at. There hain't never been nobody killed in this room."

The cowboy, who had been steadily gazing at the Swede, then spoke. "What's wrong with you, mister?"

Apparently it seemed to the Swede that he was formidably menaced. He shivered and turned white near the corners of his mouth. He sent an appealing glance in the direction of the little Easterner. During these moments he did not forget to wear his air of advanced pot-valor. "They say they don't know what I mean," he remarked mockingly to the Easterner.

The latter answered after prolonged and cautious reflection. "I don't understand you," he said, impassively.

The Swede made a movement then which announced that he thought he had encountered treachery from the only quarter where he had expected sympathy if not help. "Oh, I see you are all against me. I see——"

The cowboy was in a state of deep stupefaction. "Say," he cried, as he tumbled the deck violently down upon the board. "Say, what are you gittin' at, hey?"

The Swede sprang up with the celerity of a man escaping from a snake on the floor. "I don't want to fight!" he shouted. "I don't want to fight!"

The cowboy stretched his long legs indolently and deliberately. His hands were in his pockets. He spat into the sawdust box. "Well, who the hell thought you did?" he inquired.

The Swede backed rapidly toward a corner of the room. His hands were out protectingly in front of his chest, but he was making an obvious struggle to control his fright. "Gentlemen," he quavered, "I suppose I am going to be killed before I can leave this house! I suppose I am going to be killed before I can leave this house!" In his eyes was the dying swan look. Through the windows could be seen the snow turning blue in the shadow of dusk. The wind tore at the house and some loose thing beat regularly against the clap-boards like a spirit tapping.

A door opened, and Scully himself entered. He paused in surprise as he noted the tragic attitude of the Swede. Then he said: "What's the matter here?"

The Swede answered him swiftly and eagerly: "These men are going to kill me."

"Kill you!" ejaculated Scully. "Kill you! What are you talkin'?"

The Swede made the gesture of a martyr.

Scully wheeled sternly upon his son. "What is this, Johnnie?"

The lad had grown sullen. "Damned if I know," he answered. "I can't make no sense to it." He began to shuffle the cards, fluttering them together with an angry snap. "He says a good many men have been killed in this room, or something like that. And he says he's goin' to be killed here too. I don't know what ails him. He's crazy, I shouldn't wonder."

Scully then looked for explanation to the cowboy, but the cowboy simply shrugged his shoulders.

"Kill you?" said Scully again to the Swede. "Kill you? Man, you're off your nut."

"Oh, I know," burst out the Swede. "I know what will happen. Yes, I'm crazy—yes. Yes, of course, I'm crazy—yes. But I know one thing——" There was a sort of sweat of misery and terror upon his face. "I know I won't get out of here alive."

The cowboy drew a deep breath, as if his mind was passing into the last stages of dissolution. "Well, I'm dog-goned," he whispered to himself.

Scully wheeled suddenly and faced his son. "You've been troublin' this man!"

Johnnie's voice was loud with its burden of grievance. "Why, good Gawd, I ain't done nothin' to 'im."

The Swede broke in. "Gentlemen, do not disturb yourselves. I will leave this house. I will go 'way because——" He accused them dramatically with his glance. "Because I do not want to be killed."

Scully was furious with his son. "Will you tell me what is the matter, you young divil? What's the matter, anyhow? Speak out!"

"Blame it," cried Johnnie in despair, "don't I tell you I don't know. He—he says we want to kill him, and that's all I know. I can't tell what ails him."

The Swede continued to repeat: "Never mind, Mr. Scully, never mind. I will leave this house. I will go away, because I do not wish to be killed. Yes, of course, I am crazy—yes. But I know one thing! I will go away. I will leave this house. Never mind, Mr. Scully, never mind. I will go away."

"You will not go 'way," said Scully. "You will not go 'way until I hear the reason of this business. If anybody has troubled you I will take care of him. This is my house. You are under my roof, and I will not allow any peaceable man to be troubled here." He cast a terrible eye upon Johnnie, the cowboy, and the Easterner.

"Never mind, Mr. Scully, never mind. I will go 'way. I do not wish to be killed." The Swede moved toward the door, which opened upon the stairs. It was evidently his intention to go at once for his baggage.

"No, no," shouted Scully peremptorily; but the white-faced man slid by him and disappeared. "Now," said Scully severely, "what does this mane?"

Johnnie and the cowboy cried together: "Why, we didn't do nothin' to 'im!"

Scully's eyes were cold. "No," he said, "you didn't?"

Johnnie swore a deep oath. "Why, this is the wildest loon I ever see. We didn't do nothin' at all. We were jest sittin' here playin' cards and he——"

The father suddenly spoke to the Easterner. "Mr. Blanc," he asked, "what has these boys been doin'?"

The Easterner reflected again. "I didn't see anything wrong at all," he said at last slowly.

Scully began to howl. "But what does it mane?" He stared ferociously at his son. "I have a mind to lather you for this, me boy."

Johnnie was frantic. "Well, what have I done?" he bawled at his father.

III

"I think you are tongue-tied," said Scully finally to his son, the cowboy and the Easterner, and at the end of this scornful sentence he left the room.

Upstairs the Swede was swiftly fastening the straps of his great valise. Once his back happened to be half-turned toward the door, and hearing a noise there, he wheeled and sprang up, uttering a loud cry. Scully's wrinkled visage showed grimly in the light of the small lamp he carried. This yellow effulgence, streaming upward, colored only his prominent features, and left his eyes, for instance, in mysterious shadow. He resembled a murderer.

"Man, man!" he exclaimed, "have you gone daffy?"

"Oh, no! Oh, no!" rejoined the other. "There are people in this world who know pretty nearly as much as you do—understand?"

For a moment they stood gazing at each other. Upon the Swede's deathly pale cheeks were two spots brightly crimson and sharply edged, as if they had been carefully painted. Scully placed the light on the table and sat himself on the edge of the bed. He spoke ruminatively. "By cracky, I never heard of such a thing in my life. It's a complete muddle. I can't for the soul of me think how you ever got this idea into your head." Presently he lifted his eyes and asked: "And did you sure think they were going to kill you?"

The Swede scanned the old man as if he wished to see into his mind. "I did," he said at last. He obviously suspected that this answer might precipitate an outbreak. As he pulled on a strap his whole arm shook, the elbow wavering like a bit of paper.

Scully banged his hand impressively on the foot-board of the bed. "Why, man, we're goin' to have a line of ilictric street-cars in this town next spring."

" 'A line of electric street-cars,' " repeated the Swede stupidly.

"And," said Scully, "there's a new railroad goin' to be built down from Broken Arm to here. Not to mintion the four churches and the smashin' big brick school-house. Then there's the big factory, too. Why, in two years Romper'll be a met-tro-pol-is."

Having finished the preparation of his baggage, the Swede straightened himself. "Mr. Scully," he said with sudden hardihood, "how much do I owe you?"

"You don't owe me anythin'," said the old man angrily.

"Yes, I do," retorted the Swede. He took seventy-five cents from his pocket and tendered it to Scully; but the latter snapped his fingers in disdainful refusal. However, it happened that they both stood gazing in a strange fashion at three silver pieces on the Swede's open palm.

"I'll not take your money," said Scully at last. "Not after what's been goin' on here." Then a plan seemed to strike him. "Here," he cried, picking up his lamp and moving toward the door. "Here! Come with me a minute."

"No," said the Swede in overwhelming alarm.

"Yes," urged the old man. "Come on! I want you to come and see a picter—just across the hall—in my room."

The Swede must have concluded that his hour was come. His jaw dropped and his teeth showed like a dead man's. He ultimately followed Scully across the corridor, but he had the step of one hung in chains.

Scully flashed the light high on the wall of his own chamber. There was revealed a ridiculous photograph of a little girl. She was leaning against a balustrade of gorgeous decoration, and the formidable bang to her hair was prominent. The figure was as graceful as an upright sled-stake, and, withal, it was of the hue of lead. "There," said Scully tenderly. "That's the picter of my little girl that died. Her name was Carrie. She had the purtiest hair you ever saw! I was that fond of her, she——"

Turning then he saw that the Swede was not contemplating the picture at all, but, instead, was keeping keen watch on the gloom in the rear.

"Look, man!" shouted Scully heartily. "That's the picter of my little gal that died. Her name was Carrie. And then here's the picter of my oldest boy, Michael. He's a lawyer in Lincoln an' doin' well. I gave that boy a grand eddycation, and I'm glad for it now. He's a fine boy. Look at 'im now. Ain't he bold as blazes, him there in Lincoln, an honored an' respicted gintleman. An honored an' respicted gintleman," concluded Scully with a flourish. And so saying, he smote the Swede jovially on the back.

The Swede faintly smiled.

"Now," said the old man, "there's only one more thing." He dropped suddenly to the floor and thrust his head beneath the bed. The Swede could hear his muffled voice. "I'd keep it under me piller if it wasn't for that boy Johnnie. Then there's the old woman—— Where is it now? I never put it twice in the same place. Ah, now come out with you!"

Presently he backed clumsily from under the bed, dragging with him an old coat rolled into a bundle. "I've fetched him," he muttered. Kneeling on the floor he unrolled the coat and extracted from its heart a large yellow-brown whisky bottle.

His first maneuver was to hold the bottle up to the light. Reassured, apparently, that nobody had been tampering with it, he thrust it with a generous movement toward the Swede.

The weak-kneed Swede was about to eagerly clutch this element of strength, but he suddenly jerked his hand away and cast a look of horror upon Scully.

"Drink," said the old man affectionately. He had arisen to his feet, and now stood facing the Swede.

There was a silence. Then again Scully said: "Drink!"

The Swede laughed wildly. He grabbed the bottle, put it to his mouth, and as his lips curled absurdly around the opening and his throat worked, he kept his glance burning with hatred upon the old man's face.

IV

After the departure of Scully the three men, with the cardboard still upon their knees, preserved for a long time an astounded silence. Then Johnnie said: "That's the dod-dangest Swede I ever see."

"He ain't no Swede," said the cowboy scornfully.

"Well, what is he then?" cried Johnnie. "What is he then?"

"It's my opinion," replied the cowboy deliberately, "he's some kind of a Dutchman." It was a venerable custom of the country to entitle as Swedes all light-haired men who spoke with a heavy tongue. In consequence the idea of the cowboy was not without its daring. "Yes, sir," he repeated. "It's my opinion this feller is some kind of a Dutchman."

"Well, he says he's a Swede, anyhow," muttered Johnnie sulkily. He turned to the Easterner: "What do you think, Mr. Blanc?"

"Oh, I don't know," replied the Easterner.

"Well, what do you think makes him act that way?" asked the cowboy.

"Why, he's frightened!" The Easterner knocked his pipe against a rim of the stove. "He's clear frightened out of his boots."

"What at?" cried Johnnie and cowboy together.

The Easterner reflected over his answer.

"What at?" cried the others again.

"Oh, I don't know, but it seems to me this man has been reading dime-novels, and he thinks he's right out in the middle of it—the shootin' and stabbin' and all."

"But," said the cowboy, deeply scandalized, "this ain't Wyoming, ner none of them places. This is Nebrasker."

"Yes," added Johnnie, "an' why don't he wait till he gits *out West*?"

The traveled Easterner laughed. "It isn't different there even —not in these days. But he thinks he's right in the middle of hell."

Johnnie and the cowboy mused long.

"It's awful funny," remarked Johnnie at last.

"Yes," said the cowboy. "This is a queer game. I hope we don't git snowed in, because then we'd have to stand this here man bein' around with us all the time. That wouldn't be no good."

"I wish pop would throw him out," said Johnnie.

Presently they heard a loud stamping on the stairs, accompanied by ringing jokes in the voice of old Scully, and laughter, evidently from the Swede. The men around the stove stared vacantly at each other. "Gosh," said the cowboy. The door flew open, and old Scully, flushed and anecdotal, came into the room. He was jabbering at the Swede, who followed him, laughing bravely. It was the entry of two roysterers from a banquet hall.

"Come now," said Scully sharply to the three seated men, "move up and give us a chance at the stove." The cowboy and the Easterner obediently sidled their chairs to make room for the newcomers. Johnnie, however, simply arranged himself in a more indolent attitude, and then remained motionless.

"Come! Git over, there," said Scully.

"Plenty of room on the other side of the stove," said Johnnie.

"Do you think we want to sit in the draught?" roared the father.

But the Swede here interposed with a grandeur of confidence. "No, no. Let the boy sit where he likes," he cried in a bullying voice to the father.

"All right! All right!" said Scully deferentially. The cowboy and the Easterner exchanged glances of wonder.

The five chairs were formed in a crescent about one side of the stove. The Swede began to talk; he talked arrogantly, profanely, angrily. Johnnie, the cowboy and the Easterner maintained a morose silence, while old Scully appeared to be receptive and eager, breaking in constantly with sympathetic ejaculations.

Finally the Swede announced that he was thirsty. He moved in his chair, and said that he would go for a drink of water.

"I'll git it for you," cried Scully at once.

"No," said the Swede contemptuously. "I'll get it for myself." He arose and stalked with the air of an owner off into the executive parts of the hotel.

As soon as the Swede was out of hearing Scully sprang to his feet and whispered intensely to the others. "Upstairs he thought I was tryin' to poison 'im."

"Say," said Johnnie, "this makes me sick. Why don't you throw 'im out in the snow?"

"Why, he's all right now," declared Scully. "It was only that he was from the East and he thought this was a tough place. That's all. He's all right now."

The cowboy looked with admiration upon the Easterner. "You were straight," he said. "You were on to that there Dutchman."

"Well," said Johnnie to his father, "he may be all right now, but I don't see it. Other time he was scared, and now he's too fresh."

Scully's speech was always a combination of Irish brogue and idiom, Western twang and idiom, and scraps of curiously formal diction taken from the story-books and newspapers. He now hurled a strange mass of language at the head of his son. "What do I keep? What do I keep? What do I keep?" he demanded in a voice of thunder. He slapped his knee impressively, to indicate that he himself was going to make reply, and that all should heed. "I keep a hotel," he shouted. "A hotel, do you mind? A guest under my roof has sacred privileges. He is to be intimidated by none. Not one word shall he hear that would prijudice him in favor of goin' away. I'll not have it. There's no place in this here town where they can say they iver took in a guest of mine because he was afraid to stay here." He wheeled suddenly upon the cowboy and the Easterner. "Am I right?"

"Yes, Mr. Scully," said the cowboy, "I think you're right."

"Yes, Mr. Scully," said the Easterner, "I think you're right."

V

At six-o'clock supper, the Swede fizzed like a fire-wheel. He sometimes seemed on the point of bursting into riotous song, and in all his madness he was encouraged by old Scully. The Easterner was incased in reserve; the cowboy sat in wide-mouthed amazement, forgetting to eat, while Johnnie wrathily demolished great plates of food. The daughters of the house when they were obliged to replenish the biscuits approached as warily as Indians, and, having succeeded in their purposes, fled with ill-concealed trepidation. The Swede domineered the whole feast, and he gave it the appearance of a cruel bacchanal. He seemed to have grown suddenly taller; he gazed, brutally disdainful, into every face. His voice rang through the room. Once when he jabbed out harpoon-fashion with his fork to pinion a biscuit the weapon nearly impaled the hand of the Easterner which had been stretched quietly out for the same biscuit.

After supper, as the men filed toward the other room, the

Swede smote Scully ruthlessly on the shoulder. "Well, old boy, that was a good square meal." Johnnie looked hopefully at his father; he knew that shoulder was tender from an old fall; and indeed it appeared for a moment as if Scully was going to flame out over the matter, but in the end he smiled a sickly smile and remained silent. The others understood from his manner that he was admitting his responsibility for the Swede's new viewpoint.

Johnnie, however, addressed his parent in an aside. "Why don't you license somebody to kick you downstairs?" Scully scowled darkly by way of reply.

When they were gathered about the stove, the Swede insisted on another game of High-Five. Scully gently deprecated the plan at first, but the Swede turned a wolfish glare upon him. The old man subsided, and the Swede canvassed the others. In his tone there was always a great threat. The cowboy and the Easterner both remarked indifferently that they would play. Scully said that he would presently have to go to meet the 6.58 train, and so the Swede turned menacingly upon Johnnie. For a moment their glances crossed like blades, and then Johnnie smiled and said: "Yes, I'll play."

They formed a square with the little board on their knees. The Easterner and the Swede were again partners. As the play went on, it was noticeable that the cowboy was not board-whacking as usual. Meanwhile, Scully, near the lamp, had put on his spectacles and, with an appearance curiously like an old priest, was reading a newspaper. In time he went out to meet the 6.58 train, and, despite his precautions, a gust of polar wind whirled into the room as he opened the door. Besides scattering the cards, it chilled the players to the marrow. The Swede cursed frightfully. When Scully returned, his entrance disturbed a cozy and friendly scene. The Swede again cursed. But presently they were once more intent, their heads bent forward and their hands moving swiftly. The Swede had adopted the fashion of board-whacking.

Scully took up his paper and for a long time remained immersed in matters which were extraordinarily remote from him. The lamp burned badly, and once he stopped to adjust the wick. The newspaper as he turned from page to page rustled with a slow and comfortable sound. Then suddenly he heard three terrible words: "You are cheatin'!"

Such scenes often prove that there can be little of dramatic import in environment. Any room can present a tragic front; any room can be comic. This little den was now hideous as a torture-chamber. The new faces of the men themselves had changed it upon the instant. The Swede held a huge fist in front of Johnnie's face, while the latter looked steadily over it into the blazing orbs of his accuser. The Easterner had grown pallid; the cowboy's jaw had dropped in that expression of bovine amazement which was one of his important mannerisms. After the three words, the first sound in the room was made by Scully's paper as it floated forgotten to his feet. His spectacles had also fallen from his nose, but by a clutch he had saved them in air. His hand, grasping the spectacles, now remained poised awkwardly and near his shoulder. He stared at the card-players.

Probably the silence was while a second elapsed. Then, if the floor had been suddenly twitched out from under the men they could not have moved quicker. The five had projected themselves headlong toward a common point. It happened that Johnnie in rising to hurl himself upon the Swede had stumbled slightly because of his curiously instinctive care for the cards and the board. The loss of the moment allowed time for the arrival of Scully, and also allowed the cowboy time to give the Swede a great push which sent him staggering back. The men found tongue together, and hoarse shouts of rage, appeal or fear burst from every throat. The cowboy pushed and jostled feverishly at the Swede, and the Easterner and Scully clung wildly to Johnnie; but, through the smoky air, above the swaying bodies of the peace-compellers, the eyes of the two warriors ever sought each other in glances of challenge that were at once hot and steely.

Of course the board had been overturned, and now the whole company of cards was scattered over the floor, where the boots of the men trampled the fat and painted kings and queens as they gazed with their silly eyes at the war that was waging above them.

Scully's voice was dominating the yells. "Stop now! Stop, I say! Stop, now——"

Johnnie, as he struggled to burst through the rank formed by Scully and the Easterner, was crying: "Well, he says I cheated! He says I cheated! I won't allow no man to say I cheated! If he says I cheated, he's a——— ———!"

The cowboy was telling the Swede: "Quit, now! Quit, d'ye hear——"

The screams of the Swede never ceased. "He did cheat! I saw him! I saw him——"

As for the Easterner, he was importuning in a voice that was not heeded. "Wait a moment, can't you? Oh, wait a moment. What's the good of a fight over a game of cards? Wait a moment——"

In this tumult no complete sentences were clear. "Cheat"— "Quit"—"He says"—These fragments pierced the uproar and rang out sharply. It was remarkable that whereas Scully undoubtedly made the most noise, he was the least heard of any of the riotous band.

Then suddenly there was a great cessation. It was as if each man had paused for breath, and although the room was still lighted with the anger of men, it could be seen that there was no danger of immediate conflict, and at once Johnnie, shouldering his way forward, almost succeeded in confronting the Swede. "What did you say I cheated for? What did you say I cheated for? I don't cheat and I won't let no man say I do!"

The Swede said: "I saw you! I saw you!"

"Well," cried Johnnie, "I'll fight any man what says I cheat!"

"No, you won't," said the cowboy. "Not here."

"Ah, be still, can't you?" said Scully, coming between them.

The quiet was sufficient to allow the Easterner's voice to be heard. He was repeating: "Oh, wait a moment, can't you? What's the good of a fight over a game of cards? Wait a moment."

Johnnie, his red face appearing above his father's shoulder, hailed the Swede again. "Did you say I cheated?"

The Swede showed his teeth. "Yes."

"Then," said Johnnie, "we must fight."

"Yes, fight," roared the Swede. He was like a demoniac. "Yes, fight! I'll show you what kind of a man I am! I'll show you who you want to fight! Maybe you think I can't fight! Maybe you think

I can't! I'll show you, you skin, you card-sharp! Yes, you cheated! You cheated! You cheated!"

"Well, let's git at it, then, mister," said Johnnie coolly.

The cowboy's brow was beaded with sweat from his efforts in intercepting all sorts of raids. He turned in despair to Scully. "What are you goin' to do now?"

A change had come over the Celtic visage of the old man. He now seemed all eagerness; his eyes glowed.

"We'll let them fight," he answered stalwartly. "I can't put up with it any longer. I've stood this damned Swede till I'm sick. We'll let them fight."

VI

The men prepared to go out of doors. The Easterner was so nervous that he had great difficulty in getting his arms into the sleeves of his new leather-coat. As the cowboy drew his fur-cap down over his ears his hands trembled. In fact, Johnnie and old Scully were the only ones who displayed no agitation. These preliminaries were conducted without words.

Scully threw open the door. "Well, come on," he said. Instantly a terrific wind caused the flame of the lamp to struggle at its wick, while a puff of black smoke sprang from the chimney-top. The stove was in mid-current of the blast, and its voice swelled to equal the roar of the storm. Some of the scarred and bedabbled cards were caught up from the floor and dashed helplessly against the further wall. The men lowered their heads and plunged into the tempest as into a sea.

No snow was falling, but great whirls and clouds of flakes, swept up from the ground by the frantic winds, were streaming southward with the speed of bullets. The covered land was blue with the sheen of an unearthly satin, and there was no other hue save where at the low black railway station—which seemed incredibly distant—one light gleamed like a tiny jewel. As the men floundered into a thigh-deep drift, it was known that the Swede was bawling out something. Scully went to him, put a hand on his shoulder and projected an ear. "What's that you say?" he shouted.

"I say," bawled the Swede again, "I won't stand much show against this gang. I know you'll all pitch on me."

Scully smote him reproachfully on the arm. "Tut, man," he yelled. The wind tore the words from Scully's lips and scattered them far a-lee.

"You are all a gang of——" boomed the Swede, but the storm also seized the remainder of this sentence.

Immediately turning their backs upon the wind, the men had swung around a corner to the sheltered side of the hotel. It was the function of the little house to preserve here, amid this great devastation of snow, an irregular V-shape of heavily-incrusted grass, which crackled beneath the feet. One could imagine the great drifts piled against the windward side. When the party reached the comparative peace of this spot it was found that the Swede was still bellowing.

"Oh, I know what kind of a thing this is! I know you'll all pitch on me. I can't lick you all!"

Scully turned upon him panther-fashion. "You'll not have to whip all of us. You'll have to whip my son Johnnie. An' the man what troubles you durin' that time will have me to dale with."

The arrangements were swiftly made. The two men faced each other, obedient to the harsh commands of Scully, whose face, in the subtly luminous gloom, could be seen set in the austere impersonal lines that are pictured on the countenances of the Roman veterans. The Easterner's teeth were chattering, and he was hopping up and down like a mechanical toy. The cowboy stood rock-like.

The contestants had not stripped off any clothing. Each was in his ordinary attire. Their fists were up, and they eyed each other in a calm that had the elements of leonine cruelty in it.

During this pause, the Easterner's mind, like a film, took lasting impressions of three men—the iron-nerved master of the ceremony; the Swede, pale, motionless, terrible; and Johnnie, serene yet ferocious, brutish yet heroic. The entire prelude had in it a tragedy greater than the tragedy of action, and this aspect was accentuated by the long mellow cry of the blizzard, as it sped the tumbling and wailing flakes into the black abyss of the south.

"Now!" said Scully.

The two combatants leaped forward and crashed together like bullocks. There was heard the cushioned sound of blows, and of a curse squeezing out from between the tight teeth of one.

As for the spectators, the Easterner's pent-up breath exploded from him with a pop of relief, absolute relief from the tension of the preliminaries. The cowboy bounded into the air with a yowl. Scully was immovable as from supreme amazement and fear at the fury of the fight which he himself had permitted and arranged.

For a time the encounter in the darkness was such a perplexity of flying arms that it presented no more detail than would a swiftly-revolving wheel. Occasionally a face, as if illumined by a flash of light, would shine out, ghastly and marked with pink spots. A moment later, the men might have been known as shadows, if it were not for the involuntary utterance of oaths that came from them in whispers.

Suddenly a holocaust of warlike desire caught the cowboy, and he bolted forward with the speed of a broncho. "Go it, Johnnie; go it! Kill him! Kill him!"

Scully confronted him. "Kape back," he said; and by his glance the cowboy could tell that this man was Johnnie's father.

To the Easterner there was a monotony of unchangeable fighting that was an abomination. This confused mingling was eternal to his sense, which was concentrated in a longing for the end, the priceless end. Once the fighters lurched near him, and as he scrambled hastily backward, he heard them breathe like men on the rack.

"Kill him, Johnnie! Kill him! Kill him! Kill him!" The cowboy's face was contorted like one of those agony-masks in museums.

"Keep still," said Scully icily.

Then there was a sudden loud grunt, incomplete, cut-short, and Johnnie's body swung away from the Swede and fell with sickening heaviness to the grass. The cowboy was barely in time to prevent the mad Swede from flinging himself upon his prone adversary. "No, you don't," said the cowboy, interposing an arm. "Wait a second."

Scully was at his son's side. "Johnnie! Johnnie, me boy?" His voice had a quality of melancholy tenderness. "Johnnie? Can you go on with it?" He looked anxiously down into the bloody pulpy face of his son.

There was a moment of silence, and then Johnnie answered in his ordinary voice: "Yes, I—it—yes."

Assisted by his father he struggled to his feet. "Wait a bit now till you git your wind," said the old man.

A few paces away the cowboy was lecturing the Swede. "No, you don't! Wait a second!"

The Easterner was plucking at Scully's sleeve. "Oh, this is enough," he pleaded. "This is enough! Let it go as it stands. This is enough!"

"Bill," said Scully, "git out of the road." The cowboy stepped aside. "Now." The combatants were actuated by a new caution as they advanced toward collision. They glared at each other, and then the Swede aimed a lightning blow that carried with it his entire weight. Johnnie was evidently half-stupid from weakness, but he miraculously dodged, and his fist sent the over-balanced Swede sprawling.

The cowboy, Scully and the Easterner burst into a cheer that was like a chorus of triumphant soldiery, but before its conclusion the Swede had scuffled agilely to his feet and come in berserk abandon at his foe. There was another perplexity of flying arms, and Johnnie's body again swung away and fell, even as a bundle might fall from a roof. The Swede instantly staggered to a little wind-waved tree and leaned upon it, breathing like an engine, while his savage and flame-lit eyes roamed from face to face as the men bent over Johnnie. There was a splendor of isolation in his situation at this time which the Easterner felt once when, lifting his eyes from the man on the ground, he beheld that mysterious and lonely figure, waiting.

"Are you any good yet, Johnnie?" asked Scully in a broken voice.

The son gasped and opened his eyes languidly. After a moment he answered: "No—I ain't—any good—any—more." Then, from shame and bodily ill, he began to weep, the tears furrowing down through the blood-stains on his face. "He was too—too—too heavy for me."

Scully straightened and addressed the waiting figure. "Stranger," he said, evenly, "it's all up with our side." Then his voice changed into that vibrant huskiness which is commonly the tone of the most simple and deadly announcements. "Johnnie is whipped."

Without replying, the victor moved off on the route to the front door of the hotel.

The cowboy was formulating new and unspellable blasphemies. The Easterner was startled to find that they were out in a wind that seemed to come direct from the shadowed arctic floes. He heard again the wail of the snow as it was flung to its grave in the south. He knew now that all this time the cold had been sinking into him deeper and deeper, and he wondered that he had not perished. He felt indifferent to the condition of the vanquished man.

"Johnnie, can you walk?" asked Scully.

"Did I hurt—hurt him any?" asked the son.

"Can you walk, boy? Can you walk?"

Johnnie's voice was suddenly strong. There was a robust impatience in it. "I asked you whether I hurt him any!"

"Yes, yes, Johnnie," answered the cowboy consolingly; "he's hurt a good deal."

They raised him from the ground, and as soon as he was on his feet he went tottering off, rebuffing all attempts at assistance. When the party rounded the corner they were fairly blinded by the pelting of the snow. It burned their faces like fire. The cowboy carried Johnnie through the drift to the door. As they entered some cards again rose from the floor and beat against the wall.

The Easterner rushed to the stove. He was so profoundly chilled that he almost dared to embrace the glowing iron. The Swede was not in the room. Johnnie sank into a chair, and folding his arms on his knees, buried his face in them. Scully, warming one foot and then the other at a rim of the stove, muttered to himself with Celtic mournfulness. The cowboy had removed his fur-cap, and with a dazed and rueful air he was now running one hand through his tousled locks. From overhead they could hear the creaking of boards, as the Swede tramped here and there in his room.

The sad quiet was broken by the sudden flinging open of a door that led toward the kitchen. It was instantly followed by an inrush of women. They precipitated themselves upon Johnnie amid a chorus of lamentation. Before they carried their prey off to the kitchen, there to be bathed and harangued with that mixture of sympathy and abuse which is a feat of their sex, the mother straightened herself and fixed old Scully with an eye of stern reproach. "Shame be upon you, Patrick Scully!" she cried. "Your own son, too. Shame be upon you!"

"There, now! Be quiet, now!" said the old man weakly.

"Shame be upon you, Patrick Scully!" The girls, rallying to this slogan, sniffed disdainfully in the direction of those trembling accomplices, the cowboy and the Easterner. Presently they bore Johnnie away, and left the three men to dismal reflection.

VII

"I'd like to fight this here Dutchman myself," said the cowboy, breaking a long silence.

Scully wagged his head sadly. "No, that wouldn't do. It wouldn't be right. It wouldn't be right."

"Well, why wouldn't it?" argued the cowboy. "I don't see no harm in it."

"No," answered Scully with mournful heroism. "It wouldn't be right. It was Johnnie's fight, and now we mustn't whip the man just because he whipped Johnnie."

"Yes, that's true enough," said the cowboy; "but—he better not get fresh with me, because I couldn't stand no more of it."

"You'll not say a word to him," commanded Scully, and even then they heard the tread of the Swede on the stairs. His entrance was made theatric. He swept the door back with a bang and swaggered to the middle of the room. No one looked at him. "Well," he cried, insolently, at Scully, "I s'pose you'll tell me now how much I owe you?"

The old man remained stolid. "You don't owe me nothin'."

"Huh!" said the Swede, "huh! Don't owe 'im nothin'."

The cowboy addressed the Swede. "Stranger, I don't see how you come to be so gay around here."

Old Scully was instantly alert. "Stop!" he shouted, holding his hand forth, fingers upward. "Bill, you shut up!"

The cowboy spat carelessly into the sawdust box. "I didn't say a word, did I?" he asked.

"Mr. Scully," called the Swede, "how much do I owe you?" It was seen that he was attired for departure, and that he had his valise in his hand.

"You don't owe me nothin'," repeated Scully in his same imperturbable way.

"Huh!" said the Swede. "I guess you're right. I guess if it was any way at all, you'd owe me somethin'. That's what I guess." He turned to the cowboy. " 'Kill him! Kill him! Kill him!' " he mimicked, and then guffawed victoriously. " 'Kill him!' " He was convulsed with ironical humor.

But he might have been jeering the dead. The three men were immovable and silent, staring with glassy eyes at the stove.

The Swede opened the door and passed into the storm, giving one derisive glance backward at the still group.

As soon as the door was closed, Scully and the cowboy leaped to their feet and began to curse. They trampled to and fro, waving their arms and smashing into the air with their fists. "Oh, but that was a hard minute!" wailed Scully. "That was a hard minute! Him there leerin' and scoffin'! One bang at his nose was worth forty dollars to me that minute! How did you stand it, Bill?"

"How did I stand it?" cried the cowboy in a quivering voice. "How did I stand it? Oh!"

The old man burst into sudden brogue. "I'd loike to take that Swade," he wailed, "and hould 'im down on a shtone flure and bate 'im to a jelly wid a shtick!"

The cowboy groaned in sympathy. "I'd like to git him by the neck and ha-ammer him"—he brought his hand down on a chair with a noise like a pistol-shot—"hammer that there Dutchman until he couldn't tell himself from a dead coyote!"

"I'd bate 'im until he——"

"I'd show *him* some things——"

And then together they raised a yearning fanatic cry. "Oh-o-oh! if we only could——"

"Yes!"

"Yes!"

"And then I'd——"

"O-o-oh!"

VIII

The Swede, tightly gripping his valise, tacked across the face of the storm as if he carried sails. He was following a line of little naked gasping trees, which he knew must mark the way of the road. His face, fresh from the pounding of Johnnie's fists, felt more pleasure than pain in the wind and the driving snow. A number of square shapes loomed upon him finally, and he knew them as the houses of the main body of the town. He found a street and made travel along it, leaning heavily upon the wind whenever, at a corner, a terrific blast caught him.

He might have been in a deserted village. We picture the world as thick with conquering and elate humanity, but here, with the bugles of the tempest pealing, it was hard to imagine a peopled earth. One viewed the existence of man then as a marvel, and conceded a glamour of wonder to these lice which were caused to cling to a whirling, fire-smote, ice-locked, disease-stricken, space-lost bulb. The conceit of man was explained by this storm to be the very engine of life. One was a coxcomb not to die in it. However, the Swede found a saloon.

In front of it an indomitable red light was burning, and the snow-flakes were made blood-color as they flew through the circumscribed territory of the lamp's shining. The Swede pushed open the door of the saloon and entered. A sanded expanse was before him, and at the end of it four men sat about a table drinking. Down one side of the room extended a radiant bar, and its guardian was leaning upon his elbows listening to the talk of the men at the table. The Swede dropped his valise upon the floor, and, smiling fraternally upon the barkeeper, said: "Gimme some whisky, will you?" The man placed a bottle, a whisky-glass, and a glass of ice-thick water upon the bar. The Swede poured himself an abnormal portion of whisky and drank it in three gulps. "Pretty bad night," remarked the bartender indifferently. He was making the pretension of blindness, which is usually a distinction of his class; but it could have been seen that he was furtively studying the half-erased blood-stains on the face of the Swede. "Bad night," he said again.

"Oh, it's good enough for me," replied the Swede, hardily, as he poured himself some more whisky. The barkeeper took his coin and maneuvered it through its reception by the highly-nickeled cash-machine. A bell rang; a card labeled "20 cts." had appeared.

"No," continued the Swede, "this isn't too bad weather. It's good enough for me."

"So?" murmured the barkeeper languidly.

The copious drams made the Swede's eyes swim, and he breathed a trifle heavier. "Yes, I like this weather. I like it. It suits me." It was apparently his design to impart a deep significance to these words.

"So?" murmured the bartender again. He turned to gaze dreamily at the scroll-like birds and bird-like scrolls which had been drawn with soap upon the mirrors back of the bar.

"Well, I guess I'll take another drink," said the Swede presently. "Have something?"

"No, thanks; I'm not drinkin'," answered the bartender. Afterward he asked: "How did you hurt your face?"

The Swede immediately began to boast loudly. "Why, in a fight. I thumped the soul out of a man down here at Scully's hotel."

The interest of the four men at the table was at last aroused. "Who was it?" said one.

"Johnnie Scully," blustered the Swede. "Son of the man what runs it. He will be pretty near dead for some weeks, I can tell you. I made a nice thing of him, I did. He couldn't get up. They carried him in the house. Have a drink?"

Instantly the men in some subtle way incased themselves in reserve. "No, thanks," said one. The group was of curious formation. Two were prominent local business men; one was the district-attorney; and one was a professional gambler of the kind known as "square." But a scrutiny of the group would not have enabled an observer to pick the gambler from the men of more reputable pursuits. He was, in fact, a man so delicate in manner, when among people of fair class, and so judicious in his choice of victims, that in the strictly masculine part of the town's life he had come to be explicitly trusted and admired. People called him a thoroughbred. The fear and contempt with which his craft was regarded was undoubtedly the reason that his quiet dignity shone conspicuous above the quiet dignity of men who might be merely hatters, billiard-markers or grocery clerks. Beyond an occasional unwary traveler, who came by rail, this gambler was supposed to prey solely upon reckless and senile farmers, who, when flush with good crops, drove into town in all the pride and confidence of an absolutely invulnerable stupidity. Hearing at times in circuitous fashion of the despoilment of such a farmer, the important men of Romper invariably laughed in contempt of the victim, and if they thought of the wolf at all, it was with a kind of pride at the knowledge that he would never dare think of attacking their wisdom and courage. Besides, it was popular that this gambler had a real wife and two real children in a neat cottage in a suburb, where he led an exemplary home life, and when any one even suggested a discrepancy in his character, the crowd immediately vociferated descriptions of this virtuous family circle. Then men who led exemplary home lives, and men who did not lead exemplary home lives, all subsided in a bunch, remarking that there was nothing more to be said.

However, when a restriction was placed upon him—as, for instance, when a strong clique of members of the new Pollywog Club refused to permit him, even as a spectator, to appear in the rooms of the organization—the candor and gentleness with which he accepted the judgment disarmed many of his foes and made his friends more desperately partisan. He invariably distinguished between himself and a respectable Romper man so quickly and frankly that his manner actually appeared to be a continual broadcast compliment.

And one must not forget to declare the fundamental fact of his entire position in Romper. It is irrefutable that in all affairs outside of his business, in all matters that occur eternally and commonly between man and man, this thieving card-player was so generous, so just, so moral, that, in a contest, he could have put to flight the consciences of nine-tenths of the citizens of Romper.

And so it happened that he was seated in this saloon with the two prominent local merchants and the district-attorney.

The Swede continued to drink raw whisky, meanwhile babbling at the barkeeper and trying to induce him to indulge in potations. "Come on. Have a drink. Come on. What—no? Well, have a little one then. By gawd, I've whipped a man to-night, and

I want to celebrate. I whipped him good, too. Gentlemen," the Swede cried to the men at the table, "have a drink?"

"Ssh!" said the barkeeper.

The group at the table, although furtively attentive, had been pretending to be deep in talk, but now a man lifted his eyes toward the Swede and said shortly: "Thanks. We don't want any more."

At this reply the Swede ruffled out his chest like a rooster. "Well," he exploded, "it seems I can't get anybody to drink with me in this town. Seems so, don't it? Well!"

"Ssh!" said the barkeeper.

"Say," snarled the Swede, "don't you try to shut me up. I won't have it. I'm a gentleman, and I want people to drink with me. And I want 'em to drink with me now. *Now*—do you understand?" He rapped the bar with his knuckles.

Years of experience had calloused the bartender. He merely grew sulky. "I hear you," he answered.

"Well," cried the Swede, "listen hard then. See those men over there? Well, they're going to drink with me, and don't you forget it. Now you watch."

"Hi!" yelled the barkeeper, "this won't do!"

"Why won't it?" demanded the Swede. He stalked over to the table, and by chance laid his hand upon the shoulder of the gambler. "How about this?" he asked, wrathfully. "I asked you to drink with me."

The gambler simply twisted his head and spoke over his shoulder. "My friend, I don't know you."

"Oh, hell!" answered the Swede, "come and have a drink."

"Now, my boy," advised the gambler kindly, "take your hand off my shoulder and go 'way and mind your own business." He was a little slim man, and it seemed strange to hear him use this tone of heroic patronage to the burly Swede. The other men at the table said nothing.

"What? You won't drink with me, you little dude! I'll make you then! I'll make you!" The Swede had grasped the gambler frenziedly at the throat, and was dragging him from his chair. The other men sprang up. The barkeeper dashed around the corner of his bar. There was a great tumult, and then was seen a long blade in the hand of the gambler. It shot forward, and a human body, this citadel of virtue, wisdom, power, was pierced as easily as if it had been a melon. The Swede fell with a cry of supreme astonishment.

The prominent merchants and the district-attorney must have at once tumbled out of the place backward. The bartender found himself hanging limply to the arm of a chair and gazing into the eyes of a murderer.

"Henry," said the latter, as he wiped his knife on one of the towels that hung beneath the bar-rail, "you tell 'em where to find me. I'll be home, waiting for 'em." Then he vanished. A moment afterward the barkeeper was in the street dinning through the storm for help, and, moreover, companionship.

The corpse of the Swede, alone in the saloon, had its eyes fixed upon a dreadful legend that dwelt a-top of the cash-machine. "This registers the amount of your purchase."

IX

Months later, the cowboy was frying pork over the stove of a little ranch near the Dakota line, when there was a quick thud of hoofs outside, and, presently, the Easterner entered with the letters and the papers.

"Well," said the Easterner at once, "the chap that killed the Swede has got three years. Wasn't much, was it?"

"He has? Three years?" The cowboy poised his pan of pork, while he ruminated upon the news. "Three years. That ain't much."

"No. It was a light sentence," replied the Easterner as he unbuckled his spurs. "Seems there was a good deal of sympathy for him in Romper."

"If the bartender had been any good," observed the cowboy thoughtfully, "he would have gone in and cracked that there Dutchman on the head with a bottle in the beginnin' of it and stopped all this here murderin'."

"Yes, a thousand things might have happened," said the Easterner tartly.

The cowboy returned his pan of pork to the fire, but his philosophy continued. "It's funny, ain't it? If he hadn't said

Johnnie was cheatin' he'd be alive this minute. He was an awful fool. Game played for fun, too. Not for money. I believe he was crazy."

"I feel sorry for that gambler," said the Easterner.

"Oh, so do I," said the cowboy. "He don't deserve none of it for killin' who he did."

"The Swede might not have been killed if everything had been square."

"Might not have been killed?" exclaimed the cowboy. "Everythin' square? Why, when he said that Johnnie was cheatin' and acted like such a jackass? And then in the saloon he fairly walked up to git hurt?" With these arguments the cowboy browbeat the Easterner and reduced him to rage.

"You're a fool!" cried the Easterner viciously. "You're a bigger jackass than the Swede by a million majority. Now let me tell you one thing. Let me tell you something. Listen! Johnnie *was* cheating!"

" 'Johnnie,' " said the cowboy blankly. There was a minute of silence, and then he said robustly: "Why, no. The game was only for fun."

"Fun or not," said the Easterner, "Johnnie was cheating. I saw him. I know it. I saw him. And I refused to stand up and be a man. I let the Swede fight it out alone. And you—you were simply puffing around the place and wanting to fight. And then old Scully himself! We are all in it! This poor gambler isn't even a noun. He is kind of an adverb. Every sin is the result of a collaboration. We, five of us, have collaborated in the murder of this Swede. Usually there are from a dozen to forty women really involved in every murder, but in this case it seems to be only five men—you, I, Johnnie, old Scully, and that fool of an unfortunate gambler came merely as a culmination, the apex of a human movement, and gets all the punishment."

The cowboy, injured and rebellious, cried out blindly into this fog of mysterious theory. "Well, I didn't do anythin', did I?"

TWELVE O'CLOCK

"Where were you at twelve o'clock, noon, on the 9th of June, 1875?"—
Question on intelligent cross-examination.

I

"EXCUSE *me*," said Ben Roddle with graphic gestures to a group of citizens in Nantucket's store. "Excuse *me*. When them fellers in leather pants an' six-shooters ride in, I go home an' set in th' cellar. That's what I do. When you see me pirooting through the streets at th' same time an' occasion as them punchers, you kin put me down fer bein' crazy. Excuse *me*."

"Why, Ben," drawled old Nantucket, "you ain't never really seen 'em turned loose. Why, I kin remember—in th' old days—when——"

"Oh, damn yer old days!" retorted Roddle. Fixing Nantucket with the eye of scorn and contempt, he said: "I suppose you'll be sayin' in a minute that in th' old days you used to kill Injuns, won't you?"

There was some laughter, and Roddle was left free to expand his ideas on the periodic visits of cowboys to the town. "Mason Rickets, he had ten big punkins a-sittin' in front of his store, an' them fellers from the Upside-down-F ranch shot 'em up—shot 'em all up—an' Rickets lyin' on his belly in th' store a-callin' fer 'em to quit it. An' what did they do! Why, they *laughed* at 'im!—just *laughed* at 'im! That don't do a town no good. Now, how would an eastern capiterlist"—(it was the town's humor to be always gassing of phantom investors who were likely to come any moment and pay a thousand prices for everything)—"how would an eastern capiterlist like that? Why, you couldn't see 'im fer th' dust on his trail. Then he'd tell all his friends that 'their town may be all right, but ther's too much loose-handed shootin' fer my money.' An' he'd be right, too. Them rich fellers, they don't make no bad breaks with their money. They watch it all th' time b'cause they know blame well there ain't hardly room fer their feet fer th' pikers an' tin-horns an' thimble-riggers what are layin' fer 'em. I tell you, one puncher racin' his cow-pony hell-bent-fer-election down Main Street an' yellin' an' shootin' an' nothin' at all done about it, would scare away a whole herd of capiterlists. An' it ain't right. It oughter be stopped."

A pessimistic voice asked: "How you goin' to stop it, Ben?"

"Organize," replied Roddle pompously. "Organize: that's the only way to make these fellers lay down. I——"

From the street sounded a quick scudding of pony hoofs, and a party of cowboys swept past the door. One man, however, was seen to draw rein and dismount. He came clanking into the store. "Mornin', gentlemen," he said, civilly.

"Mornin'," they answered in subdued voices.

He stepped to the counter and said, "Give me a paper of fine cut, please." The group of citizens contemplated him in silence. He certainly did not look threatening. He appeared to be a young man of twenty-five years, with a tan from wind and sun, with a remarkably clear eye from perhaps a period of enforced temperance, a quiet young man who wanted to buy some tobacco. A six-shooter swung low on his hip, but at the moment it looked more decorative than warlike; it seemed merely a part of his odd gala dress—his sombrero with its band of rattlesnake skin, his great flaming neckerchief, his belt of embroidered Mexican leather, his high-heeled boots, his huge spurs. And, above all, his hair had been watered and brushed until it lay as close to his head as the fur lays to a wet cat. Paying for his tobacco, he withdrew.

Ben Roddle resumed his harangue. "Well, there you are! Looks like a calm man now, but in less'n half an hour he'll be as drunk as three bucks an' a squaw, an' then . . . . . excuse *me!*"

II

On this day the men of two outfits had come into town, but Ben Roddle's ominous words were not justified at once. The punchers spent most of the morning in an attack on whiskey which was too earnest to be noisy.

At five minutes of eleven, a tall, lank, brick-colored cowboy strode over to Placer's Hotel. Placer's Hotel was a notable place. It was the best hotel within two hundred miles. Its office was filled with arm-chairs and brown papier-maché receptacles. At one end of the room was a wooden counter painted a bright pink, and on this morning a man was behind the counter writing in a ledger. He was the proprietor of the hotel, but his customary humor was so sullen that all strangers immediately wondered why in life he had chosen to play the part of mine host. Near his left hand, double doors opened into the dining-room, which in warm weather was always kept darkened in order to discourage the flies, which was not compassed at all.

Placer, writing in his ledger, did not look up when the tall cowboy entered.

"Mornin', mister," said the latter. "I've come to see if you kin grub-stake th' hull crowd of us fer dinner t'day."

Placer did not then raise his eyes, but with a certain churlishness, as if it annoyed him that his hotel was patronized, he asked: "How many?"

"Oh, about thirty," replied the cowboy. "An' we want th' best dinner you kin raise an' scrape. Everything th' best. We don't care what it costs s'long as we git a good square meal. We'll pay a dollar a head: by God, we will! We won't kick on nothin' in the bill if you do it up fine. If you ain't got it in th' house, russle th' hull town fer it. That's our gait. So you just tear loose, an' we'll——"

At this moment the machinery of a cuckoo-clock on the wall began to whirr, little doors flew open, and a wooden bird appeared and cried, "Cuckoo!" And this was repeated until eleven o'clock had been announced, while the cowboy, stupefied, glassy-eyed, stood with his red throat gulping. At the end he wheeled upon Placer and demanded: *What in hell is that?*

Placer revealed by his manner that he had been asked this question too many times. "It's a clock," he answered shortly.

"I know it's a clock," gasped the cowboy; "but what *kind* of a clock?"

"A cuckoo-clock. Can't you see?"

The cowboy, recovering his self-possession by a violent effort, suddenly went shouting into the street. "Boys! Say, boys! Com' 'ere a minute!"

His comrades, comfortably inhabiting a near-by saloon, heard his stentorian calls, but they merely said to one another: "What's th' matter with Jake?—he's off his nut again."

But Jake burst in upon them with violence. "Boys," he yelled, "come over to th' hotel! They got a clock with a bird inside it, an' when it's eleven o'clock or anything like that, th' bird comes out an' says, 'toot-toot, toot-toot!' that way, as many times as whatever time of day it is. It's immense! Come on over!"

The roars of laughter which greeted his proclamation were of two qualities; some men laughing because they knew all about cuckoo-clocks, and other men laughing because they had concluded that the eccentric Jake had been victimized by some wise child of civilization.

Old Man Crumford, a venerable ruffian who probably had been born in a corral, was particularly offensive with his loud guffaws of contempt. "Bird a-comin' out of a clock an' a-tellin' ye th' time! Haw-haw-haw!" He swallowed his whiskey. "A bird! a-tellin' ye th' time! Haw-haw! Jake, you ben up agin some new drink. You ben drinkin' lonely an' got up agin some snake-medicine licker. A bird a-tellin' ye th' time! Haw-haw!"

The shrill voice of one of the younger cowboys piped from the background. "Brace up, Jake. Don't let 'em laugh at ye. Bring 'em that salt cod-fish of yourn what kin pick out th' ace."

"Oh, he's only kiddin' us. Don't pay no 'tention to 'im. He thinks he's smart."

A cowboy whose mother had a cuckoo-clock in her house in Philadelphia spoke with solemnity. "Jake's a liar. There's no such clock in the world. What? a bird inside a clock to tell the time? Change your drink, Jake."

Jake was furious, but his fury took a very icy form. He bent a withering glance upon the last speaker. "I don't mean a *live* bird," he said, with terrible dignity. "It's a wooden bird, an'——"

"A wooden bird!" shouted Old Man Crumford. "Wooden bird a-tellin' ye th' time! Haw-haw!"

But Jake still paid his frigid attention to the Philadelphian.

"An' if yer sober enough to walk, it ain't such a blame long ways from here to th' hotel, an' I'll bet my pile agin yours if you only got two bits."

"I don't want your money, Jake," said the Philadelphian. "Somebody's been stringin' you—that's all. I wouldn't take your money." He cleverly appeared to pity the other's innocence.

"You couldn't *git* my money," cried Jake, in sudden hot anger. "You couldn't git it. Now—since yer so fresh—let's see how much you got." He clattered some large gold pieces noisily upon the bar.

The Philadelphian shrugged his shoulders and walked away. Jake was triumphant. "Any more bluffers 'round here?" he demanded. "Any more? Any more bluffers? Where's all these here hot sports? Let 'em step up. Here's my money—come an' git it."

But they had ended by being afraid. To some of them his tale was absurd, but still one must be circumspect when a man throws forty-five dollars in gold upon the bar and bids the world come and win it. The general feeling was expressed by Old Man Crumford, when with deference he asked: "Well, this here bird, Jake—what kinder lookin' bird is it?"

"It's a little brown thing," said Jake briefly. Apparently he almost disdained to answer.

"Well—how does it work?" asked the old man meekly.

"Why in blazes don't you go an' look at it?" yelled Jake. "Want me to paint it in iles fer you? Go an' look!"

III

Placer was writing in his ledger. He heard a great trample of feet and clink of spurs on the porch, and there entered quietly the band of cowboys, some of them swaying a trifle, and these last being the most painfully decorous of all. Jake was in advance. He waved his hand toward the clock. "There she is," he said laconically. The cowboys drew up and stared. There was some giggling, but a serious voice said half-audibly, "I don't see no bird."

Jake politely addressed the landlord. "Mister, I've fetched these here friends of mine in here to see yer clock——"

Placer looked up suddenly. "Well, they can see it, can't they?" he asked in sarcasm. Jake, abashed, retreated to his fellows.

There was a period of silence. From time to time the men shifted their feet. Finally, Old Man Crumford leaned toward Jake, and in a penetrating whisper demanded, "Where's th' bird?" Some frolicsome spirits on the outskirts began to call "Bird! Bird!" as men at a political meeting call for a particular speaker.

Jake removed his big hat and nervously mopped his brow.

The young cowboy with the shrill voice again spoke from the skirts of the crowd. "Jake, is ther' sure-'nough a bird in that thing?"

"Yes. Didn't I tell you once?"

"Then," said the shrill-voiced man, in a tone of conviction, "it ain't a clock at all. It's a bird-cage."

"I tell you it's a clock," cried the maddened Jake, but his retort could hardly be heard above the howls of glee and derision which greeted the words of him of the shrill voice.

Old Man Crumford was again rampant. "Wooden bird a-tellin' ye th' time! Haw-haw!"

Amid the confusion Jake went again to Placer. He spoke almost in supplication. "Say, mister, what time does this here thing go off agin?"

Placer lifted his head, looked at the clock, and said: "Noon."

There was a stir near the door, and Big Watson of the Square-X outfit, and at this time very drunk indeed, came shouldering his way through the crowd and cursing everybody. The men gave him much room, for he was notorious as a quarrelsome person when drunk. He paused in front of Jake, and spoke as through a wet blanket. "What's all this —— monkeyin' about?"

Jake was already wild at being made a butt for everybody, and he did not give backward. "None a' your damn business, Watson."

"Huh?" growled Watson, with the surprise of a challenged bull.

"I said," repeated Jake distinctly, "it's none a' your damn business."

Watson whipped his revolver half out of its holster. "I'll make it m' business, then, you ——"

But Jake had backed a step away, and was holding his left-hand palm outward toward Watson, while in his right he held his six-shooter, its muzzle pointing at the floor. He was shouting in a frenzy,—"No—don't you try it, Watson! Don't you dare try it, or, by Gawd, I'll kill you, sure—*sure!*"

He was aware of a torment of cries about him from fearful men; from men who protested, from men who cried out because they cried out. But he kept his eyes on Watson, and those two glared murder at each other, neither seeming to breathe, fixed like statues.

A loud new voice suddenly rang out: "Hol' on a minute!" All spectators who had not stampeded turned quickly, and saw Placer standing behind his bright pink counter, with an aimed revolver in each hand.

"Cheese it!" he said. "I won't have no fightin' here. If you want to fight, git out in the street."

Big Watson laughed, and, speeding up his six-shooter like a flash of blue light, he shot Placer through the throat—shot the man as he stood behind his absurd pink counter with his two aimed revolvers in his incompetent hands. With a yell of rage and despair, Jake smote Watson on the pate with his heavy weapon, and knocked him sprawling and bloody. Somewhere a woman shrieked like windy, midnight death. Placer fell behind the counter, and down upon him came his ledger and his ink-stand, so that one could not have told blood from ink.

The cowboys did not seem to hear, see, or feel, until they saw numbers of citizens with Winchesters running wildly upon them. Old Man Crumford threw high a passionate hand. "Don't shoot! We'll not fight ye fer 'im."

Nevertheless two or three shots rang, and a cowboy who had been about to gallop off suddenly slumped over on his pony's neck, where he held for a moment like an old sack, and then slid to the ground, while his pony, with flapping rein, fled to the prairie.

"In God's name, don't shoot!" trumpeted Old Man Crumford. "We'll not fight ye fer 'im!"

"It's murder," bawled Ben Roddle.

In the chaotic street it seemed for a moment as if everybody would kill everybody. "Where's the man what done it?" These hot cries seemed to declare a war which would result in an absolute annihilation of one side. But the cowboys were singing out against it. They would fight for nothing—yes—they often fought for nothing—but they would not fight for this dark something.

At last, when a flimsy truce had been made between the inflamed men, all parties went to the hotel. Placer, in some dying whim, had made his way out from behind the pink counter, and, leaving a horrible trail, had travelled to the centre of the room, where he had pitched headlong over the body of Big Watson.

The men lifted the corpse and laid it at the side.

"Who done it?" asked a white, stern man.

A cowboy pointed at Big Watson. "That's him," he said huskily.

There was a curious grim silence, and then suddenly, in the death-chamber, there sounded the loud whirring of the clock's works, little doors flew open, a tiny wooden bird appeared and cried "Cuckoo"—twelve times.

MOONLIGHT ON THE SNOW

I

THE town of War Post had an evil name for three hundred miles in every direction. It radiated like the shine from some stupendous light. The citizens of the place had been for years grotesquely proud of their fame as a collection of hard-shooting gentlemen who invariably "got" the men who came up against them. When a citizen went abroad in the land he said, "I'm f'm War Post." And it was as if he had said, "I am the devil himself."

But ultimately it became known to War Post that the serene-browed angel of peace was in the vicinity. The angel was full of projects for taking comparatively useless bits of prairie and sawing them up into town lots, and making chaste and beautiful maps of his handiwork which shook the souls of people who had never been in the West. He commonly traveled here and there in a light wagon, from the tail-board of which he made orations which soared into the empyrean regions of true hydrogen gas. Towns far and near listened to his voice and followed him singing, until in all that territory you couldn't throw a stone at a jack-rabbit without hitting the site of a projected mammoth hotel; estimated cost, fifteen thousand dollars. The stern and lonely buttes were given titles like grim veterans awarded tawdry patents of nobility—Cedar Mountain, Red Cliffs, Lookout Peak. And from the East came both the sane and the insane with hope, with courage, with hoarded savings, with cold decks, with Bibles, with knives in boots, with humility and fear, with bland impudence. Most came with their own money; some came with money gained during a moment of inattention on the part of somebody in the East. And high in the air was the serene-browed angel of peace, with his endless gabble and his pretty maps. It was curious to walk out of an evening to the edge of a vast silent sea of prairie, and to reflect that the angel had parceled this infinity into building lots.

But no change had come to War Post. War Post sat with her reputation for bloodshed pressed proudly to her bosom and saw her mean neighbors leap into being as cities. She saw drunken old reprobates selling acres of red-hot dust and becoming wealthy men of affairs, who congratulated themselves on their shrewdness in holding land which, before the boom, they would have sold for enough to buy a treat all 'round in the Straight Flush Saloon—only nobody would have given it.

War Post saw dollars rolling into the coffers of a lot of contemptible men who couldn't shoot straight. She was amazed and indignant. She saw her standard of excellence, her creed, her reason for being great, all tumbling about her ears, and after the preliminary gasps she sat down to think it out.

The first man to voice a conclusion was Bob Hether, the popular barkeeper in Stevenson's Crystal Palace. "It's this here gun-fighter business," he said, leaning on his bar, and, with the gentle, serious eyes of a child, surveying a group of prominent citizens who had come in to drink at the expense of Tom Larpent, a gambler. They solemnly nodded assent. They stood in silence, holding their glasses and thinking.

Larpent was a chief factor in the life of the town. His gambling-house was the biggest institution in War Post. Moreover, he had been educated somewhere, and his slow speech had a certain mordant quality which was apt to puzzle War Post, and men heeded him for the reason that they were not always certain as to what he was saying. "Yes, Bob," he drawled, "I think you are right. The value of human life has to be established before there can be theatres, water-works, street cars, women and babies."

The other men were rather aghast at this cryptic speech, but somebody managed to snigger appreciatively and the tension was eased.

Smith Hanham, who whirled roulette for Larpent, then gave his opinion.

"Well, when all this here coin is floatin' 'round, it 'pears to me we orter git our hooks on some of it. Them little tin-horns over at Crowdger's Corners are up to their necks in it, an' we ain't yit seen a centavo. Not a centavetto. That ain't right. It's all well enough to sit 'round takin' money away from innercent cow-punchers s'long's ther's nothin' better; but when these here speculators come 'long flashin' rolls as big as water-buckets, it's up to us to whirl in an' git some of it."

This became the view of the town, and, since the main stipulation was virtue, War Post resolved to be virtuous. A great meeting was held, at which it was decreed that no man should kill another man under penalty of being at once hanged by the populace. All the influential citizens were present, and asserted their determination to deal out a swift punishment which would take no note of an acquaintance or friendship with the guilty man. Bob Hether made a loud, long speech, in which he declared that he for one would help hang his "own brother" if his "own brother" transgressed this law which now, for the good of the community, must be forever held sacred. Everybody was enthusiastic save a few Mexicans, who did not quite understand; but as they were more than likely to be the victims of any affray in which they were engaged, their silence was not considered ominous.

At half-past ten on the next morning Larpent shot and killed a man who had accused him of cheating at a game. Larpent had then taken a chair by the window.

II

Larpent grew tired of sitting in the chair by the window. He went to his bedroom, which opened off the gambling hall. On the table was a bottle of rye whiskey, of a brand which he specially and secretly imported from the East. He took a long drink; he changed his coat after laving his hands and brushing his hair. He sat down to read, his hand falling familiarly upon an old copy of Scott's "Fair Maid of Perth."

In time he heard the slow trample of many men coming up the stairs. The sound certainly did not indicate haste; in fact, it declared all kinds of hesitation. The crowd poured into the gambling hall; there was low talk; a silence; more low talk. Ultimately somebody rapped diffidently on the door of the bedroom.

"Come in," said Larpent. The door swung back and disclosed War Post with a delegation of its best men in the front, and at the rear men who stood on their toes and craned their necks. There was no noise. Larpent looked up casually into the eyes of Bob Hether. "So you've come up to the scratch all right, eh, Bobbie?" he asked kindly. "I was wondering if you would weaken on the blood-curdling speech you made yesterday."

Hether first turned deadly pale and then flushed beet red. His six-shooter was in his hand, and it appeared for a moment as if his weak fingers would drop it to the floor. "Oh, never mind," said Larpent in the same tone of kindly patronage. "The community must and shall hold this law forever sacred; and your own brother lives in Connecticut, doesn't he?" He laid down his book and arose. He unbuckled his revolver belt and tossed it on the bed. A look of impatience had come suddenly upon his face. "Well, you don't want me to be master of ceremonies at my own hanging, do you? Why don't somebody say something or do something? You stand around like a lot of bottles. Where's your tree, for instance? You know there isn't a tree between here and the river. Damned little jack-rabbit town hasn't even got a tree for its hanging. Hello, Coats, you live in Crowdger's Corners, don't you? Well, you keep out of this thing, then. The Corners has had its boom, and this is a speculation in real estate which is the business solely of the citizens of War Post."

The behavior of the crowd became extraordinary. Men began to back away; eye did not meet eye; they were victims of an inexplicable influence; it was as if they had heard sinister laughter from a gloom. "I know," said Larpent considerately, "that this isn't as if you were going to hang a comparative stranger. In a sense, this is an intimate affair. I know full well you could go out and jerk a comparative stranger into kingdom come and make a sort of festal occasion of it. But when it comes to performing the same office for an old friend, even the ferocious Bobbie Hether stands around on one leg like a damned white-livered coward. In short, my milk-fed patriots, you seem fat-headed enough to believe that I am going to hang myself if you wait long enough; but unfortunately I am going to allow you to conduct your own real-estate speculations. It seems to me there should be enough men here who understand the value of corner lots in a safe and godly town, and hence should be anxious to hurry this business."

The icy tones had ceased, and the crowd breathed a great sigh, as if it had been freed of a physical pain. But still no one seemed to know where to reach for the scruff of this weird situation. Finally there was some jostling on the outskirts of the crowd, and some men were seen to be pushing old Billie Simpson forward amid some protests. Simpson was, on occasion, the voice of the town. Somewhere in his past he had been a Baptist preacher. He had fallen far, very far, and the only remnant of his former dignity was a fatal facility of speech when half drunk. War Post used him on those state occasions when it became bitten with a desire to "do the thing up in style." So the citizens pushed the blear-eyed old ruffian forward until he stood hemming and hawing in front of Larpent. It was evident at once that he was brutally sober, and hence wholly unfitted for whatever task had been planned for him. A dozen times he croaked like a frog, meanwhile wiping the back of his hand rapidly across his mouth. At last he managed to stammer, "Mister Larpent——"

In some indescribable manner Larpent made his attitude of respectful attention to be grossly contemptuous and insulting. "Yes, Mister Simpson?"

"Er—now—Mister Larpent," began the old man hoarsely, "we wanted to know——" Then obviously feeling that there was a detail which he had forgotten, he turned to the crowd and whispered, "Where is it?" Many men precipitately cleared themselves out of the way, and down this lane Larpent had an unobstructed view of the body of the man he had slain. Old Simpson again began to croak like a frog, "Mister Larpent."

"Yes, Mister Simpson."

"Do you—er—do you—admit——"

"Oh, certainly," said the gambler good-humoredly. "There can be no doubt of it, Mister Simpson, although, with your well-known ability to fog things, you may later possibly prove that you did it yourself. I shot him because he was too officious. Not quite enough men are shot on that account, Mister Simpson. As one fitted in every way by nature to be consummately officious, I hope you will agree with me, Mister Simpson."

Men were plucking old Simpson by the sleeve and giving him directions. One could hear him say, "What?" "Yes." "All right." "What?" "All right." In the end he turned hurriedly upon Larpent and blurted out, "Well, I guess we're goin' to hang you."

Larpent bowed. "I had a suspicion that you would," he said in a pleasant voice. "There has been an air of determination about the entire proceeding, Mister Simpson."

There was an awkward moment. "Well—well—well, come ahead——"

Larpent courteously relieved a general embarrassment. "Why, of course. We must be moving. Clergy first, Mister Simpson. I'll take my old friend, Bobbie Hether, on my right hand, and we'll march soberly to the business, thus lending a certain dignity to this outing of real-estate speculators."

"Tom," quavered Bob Hether, "for Gawd's sake, keep your mout' shut."

"He invokes the deity," remarked Larpent placidly. "But, no; my last few minutes I am resolved to devote to inquiries as to the welfare of my friends. Now, you, for instance, my dear Bobbie, present to-day the lamentable appearance of a rattlesnake that has been four times killed and then left in the sun to rot. It is the effect of friendship upon a highly delicate system. You suffer? It is cruel. Never mind; you will feel better presently."

III

War Post had always risen superior to her lack of a tree by making use of a fixed wooden crane which appeared over a second-story window on the front of Pigrim's general store. This crane had a long tackle always ready for hoisting merchandise to the store's loft. Larpent, coming in the midst of a slow-moving throng, cocked a bright bird-like eye at this crane.

"Mm—yes," he said.

Men began to work frantically. They called each to each in voices strenuous but low. They were in a panic to have the thing finished. Larpent's cold ironical survey drove them mad, and it entered the minds of some that it would be felicitous to hang him before he could talk more. But he occupied the time in pleasant discourse. "I see that Smith Hanham is not here. Perhaps some undue tenderness of sentiment keeps him away. Such feelings are entirely unnecessary. Don't you think so, Bobbie? Note the feverish industry with which the renegade parson works at the rope. You will never be hung, Simpson. You will be shot for fooling too near a petticoat which doesn't belong to you —the same old habit which got you flung out of the Church, you red-eyed old satyr. Ah, the Cross Trail stage coach approaches. What a situation!" The crowd turned uneasily to follow his glance, and saw, truly enough, the dusty rickety old vehicle coming at the gallop of four lean horses. Ike Boston was driving the coach, and far away he had seen and defined the throng in front of Pigrim's store. First calling out excited information to his passengers, who were all inside, he began to lash his horses and yell. As a result he rattled wildly up to the scene just as they were arranging the rope around Larpent's neck.

"Whoa!" said he to his horses.

The inhabitants of War Post peered at the windows of the coach and saw therein six pale, horror-stricken faces. The men at the rope stood hesitating. Larpent smiled blandly. There was a silence. At last a broken voice cried from the coach: "Driver! Driver! What is it? What is it?"

Ike Boston spat between the wheel horses and mumbled that he s'posed anybody could see, less'n they were blind. The door of the coach opened and out stepped a beautiful young lady. She was followed by two little girls hand clasped in hand, and a white-haired old gentleman with a venerable and peaceful face. And the rough West stood in naked immorality before the eyes of the gentle East. The leather-faced men of War Post had never imagined such perfection of feminine charm, such radiance; and as the illumined eyes of the girl wandered doubtfully, fearfully, toward the man with the rope around his neck, a certain majority of the practiced ruffians tried to look as if they were having nothing to do with the proceedings.

"Oh," she said, in a low voice, "what are you going to do?"

At first none made reply; but ultimately a hero managed to break the harrowing stillness by stammering out, "Nothin'!" And then, as if aghast at his own prominence, he shied behind the shoulders of a big neighbor.

"Oh, I know," she said, "but it's wicked. Don't you see how wicked it is? Papa, do say something to them."

The clear, deliberate tones of Tom Larpent suddenly made every one stiffen. During the early part of the interruption he had seated himself upon the steps of Pigrim's store, in which position he had maintained a slightly bored air. He now was standing with the rope around his neck and bowing. He looked handsome and distinguished and—a devil. A devil as cold as moonlight upon the ice. "You are quite right, miss. They are going to hang me, but I can give you my word that the affair is perfectly regular. I killed a man this morning, and you see these people here who look like a fine collection of premier scoundrels are really engaged in forcing a real-estate boom. In short, they are speculators, land barons, and not the children of infamy which you no doubt took them for at first."

"O—oh!" she said, and shuddered.

Her father now spoke haughtily. "What has this man done? Why do you hang him without a trial, even if you have fair proofs?"

The crowd had been afraid to speak to the young lady, but a dozen voices answered her father. "Why, he admits it." "Didn't ye hear?" "There ain't no doubt about it." "No!" "He *sez* he did."

The old man looked at the smiling gambler. "Do you admit that you committed murder?"

Larpent answered slowly. "For the first question in a temporary acquaintance that is a fairly strong beginning. Do you wish me to speak as man to man, or to one who has some kind of official authority to meddle in a thing that is none of his affair?"

"I—ah—I," stuttered the other. "Ah—man to man."

"Then," said Larpent, "I have to inform you that this morning, at about 10:30, a man was shot and killed in my gambling house. He was engaged in the exciting business of trying to grab some money out of which he claimed I had swindled him. The details are not interesting."

The old gentleman waved his arm in a gesture of terror and despair and tottered toward the coach; the young lady fainted; the two little girls wailed. Larpent sat on the steps with the rope around his neck.

IV

The chief function of War Post was to prey upon the bands of cowboys who, when they had been paid, rode gayly into town to look for sin. To this end there were in War Post many thugs and thieves. There was treachery and obscenity and merciless greed in every direction. Even Mexico was levied upon to furnish a kind of ruffian which appears infrequently in the northern races. War Post was not good; it was not tender; it was not chivalrous; but——

But——

There was a quality to the situation in front of Pigrim's store which made War Post wish to stampede. There were the two children, their angelic faces turned toward the sky, weeping in the last anguish of fear; there was the beautiful form of the young lady prostrate in the dust of the road, with her trembling father bending over her; on the steps sat Larpent, waiting, with a derisive smile, while from time to time he turned his head in the rope to make a forked-tongued remark as to the character and bearing of some acquaintance. All the simplicity of a mere lynching was gone from this thing. Through some bewildering inner power of its own it had carried out of the hands of its inaugurators and was marching along like a great drama and they were only spectators. To them it was ungovernable; they could do no more than stand on one foot and wonder.

Some were heartily sick of everything and wished to run away. Some were so interested in the new aspect that they had forgotten why they had originally come to the front of Pigrim's store. These were the poets. A large practical class wished to establish at once the identity of the new comers. Who were they? Where did they come from? Where were they going to? It was truthfully argued that they were the parson for the new church at Crowdger's Corners, with his family.

And a fourth class—a dark-browed, muttering class—wished to go at once to the root of all disturbance by killing Ike Boston for trundling up his old omnibus and dumping out upon their ordinary lynching party such a load of tears and inexperience and sentimental argument. In low tones they addressed vitriolic reproaches.

"But how'd I know?" he protested, almost with tears. "How'd I know ther'd be all this here kick up?"

But Larpent suddenly created a great stir. He stood up, and his face was inspired with a new, strong resolution. "Look here, boys," he said decisively, "you hang me to-morrow. Or, anyhow, later on to-day. We can't keep frightening the young lady and these two poor babies out of their wits. Ease off on the rope, Simpson, you blackguard! Frightening women and children is your game, but I'm not going to stand it. Ike Boston, take your passengers on to Crowdger's Corners, and tell the young lady that, owing to her influence, the boys changed their minds about making me swing. Somebody lift the rope where it's caught under my ear, will you? Boys, when you want me you'll find me in the Crystal Palace."

His tone was so authoritative that some obeyed him at once involuntarily; but, as a matter of fact, his plan met with general approval. War Post heaved a great sigh of relief. Why had nobody thought earlier of so easy a way out of all these here tears?

V

Larpent went to the Crystal Palace, where he took his comfort like a gentleman, conversing with his friends and drinking. At nightfall two men rode into town, flung their bridles over a convenient post and clanked into the Crystal Palace. War Post knew them in a glance. Talk ceased and there was a watchful squaring back.

The foremost was Jack Potter, a famous town marshal of Yellow Sky, but now sheriff of the county; the other was Scratchy Wilson, once a no less famous desperado. They were both two-handed men of terrific prowess and courage, but War Post could hardly believe her eyes at view of this daring invasion. It was unprecedented.

Potter went straight to the bar, behind which frowned Bobbie Hether.

"You know a man by the name of Larpent?"

"Supposin' I do?" said Bobbie sourly.

"Well, I want him. Is he in the saloon?"

"Maybe he is an' maybe he isn't," said Bobbie.

Potter went back among the glinting eyes of the citizens. "Gentlemen, I want a man named Larpent. Is he here?"

War Post was sullen, but Larpent answered lazily for himself. "Why, you must mean me. My name is Larpent. What do you want?"

"I've got a warrant for your arrest."

There was a movement all over the room as if a puff of wind had come. The swing of a hand would have brought on a murderous mêlée. But after an instant the rigidity was broken by Larpent's laughter.

"Why, you're sold, sheriff!" he cried. "I've got a previous engagement. The boys are going to hang me to-night."

If Potter was surprised he betrayed nothing.

"The boys won't hang you to-night, Larpent," he said calmly, "because I'm goin' to take you in to Yellow Sky."

Larpent was looking at the warrant. "Only grand larceny," he observed. "But still, you know, I've promised these people to appear at their performance."

"You're goin' in with me," said the impassive sheriff.

"You bet he is, sheriff!" cried an enthusiastic voice, and it belonged to Bobbie Hether. The barkeeper moved down inside his rail, and, inspired like a prophet, he began a harangue to the citizens of War Post. "Now, look here, boys, that's jest what we want, ain't it? Here we were goin' to hang Tom Larpent jest for the reputation of the town, like. 'Long comes Sheriff Potter, the reg-u-lerly cons-ti-tuted officer of the law, an' he says, 'No; the man's mine.' Now, we want to make the reputation of the town as a law-abidin' place, so what do we say to Sheriff Potter? We says, 'A-a-ll right, sheriff; you're reg'lar; we ain't; he's your man.' But supposin' we go to fightin' over it? Then what becomes of the reputation of the town which we was goin' to swing Tom Larpent for?"

The immediate opposition to these views came from a source which a stranger might have difficulty in imagining. Men's foreheads grew thick with lines of obstinacy and disapproval. They were perfectly willing to hang Larpent yesterday, to-day, or to-morrow as a detail in a set of circumstances at War Post; but when some outsider from the alien town of Yellow Sky came into the sacred precincts of War Post and proclaimed the intention of extracting a citizen for cause, any citizen for any cause, the stomach of War Post was fed with a clan's blood, and her children gathered under one invisible banner, prepared to fight as few people in few ages were enabled to fight for their—points of view. There was a guttural murmuring.

"No; hold on!" screamed Bobbie, flinging up his hands. "He'll come clear all right. Tom," he appealed wildly to Larpent, "you never committed no —— —— low-down grand larceny?"

"No," said Larpent coldly.

"But how was it? Can't you tell us how it was?"

Larpent answered with plain reluctance. He waved his hand to indicate that it was all of little consequence. "Well, he was a tenderfoot, and he played poker with me, and he couldn't play quite good enough. But he thought he could; he could play extremely well, he thought. So he lost his money. I thought he'd squeal."

"Boys," begged Bobbie, "let the sheriff take him."

Some answered at once, "Yes!" Others continued to mutter. The sheriff had held his hand because, like all quiet and honest men, he did not wish to perturb any progress toward a peaceful solution; but now he decided to take the scene by the nose and make it obey him.

"Gentlemen," he said formally, "this man is comin' with me. Larpent, get up and come along."

This might have been the beginning, but it was practically the end. The two opinions in the minds of War Post fought in the air and, like a snow-squall, discouraged all action. Amid general confusion Jack Potter and Scratchy Wilson moved to the door with their prisoner. The last thing seen by the men in the Crystal Palace was the bronze countenance of Jack Potter as he backed from the place.

A man filled with belated thought suddenly cried out, "Well, they'll hang him fer this here shootin' game, anyhow."

Bobbie Hether looked disdain upon the speaker.

"Will they! An' where'll they get their witnesses? From here, do y' think? No; not a single one. All he's up against is a case of grand larceny; and—even supposin' he done it—what in hell does grand larceny amount to?"

A POKER GAME

USUALLY a poker game is a picture of peace. There is no drama so low-voiced and serene and monotonous. If an amateur loser does not softly curse there is no orchestral support. Here is one of the most exciting and absorbing occupations known to intelligent American manhood, here a year's reflection is compressed into a moment of thought, here the nerves may stand on end and scream to themselves, but a tranquility as from heaven is only interrupted by the click of chips. The higher the stakes, the more quiet the scene; this is a law that applies everywhere save on the stage.

And yet sometimes in a poker game things happen. Everybody remembers the celebrated corner on bay rum that was triumphantly consummated by Robert F. Cinch of Chicago assisted by the United States courts and whatever other federal power he needed. Robert F. Cinch enjoyed his victory four months. Then he died and young Bobbie Cinch came to New York in order to more clearly demonstrate that there was a good deal of fun in twenty-two million dollars.

Old Henry Spuytendyvil owns all the real estate in New York save that previously appropriated by the hospitals and Central Park. He had been a friend of Bob's father. When Bob appeared in New York, Spuytendyvil entertained him correctly. It came to pass that they just naturally played poker.

One night they were having a small game in an up-town hotel. There were five of them, including two lawyers and a politician. The stakes depended on the ability of the individual fortune.

Bobbie Cinch had won rather heavily. He was as generous as sunshine and when luck chases a generous man it chases him hard, even though he cannot bet with all the skill of his opponents.

Old Spuytendyvil had lost a considerable amount. One of the

lawyers from time to time smiled quietly because he knew Spuy-tendyvil well and he knew that anything with the name of loss attached to it sliced the old man's heart into sections.

At midnight, Archie Bracketts, the actor, came into the room. "How you holding 'em, Bob?" said he.

"Pretty well," said Bob.

"Having any luck, Mr. Spuytendyvil?"

"Blooming bad," grunted the old man.

Bracketts laughed and put his foot on the round of Spuytendy-vil's chair. "There," said he. "I'll queer your luck for you." Spuy-tendyvil sat at the end of the table. "Bobbie," said the actor presently, as young Cinch won another pot, "I guess I better knock your luck." So he took his foot from the old man's chair and placed it on Bob's chair. The lad grinned good-naturedly and said he didn't care.

Bracketts was in a position to scan both of the hands. It was Bob's ante and old Spuytendyvil threw in a red chip. Everybody passed out up to Bobbie. He filled in the pot and drew a card.

Spuytendyvil drew a card. Bracketts, looking over his shoulder, saw him holding the ten, nine, eight and seven of diamonds. Theatrically speaking, straight flushes are as frequent as berries on a juniper tree but as a matter of truth the reason that straight flushes are so admired is because they are not as common as berries on a juniper tree. Bracketts stared; drew a cigar slowly from his pocket and placing it between his teeth, forgot its existence.

Bobbie was the only other stayer. Bracketts flashed an eye for the lad's hand and saw the nine, eight, six and five of hearts. Now there are but six hundred and forty-five emotions possible to the human mind and Bracketts immediately had them all. Under the impression that he had finished his cigar, he took it from his mouth and tossed it toward the grate without turning his eyes to follow its flight.

There happened to be a complete silence around the green-clothed table. Spuytendyvil was studying his hand with a kind of contemptuous smile but in his eyes there perhaps was to be seen a cold stern light expressing something sinister and relentless.

Young Bob sat as he had sat. As the pause grew longer, he looked up once inquiringly at Spuytendyvil.

The old man reached for a white chip. "Well, mine are worth about that much," said he, tossing it into the pot. Thereupon he leaned back comfortably in his chair and renewed his stare at the five straight diamonds. Young Bob extended his hand leisurely toward his stack. It occurred to Bracketts that he was smoking but he found no cigar in his mouth.

The lad fingered his chips and looked pensively at his hand. The silence of these moments oppressed Bracketts like the smoke from a conflagration.

Bobbie Cinch continued for some moments to coolly observe his cards. At last he breathed a little sigh and said: "Well, Mr. Spuytendyvil, I can't play a sure thing against you." He threw in a white chip. "I'll just call you. I've got a straight flush." He faced down his cards.

Old Spuytendyvil's roar of horror and rage could only be equaled in volume to a small explosion of gasolene. He dashed his cards upon the table. "There!" he shouted glaring frightfully at Bobbie. "I've got a straight flush, too! And mine is Jack high!"

Bobbie was at first paralyzed with amazement but in a moment he recovered and apparently observing something amusing in the situation he grinned.

Archie Bracketts, having burst his bond of silence, yelled for joy and relief. He smote Bobbie on the shoulder. "Bob, my boy," he cried exuberantly, "you're no gambler but you're a mighty good fellow and if you hadn't been you would be losing a good many dollars this minute."

Old Spuytendyvil glowered at Bracketts. "Stop making such an infernal din, will you, Archie," he said morosely. His throat seemed filled with pounded glass. "Pass the whiskey."

APPENDIXES

TEXTUAL NOTES

THE PACE OF YOUTH

4.18 the manner] This is the first of five changes made by E1 from $N 'the' to 'a', with one alteration in reverse—from 'a' to 'the'—at 5.21. On the evidence of a similar change from 'the' to 'a' made no doubt inadvertently by the *Kansas City Star* at 11.18, such variation is to be expected sporadically and unauthoritatively. However, five times in one story goes beyond the possibility of chance. Thus only two alternatives present themselves: (1) these are authentic stylistic changes which Crane made when marking printer's copy for Heinemann; or (2) the English compositor or press reader of this section had his own strong ideas about idiom. The first is unsupported by other examples of similar changes in E1, or elsewhere in Crane on a demonstrably authoritative basis. Moreover, although several of these may be indifferent (as at 12.25), normal idiom seems violated here at 4.18 and certainly at 12.7, where the E1 version 'his whole expedition was a tottering upon a trail of birds' is unnatural. The change at 10.8 may seem odd: the indefinite 'a dull, sultry afternoon' of E1 may seem to clash with the precision of the opening 'One day', and $N 'One day, when business paused during the dull, sultry afternoon' is almost required. On the other hand, since these peculiar changes are confined to only one story in this collection, it might seem easier to assign them to Crane since he was definitely engaged in a stylistic revision of this material, whereas a mechanical explanation confined to a single literary unit is more difficult to accept. Nevertheless, the difficulty of viewing these six exchanges of 'the' and 'a' as truly revisory is acute unless one were to believe that the copy for E1 was a new typescript. It may be that a similar change made in "One Dash—Horses" is significant, although whether it was inadvertent or conscious on the part of the English compositor is difficult to establish. At any rate, the alteration from 'the knife' to 'a knife' at 18.22 (and the reverse at 14.22) took place not in E1 but earlier in the *New Review* text, which Crane did not oversee, and thus he cannot be held responsible for it. Yet it is precisely the sort of idiomatic change made in "The Pace of Youth" and hence may lend some support to the hypothesis of the present editor that on the whole English tinkering with American style may be preferable as an explanation for this anomaly instead of authorial revision. These five changes, then, as well as the sixth in reverse, have been rejected in the present text.

10.2 crowd] E1 'crowds' appears to be an error caused by contamination from the plurals 'stars' and 'lights'. That the crowd is singular, as in $N,

is clear from references at 8.13 and 8.32. It may seem farfetched to take it
that Crane thought of one crowd as replacing, or exchanging with, another
and therefore altered the copy to the plural.

10.7 mystic lands] With some strain, perhaps, the E1 variant 'mystic
bands' might be justified as the bonds of love and marriage that are to
unite the couple in the future. But it would seem that E1 is a misprint and
that $N 'mystic lands' should hold. The emphasis has been on this 'fairy
scene of the night . . . the purple sea, the yellow stars, the changing
crowd'. The gay paper lanterns reflected in the waters of the lake promise
the couple a habitation in the future for their feelings that is as romantic
and sublime as this present 'fairy scene', far removed from the mundane
pattern of ordinary life. Professor Levenson has suggested the following
exact parallel from Crane's "Experiment in Luxury": 'The head of the
family, the famous millionaire, sat on a low stool before the fire. He was
deeply absorbed in the gambols of a kitten. . . . There was never such a
case of abstraction, of want of care. The man of millions was in a far
land where mechanics and bricklayers go, a mystic land of little, universal
emotions, and he had been guided to it by the quaint gestures of a kitten's
furry paws. His wife, who stood near, was apparently not at all a dweller
in thought lands. She was existing very much in the present. Evidently she
had been wishing to consult with her husband on some tremendous
domestic question'.

11.38 clinched] So far as the evidence of Crane's manuscripts goes, he
never in his life wrote 'clenched' but always 'clinched'. In the present example, therefore, one is faced with the possibility that all texts except for
the New York *Press* edited the word to its usual form, or else that an intermediate typescript which had made the change to 'clenched' was the copy
for the Bacheller proof and the *Press* independently styled as 'clinched'.

12.15 The dust rose . . .] The closing by E1 at this point of a paragraph
present in $N and the opening of a paragraph indention at 'The highway
vanished' at 12.16 is one of the few cases that E1 alters N paragraphing
except in connection with the styling of dialogue. Since the copy for E1
was generally revised by Crane, any variant must be analyzed respectfully.
However, the present seems to be an arbitrary act by the English compositor, or the typist of an intermediate manuscript as copy for E1, tempted
perhaps by what seemed to be a most acute conjunction of detail. That is,
Stimson's revery that leads him to 'that time when his bones must be laid
in earth' seems only fittingly followed by the detail that the dust rose from
the road to stifle his nostrils. On the other hand, the original N paragraphing does not thrust this parallel at the reader so resolutely and is demonstrably of a piece. Stimson's thoughts lead to an internal relaxation of his
anger. Externally, the physical difficulties act to cause the pursuit to become increasingly useless. Stimson is made uncomfortable by the heat and
the dust, and, finally, the youthful buggy is easily outdistancing his aged
hack. The dust, then, is not of the grave, primarily, but of the here and
now operating on him to influence his acceptance of defeat. The E1 alteration is superficially clever but it is either a true distortion or else an over-
explicit signpost to a latent reference.

ONE DASH—HORSES

15.22 North] On the example of 'eastern' in the manuscript of "The Five White Mice" (48.26), the manuscript of "One Dash—Horses" very likely read 'north' as in N³⁻⁵, PM, and NR. However, Crane's practice may not have been invariable, and in any event the reading 'North' of N¹⁻² is required, although it may most properly be regarded as an emendation.

15.31 quavering] The *New Review*, which represents an earlier state of the text than that in the proof that lies behind the newspapers and the *Pocket Magazine*, reads 'quavering'—a reading thence transferred to E1. The N,PM reading 'quivering', which is passed on to A1 without alteration there, appears to be a compositorial sophistication in the proof, the pure reading of the typescript (and manuscript) being preserved in the copy sent to England. In the present story 'quivering' appears four times: at 13.18 Richardson's horse 'breathed quiveringly'; at 20.25 Richardson heard his horse 'breathe a quivering sigh of excitement'; at 22.21 José's moans and cries 'broke continually from his quivering lips'; and at 23.10 the black horse 'quivering and breathing heavily he made a great effort'. But these examples do not apply to the voice. In *George's Mother*, in Volume 1 of this edition of Crane's *Works*, 119.14–15, the mother's voice 'quavered and trembled out into the air' and in "The Five White Mice" (44.39) the New York Kid hears the drunken 'quavering voices' of the 'Frisco Kid and Benson. In "Three Miraculous Soldiers" (VI, TALES OF WAR), the girl 'was quivering' with excitement as she watched the Union soldiers coming down the road (23.30), but her voice 'quavered' as she spoke to her mother (25.4). It follows that in "One Dash—Horses" 'They [the twenty voices] rose in quavering shrillness, as from men badly drunk' is the right reading, as found in NR.

17.26–27 as rigidly] The omission of this phrase in NR is accompanied by signs of newspaper difficulty as in N¹ 'at rigidly' and N⁵ 'as rigorously'. Some corruption in the original typescript independently transferred to the proof and to the NR copy may have occurred and been solved in various ways by the compositors. Another such corruption may have occurred in 'that way' at 20.34, although here perhaps the trouble was confined to the proof.

18.3 this—,"] It is tempting to speculate if Crane intended the fat Mexican's speech to end with 'this' and then trail off, or whether the dash was supposed to stand for an epithet. In favor of the first, or suspension of the speech, is the word 'began'; but, more concretely, every text prints the dash close up to 'this' and not with space between as if the dash stood for a word. According to the documentary evidence, therefore, the meaning is not in question. The comma after the dash is not typical of Crane, but some compositors (and typists) styled copy with it in this position.

18.35 vibrating and] This E1 reading substitutes for $N,PM,NR 'mystic and' and is part of a systematic process of weeding out in early stories the use of the word 'mystic', a process commented on in the sections of the Textual Introduction on "The Pace of Youth" and "A Man and Some Others." Interestingly, in "One Dash—Horses" the sole A1 revision is the simple omission of this 'mystic and' found in the PM copy. The difference in treatment between the revision for the English and the American editions of *The Open Boat* suggests that the more systematic alterations of E1 (even disregarding such thoroughgoing E1 revision as took place in "The Pace of Youth") were made in the copy that Crane sent to Heinemann, usually from English magazine publication when available. The difference in the printer's copy, whereby the American *Open Boat* was always set from American periodicals, also suggests that Crane had not himself assembled and marked this copy but instead had merely indicated to his American agent or publisher where copy could be found. If this is so, then the authoritative changes made in A1 stem from actual proof correction, and they are few enough to conform to such a pattern. Although the E1 variants might also have been made in proof, their greater frequency and their almost complete lack of relationship to the A1 variants suggest instead that in general they originated in the printer's copy. (Of course, any further changes made in the E1 proof could not be distinguished.) This difference in the treatment of the texts for the two book editions would readily enough account for Crane's variable revision of the PM,NR phrase 'mystic and'. He seems to have read proof for A1 without recollection of the changes he had made in the copy for Heinemann and to have altered A1 proof independently. Under these conditions it is proper to retain here the E1 revision, since it is part of a systematic review of the text, and to ignore the omission of the phrase which occurred during a casual proofreading of A1.

THE WISE MEN

26.15 Kids] The manuscript of "The Five White Mice," followed by the two United States texts, reads 'Kids' with a capital except for two slips, although E1 persists in 'kids'. On the other hand, in "The Wise Men" 'kids' must have stood in the manuscript and in the two basic typescripts in order to produce the agreement by LB, LM, and E1 in the lower-case form. Under these circumstances, the invariable capitalization 'Kids' in A1 is unlikely to represent house styling and must reproduce the marking in the copy for A1 that was part of its revision.

26.29–30 is set . . . windows] Crane's uncertain grammar, no doubt appearing in the original manuscript, is probably retained in the typescript furnished the LM and E1 copy since in the English versions the reading is 'is set . . . windows'. One may only speculate whether the typist of the copy made for the United States altered the reading to 'are' (as is assumed in the present edition) or whether it is one of the series of apparently authoritative variants between the two textual traditions.

28.14 mean] The LB variant 'means' could hypothetically have followed the typescript for America (either corrected or house-styled to 'mean' in A1) but with the typescript for LM and E1 reading 'mean'. This would follow the principle of the harder reading. On the other hand it is much simpler to conjecture that both typescripts read 'mean' but that the LB compositor was misled by contamination into taking 'form' as the referent of 'which', not the correct 'qualities'.

29.38 They thought he intended] Twice in this story (here and at 32.8) A1 uniquely inserts a 'that' where clearly neither of the two typescripts had one. The question arises whether these insertions were part of Crane's revision of the text in A1 or were editorial. It is perhaps a question of plus or of minus whether compositors or typists are more inclined to omit the relative 'that' in colloquial speech or to add it. In general, however, the probability is that an inserted 'that' is a sophistication. The pull toward regularity of syntax may be seen at 32.5, where E1 joins A1 in adding a 'that' not present in LB and LM, and also at 32.37, where the typescripts themselves seem to have diverged since the 'that' found in LB,A1 is wanting in LM,E1.

32.32 It's a go?] The A1 alteration to 'is it a go?' must be viewed with considerable suspicion since the question mark would readily suggest the change. Something of a parallel may exist in ' "Ten, is it? All right; that goes." ' (31.36), but the parallel is scarcely an exact one. Nor is the parallel exact at 51.19–20 in "The Five White Mice" of ' "Well, señor, it is finished?" ' because here a Mexican is speaking unidiomatic English.

33.16 *calle*] The italics in A1 but not elsewhere are perhaps as likely to be compositorial as an authorial correction. It is interesting that in "The Five White Mice" manuscript the word 'calle' is underlined on its first appearance (40.9) but not on its second (46.3).

33.18 class] The A1 change to 'classes' may be a sophistication affected by 'their' at 33.19,20 and especially by 'classes' at 33.20. That the manuscript read 'class' seems to be established by the agreement of LB, LM, and E1. The manuscript reading may have been an error, of course; but it is also possible that Crane was identifying only one top class but more than one type of lower class, such as Mexicans and Indians, or else distinguishable traits within the lower classes but uniformity in the upper class.

33.22 pave] The LM alteration of 'pave' in the other texts to 'pavé' obviously cannot be authorial and is, in fact, unnecessary since 'pave' as cited in *O.E.D.* and used by Walt Whitman seems to be a rare American form.

36.3 buskins] The LB variant 'buckskins' is more likely, perhaps, to be the compositor's rationalization of what may have been an unfamiliar word than a typist's error in the American line corrected in A1. Fortunately, no doubt can exist about the correct reading. *Buckskins* are scarcely characteristic of the European 'Old World' that Crane is evoking; moreover, the 'cavalcades of steel' that are next related to the stones are evidently the charges of knights in armor.

37.39 jeer] Although 'jibe'—the reading of LB, LM, E1—is a characteristic Crane spelling for *gibe* and thus almost certainly the reading of the manuscript, the A1 alteration to 'jeer' is probably not a sophistication but an authentic revision: in the manuscript for "The Five White Mice" at 43.13 one finds 'a man would suddenly jeer a finger at the Kid' where 'jeer' has been interlined above deleted 'thrust'.

38.3 hollo] This unique A1 variant for LB,LM,E1 'hello' might be thought a simple misprint were it not for two pieces of evidence in its favor. First, 37.39 carries the Kids' jeering question to Benson, and after Benson's explanation how he came to lose his handkerchief it would be quite inane for the Kids to respond with the greeting 'hello'. Second, both LM and E1 punctuate ' "Why, hello! Benson," ' which is an odd exclamation point for an ordinary greeting. It would seem that the Kids by their jocular *holloo* are encouraging Benson to seek the trail of his lost handkerchief. The EM,E1 exclamation would be appropriate after 'holloo' or its equivalent 'hollo', and thus seems to have stood in the basic typescript behind the English versions although not behind the American. The probability is that both typescripts contained the error 'hello' and that 'hollo' is a Crane change in the A1 copy. This is easier to accept than a triple false rationalization by LB, LM, and E1 of typescript 'hallo', especially since we know that A1 was a corrected text. One may compare the hail "Halloa' from the cruiser in "The Revenge of the *Adolphus*" (VII, TALES OF WAR) at 160.2.

THE FIVE WHITE MICE

41.1 in] That MS,E1 to blow 'in the cup' in order to perform magic is correct, and not 'on the cup' as in W,A1, may be indicated by 42.7–8, 'He addressed a gambler's slogan to the interior of the cup.'

42.19 All of the] Although in MS the 'of' is squeezed in and possibly may have been overlooked by the E1 compositor, he seems to have been motivated by a reversion to the English idiom as in "All the King's horses . . ."

44.1 They stuck me] Although the reading is largely indifferent, the W,A1 concurrence in 'They've' for MS,E1 'They' shows that it was in the typescript. On the evidence of the form 'They stuck' in all texts at 43.36–37 and 44.8, it seems more probable that the typist was led to contaminate MS 'They' from the following 'I've' than that Crane altered this one reading in the typescript and ignored the others.

44.3–6 "Oh . . . feet."] The concurrence of W with MS,E1 demonstrates that the A1 punctuation of each sentence with quotation marks to mark off the alternating speeches of the 'Frisco Kid and Benson was either the A1 compositor's sophistication or else Crane's proof corrections in A1. In "The Wise Men" at 33.29–31 speeches of this order are each given a separate line and their own quotation marks as normal dialogue, but at 35.30, probably at 37.3, and certainly at 37.8–10, mixed remarks from various nameless persons are treated, as in MS here, as part of only one quotation. However, the parallel is not an exact one, and it may be significant that at 37.11–14, immediately following the mixed dialogue treated as one speech in lines 8–10, when the cries begin to sort themselves out, each is again given a separate line of dialogue with its proper quotes. Crane's practice was not, perhaps, invariable but in this case the evidence of "The Shrapnel of Their Friends" (VI, TALES OF WAR, 304.30–31) appears to be decisive. Here two independently derived texts—*Ainslee's Magazine*, *Black and White*, and then a later typescript, the carbon of which served as printer's copy for *Last Words*—read as follows: 'Men stumbled; men fell; men swore. There were cries: "This way! Come this way! Don't go that way! You can't get up that way!"' But the wholly unauthoritative *Last Words* text, set from the typescript copy in the exact form given above, takes it upon itself to put quotes about each individual cry. The assumption is that in "The Five White Mice" the A1 quotes are precisely in the same category.

44.23 comic, foolish, wise] The E1 variant 'foolish-wise clown', though sometimes quoted with approval because of its appearance in Follett's text, seems to be the English compositor's rationalization of a typical Crane series of adjectives without commas in the MS printer's copy.

45.1 Comere] MS had originally been written 'Com' ere' but then an 'h' seems to have been interlined and later deleted. At this time the apostrophe was deleted and the 'm' and 'e' carefully joined. In view of this evidence the intended reading is certain, and it would seem that the E1 compositor and the typist mistook the markings in the MS.

45.11 'round] It is possible that the English typist altered MS 'around' to 'round', as it appears in W,A1, just as English compositors were apt to make this alteration in Crane. On the other hand, 'round' is not unknown in Crane—''round' appears in informal speech in "The Wise Men" 31.8—and it is much more appropriate here to the other drunken elisions than is 'around'. Since Crane took particular care with dialect speech, it is likely that he made this alteration in the typescript. Just possibly the apostrophe in W 'Cer'ly' at 45.13 (A1 'Ce'r'ly') is another such small attention, especially in view of the W,A1 form 'ain'' for MS 'aint' at 46.23. At first sight an apostrophe in 'Cerly' seems to violate the system of run-together words like 'Comere'; but the two cases are different, for 'Cer'ly' indicates only the elided syllable in a single word, like 'reg'lar' at 46.23.

THE OPEN BOAT

69.38 doubtlessly] It is difficult to assess the authority of the change in A1 to 'doubtless' within parenthetical commas. Although the more usual form, as in A1, is found at 71.8—'but they all doubtless possessed this sense of the situation'—yet the agreement of all three texts in 'Previously to the foundering' at 74.37 may seem decisive in favor of retaining the Sc,E1 'doubtlessly' as the more likely to be authoritative.

72.25 light-house] In Sc this word is unhyphenated in its first three appearances here and at 72.28, 73.2, but is hyphenated regularly thereafter at 74.3, 74.9, 75.9, and 76.8. Whether this anomaly is the result of a change of compositors in Sc or whether the copy was hyphenated throughout and house style was imposed only on the first appearances—or vice versa—cannot be determined. In Chapter xii of the holograph manuscript of *The O'Ruddy* the form is 'light-house'.

74.5–7 The man . . . shadow.] An anomaly is present here. We know that the boat had only two oars (68.18). At 73.32–74.2 a sail is rigged using the captain's overcoat with one of the oars for a mast. The second oar was then used by the oiler for steering. Thus at 74.5–7 when the boat was under sail, no man would be at the oars and prevented from turning his head to glimpse the shadow. It will not do, either, to try to emend to 'oar' by making this man the cook and correspondent who hold up the oar-mast. Crane's inadvertent slip could be repaired only by the omission of the present sentence. When the wind later dies down the sail is given over and rowing resumed (74.16–20).

79.27 those] The reading of all texts, 'one of these big hotel omnibuses', is not impossible but the odds favor it as an error. One may compare 'one of those big yawls' (80.29); 'Don't talk about those things' (82.2); and ' "We'll give those boys a chance to get into shape again" ' (87.10), the two latter, especially, being occasions when *these* would have been more appropriate than at 79.27. On the other hand, *these* is very properly employed at 82.8–9: 'These two lights were the furniture of the world.' Just such a confusion of 'these' and 'those' is also found in "A Tale of Mere Chance."

85.24 never more shall see] This is a correction in A1 of the Sc,E1 limping 'shall never see', the correction coming from the true reading of the Caroline E. S. Norton poem, "Bingen on the Rhine." Crane has taken liberties with the text by deftly condensing the original:

A soldier of the Legion lay dying in Algiers;
There was lack of woman's nursing, there was dearth of woman's tears;
But a comrade stood beside him, while his life-blood ebb'd away,
And bent, with pitying glances, to hear what he might say.
The dying soldier falter'd as he took that comrade's hand,
And he said, "I never more shall see my own, my native land. . . ."
(Philadelphia: Porter and Coates, 1883)

FLANAGAN AND HIS SHORT FILIBUSTERING ADVENTURE

93.12 afterward] Although it is unlikely that 'afterward' in A1 for 'afterwards' in the other texts is a proof correction, the agreement of McC and of A1 at 106.13 in 'afterward', a Crane form, suggests that the English form here and at 100.10 in McC did not reflect the manuscript and perhaps not the typescript.

101.37 said he] The inversion is so characteristic of Crane (as in *Maggie*), although decreasing in his later style, as to lead to the belief that this may well be an authorial proof revision in A1. The A1 correction of McC at 103.5–6 (see Textual Note below) encourages the conclusion that

"Flanagan" was not passed over but was casually marked in proof as were most of the other stories in the American edition.

103.5–6 engine-rooms] Just possibly the ILN plural is a sophistication of the typescript and McC singular. But the curious appearance of the plural, again, in A1 (the second example of an A1 proof correction?) gives one some slight confidence that Crane wanted the plural and that McC had been in error. One may cite: 'In the engine-room the chief and his assistant were staring at the gong. In the stoke-room the firemen breathed through their teeth' (102.27–29). This distinction of the two rooms suggests that if 'Everyone outside of the engine-room was set on watch', as in McC, were to be literally interpreted, the stokers would have been removed for watch duty, a manifest absurdity. The plural 'engine-rooms', therefore, associates the stokehole with the engine room proper, as is necessary.

103.20 into] On the evidence of McC,ILN agreement on 'blipped into the sea' at 103.16, ILN appears to preserve the correct form here, in repetition, as against McC 'in'.

107.20 head] Whether the captain 'knocked his head on the gunwale' as in McC, or 'knocked his hand' as in ILN, is a difficult question. The usual expression of feeling in Crane involves beating the hand against an object, as in 'Scully banged his hand impressively on the foot-board of the bed' and the cowboy 'brought his hand down on a chair with a noise like a pistol-shot' ("The Blue Hotel," pp. 149.33, 164.30–31). In Chapter VIII of *The O'Ruddy*, 'Colonel Royale beat his hand passionately against the wall'. These may support the ILN reading and might even prove conclusive were it not for the curious discrepancy between the violence of 'whirled' and the comparatively moderate verb 'knocked', which differs from 'beat' or 'bang' as better suited to the head than to the hand. This impression may be an overrefined one, however. Even though McC is the superior text for substantives, there is admittedly a danger in following it here when the ILN variant reproduces Crane analogues. Yet the aptness of these must remain in question since they are all expressions of anger, whereas the captain's action is one of despair.

THE BRIDE COMES TO YELLOW SKY

109.8 coach] The change in Ch to 'train' seems to be a special alteration for the English reader for whom a *coach* is a *carriage* and *Pullman* had, at that time, little or no meaning. It was necessary, obviously, to establish immediately the fact that the couple were on a train, not in a stagecoach; after that, the Ch editor could relax and allow 'coach' to pass at 110.9 and 111.10.

110.5 trains] The Ch singular 'train' may be a sophistication or the same sort of error that produced the faulty singular 'revolver' at 117.19. The McC plural 'trains' more naturally suggests that Potter explained about the various kinds of trains on their route for the specific purpose of pointing out how much superior was their express that stopped only four times. Or, if this is too refined, one may suppose that since Mrs. Potter may never have been on a train in her life, her husband explained trains to her in general.

119.20 the glory of the marriage, the environment of the new estate] Ch reads 'of their marriage' but joins McC in 'the environment of the new estate' (Ch error: 'environments'). The agreement of the two authorities in the latter half of this vision passage demonstrates the absolute authority of 'the environment of the new estate' (at least in the basic typescript). The first half, then, is alone in question. In the first Pullman passage at 110.15–17 Crane was reproducing the thoughts of the couple ('To the minds of the pair, their surroundings reflected the glory of their marriage . . . this was the environment of their new estate'), but at 119.20 Jack Potter's thoughts alone are involved, and hence 'the' is a more appropriate reading than 'their'. Since the 'their' in the latter half of the passage repetition was changed to 'the', it is reasonable to consider that the same change was intended in the first half.

DEATH AND THE CHILD

122.16 moments] On various occasions, and in the manuscript of *The O'Ruddy*, Crane altered 'minutes' to 'moments'; his liking for this word, indeed, may put some strain on it so that unauthoritative changes could be made, as in TMs of "An Episode of War" which, copying the printed text from the magazine *The Gentlewoman*, without authority altered 'moment' to 'instant' (see VI, TALES OF WAR, 89.24). Under these circumstances—that Crane elsewhere did not alter 'moment' to something else, although changing other words to it—the A1 substitution of 'times' for 'moments' must be viewed with considerable suspicion, the more especially since 'moments' is not especially idiomatic here.

123.30 this kind] The A1 'this' for BW,HW,A1 (and therefore MS) 'his' makes the correct substitution for words often confused with each other. The context does not support any suggestion that 'his kind' could be used for Peza in the special sense Crane applied to the lieutenant in "The Clan of No-Name" and its litany. The correctness of the A1 alteration 'dwelt' for BW,HW,E1 'dwell' in the same line is open to more question. It is true that Crane's uncrossed 't' frequently resembles an 'l' but since 'dwell' was manifestly the reading in both typescripts it may be asking too much of fate to conjecture that both typists made the same misreading. The A1 preterite 'dwelt' is an easy sophistication to bring the verb into the past with the other verbs in the sentence; it is, however, an unnecessary one and appears to have no authority.

123.36 an explosion] The manuscript leaf here shows Crane, as he dictated, endeavoring to avoid the repeated use of 'one'. The sentence begins in the MS, 'Then suddenly the beats became mingled until one could'; but before Cora could quite complete the final 'd' she was stopped, 'one could' was crossed through, and the sentence continued with 'a man could hardly separate one from another. . . .' As shown by the agreement of BW,

HW, and E1 in the reading 'until one could not separate an explosion from another', in the final manuscript version drawn on by both type-scripts Crane rejected his original expedient in order to return to 'one' for 'a man', but then weakly altered 'one explosion' to 'an explosion'. In setting 'one explosion' the A1 compositor (or editor) recognized the difficulty of 'an', but the alteration need not thereby acquire any authority.

124.11 struck with] The British form of the idiom is 'struck by', as in BW,E1; not 'struck with', as in HW,A1. Although it is possible that both compositors of BW and E1 independently altered the phrase, the simpler explanation is that this marks a difference in the two typescripts. If so, there may be some reason to conjecture that the typescript behind BW and E1 was made by a different agent from that behind HW and A1 and that this agent was English. It does not necessarily follow, unfortunately, that the typist of the other transcript was an American. The typist could also have been English but one who followed copy in this word.

125.6 But] The omission of this word in A1 is probably not to be separated from the insertion of a semicolon before 'that' in the preceding line with the effect of turning a relative pronoun into a demonstrative. The reading of the three other texts is almost certainly that of MS; but the question then arises whether MS may not have been in error as it seems to have been above at 123.30 (see Textual Note). However, the case may differ somewhat from 123.30 in that 'But' could scarcely be an *error* in MS, and thus if Crane had marked it for omission in A1, the case would be one for revision, not for correction (regardless of the question of 'that'). When one analyzes the paragraph beginning at 124.31, one may see that the central idea is not love versus war, or hate, but a principle versus a living fact, isolation versus participation, the ideas that run throughout the story. The contrast, then, between Peza confronting love as an individual and the fact of war, as represented by the collective emotions of forty thousand men, requires the 'But'; otherwise, 'he felt here the vibration from the hearts of forty thousand men' would be placed in apposition to 'Love he knew that he had confronted . . .' The omission of 'But', therefore, can scarcely be an authorial revision but seems to represent a compositorial or editorial misunderstanding. This being so, the syntactical alteration in the line above loses what little virtue it might have possessed. It would seem that the compositor was misled by a more than ordinarily graceless Crane construction, which one can easily rearrange in its sense as *He knew that he had confronted love alone. . . .*

125.31 gesticulation] The plural reading 'gesticulations' in the impossible combination for authority of BW,A1 shows compositorial sophistication at work here. Thus the direction of change is sufficiently obvious: the singular 'gesticulation' of the typescripts has been corrupted by the first element in the series, 'ape-like cries'. One would not wish to argue the reverse.

127.6 ¶ The roar of the fighting] Some irregularity either of paragraph indention or of marking may have occurred in the manuscript at or near this point. HW and A1 begin a new paragraph with 'He was not averse' at

127.4, and run on with this the next sentence, 'The roar of the fighting . . .' BW, on the contrary, may reflect the manuscript, although perhaps not some direction in it, by ignoring the HW,A1 paragraphing at 127.4 but agreeing with the continuous text of 'The roar of the fighting . . .' E1 agrees with BW in ignoring the HW,A1 paragraph at 127.4 but uniquely places the paragraph indention at 127.6. According to the sense, this is the best choice if a paragraph is to be accepted at all, for 'He was not averse . . .' is closely tied with its preceding sentence, 'There was an element . . .', but not with its following, 'The roar of the fighting . . .' The HW,A1 indention, then, is wrongly placed. An editor would be tempted to follow the BW lack of paragraphing throughout (since the E1 indention at 127.6 is of doubtful authority) were it not for the misplaced HW,A1 paragraphing which would seem to suggest some notation in the manuscript intended to alter the inscription followed by BW to an indention, but which was misunderstood by the typist of the copy behind HW,A1. If so, however, the typist behind the BW,E1 prints could not have obeyed the marking, and we might seem forced to believe that the E1 indention is purely editorial. This is not a very satisfactory conclusion, and a better hypothesis would be that the typist originally overlooked the marking and typed continuous text but marked the typescript, and BW either ignored the marking or followed an unmarked carbon whereas E1 obeyed the marking.

127.15 all] The phrase at 129.9–10, 'the trees, the flowers, the grass, all tender and beautiful nature', may suggest that the A1 omission of 'all' here at 127.15 is an error, not an authorial change.

131.31 moved] Since the overall evidence does not suggest that the typescripts for either the English or the American line of the text (with the possible exception of A1) were authorially reviewed and revised independently, it follows that variations between them consist mainly of right and of wrong readings, not of original and revised readings. This being so, 'curved' may be a typist's sophistication of the manuscript's hard reading 'moved', since a critic would scarcely be persuaded by the opposite argument. Misreading of handwriting is a slight possibility to aid the typist in believing in the conventional word. Nevertheless, the case is far from open and shut. In Report #6 (see "A Fragment of Velestino" in REPORTS OF WAR, Works, IX) the second paragraph begins, "There was a wide highway, curving sinuously because of the grades." On the other hand, "Death and the Child" is explicit about this road: "At the foot of the path they came to a wide road which extended toward the battle in a yellow and straight line." After this specification, it may be better to read that the road 'moved' around the base of the hill than that it 'curved.'

135.15 sheep] That the HW,A1 'steep track' goes back to a typist's error in their copy may be indicated by 122.8–9, 'The trail wound here and there as the sheep had willed in the making of it.'

136.12 connected] The context indicates that A1 'concerted' is a sophistication, not an authorial alteration. The comparison to 'cataracts' and to a 'pealing' suggests the idea of a continuous, or 'connected', sound, not that of volleys at intervals. Moreover, by definition a volley is concerted.

Some support may be offered by Report #5 (IX, REPORTS OF WAR) which in the 5(I) text reads, "The roll of musketry was tremendous. From a distance it was like tearing a cloth; nearer, it sounded like rain on a tin roof and close up it was just a long crash after crash." The last detail seems more pertinent to the use of 'connected' here (quite definitely the reading of the typescripts) than the use of 'concert' in Report #6 in a different context although closely associated with the description of the firing: "The volleys were rattling and crackling from one end of the hill to the other. Sometimes the patter of individual firing swelled suddenly to one long, beautiful crash that had something in it of the fall of a giant pine amid his brethren of the mountain side. At times it was these things, and at times it was just the crack-crack-crackety-crack-crackle of burning timbers. Altogether, the troops on the ridge were heavily engaged, and as if by concert the plain on the right became dotted with little puffs of smoke."

136.25 fine] This omission in E1, presumably to avoid the repetition of 'fine' from 'fine scene' at 136.23–24, may be paralleled lower on the E1 page where at 137.3 the 'up' in 'held up to this business', as in the other three texts, is omitted, no doubt to avoid the repetition in immediately following 'drag them up'. It is comforting to an editor that the overall textual hypothesis removes the E1 variants from the possibility either of having been made in annotated printer's copy or in proof. He is thereby enabled to assign these as compositorial sophistication and not authorial tinkering.

MOONLIGHT ON THE SNOW

180.39 Corners] 'Crowdger's Corners' causes some textual difficulty. In FL the reading 'Crowdgers' at the start probably reflects the manuscript (i.e., its typescript copying) but whether the final two FL appearances with the apostrophe at 187.31 and 188.12 represented belated compositorial recognition or else a change in the copy itself is impossible to decide. The situation with 'Corners' versus 'Corner' is simplified by the preserved page proof for E2 in the Barrett Collection. At its first appearance here at 180.39 both texts read 'Corner', which might or might not reflect the copy. However, when next it appears, at 182.21 FL switches to the plural 'Corners', which it maintains thereafter, whereas E2 continues 'Corner' without variation. However, the Barrett page proof demonstrates that the original E2 typesetting read 'Corners' throughout but that from the first appearance at 180.39 the proof corrector, probably Cora, deleted the final 's'. Since evidence exists that in reading proof Cora was partly exercising her own notions about readings and partly bringing E2 into general conformity with the printer's copy, we have every reason to respect the original E2 'Corners' readings and very little reason to defer to Cora's unauthoritative changes. The evidence certainly suggests that the copy for both printed versions read 'Corners'. Small American towns may be named either *Corner* or *Corners*.

185.8 stage coach] That the E2 omission of 'stage', which makes it conform to 185.12,19,21; 185.25 and 186.36 where both texts have simple 'coach', is an error would be demonstrated by the legend to the fourth illustration which uses 'stage' (though not 'coach') if we could be sure that the artist F. P. Klitz drew his material from the typescript and not from a proof. But since no such proof is available, the retention of 'stage' in the present text must rest on probability alone. See note 95 in the Textual Introduction.

EDITORIAL EMENDATIONS IN THE COPY-TEXT

NOTE: Every editorial change from the copy-texts—whether manuscript, typescript, newspaper, magazine, or book version, as chosen—is recorded for the substantives, and every change in the accidentals as well save for such silent typographical alterations as are remarked in "The Text of the Virginia Edition" prefixed to Volume I of this collected edition with slight modification as indicated in the headnotes to the present apparatus. Only the direct source of the emendation, with its antecedents, is noticed; the Historical Collation may be consulted for the complete history, within the texts collated, of any substantive readings that qualify for inclusion in that listing. However, when as in syndicated newspaper versions a number of texts have equal claim to authority, all are noted in the Emendations listing. An alteration assigned to the Virginia edition (V) is made for the first time in the present edition if *by the first time* is understood *the first time in respect to the texts chosen for collation*. Asterisked readings are discussed in the Textual Notes. The note *et seq.* signifies that all following occurrences are identical and thus the same emendation has been made without further notice. The wavy dash ~ represents the same word that appears before the bracket and is used exclusively in recording punctuation or other accidentals variants. An inferior caret ᴧ indicates the absence of a punctuation mark. The dollar sign $ is taken over from a convention of bibliographical description to signify *all* editions so identified. That is, if N represents newspaper versions in general, and N$^{1-6}$ the six collated newspapers, then $N would be a shorthand symbol for all of these six texts and would be used even if one text owing to a more extensive cut than simple omission (always recorded in the Historical Collation) did not contain the reading in question. Moreover, the universal $ sign would also be used if all the subsumed texts agreed as to the point of variation being noted although disagreeing in other respects not being noted. For example, if an entry read 'laborᴧ] A1; ~ , $N' all N documents would have a comma; but some might read 'labour' without this fact being specified or interfering with the use of the $ sign, for only the punctuation was in question.]

THE PACE OF YOUTH

[The copy-text is N^1: Dayton *Daily Journal*. Other texts collated are N^2: *Kansas City Star*; N^3: *Nebraska State Journal*; N^4: New York *Press*; N^5: *Minneapolis Tribune*; N^6: San Francisco *Examiner*; and E1: *The Open Boat*, Heinemann, 1898.]

3.0   I] N²,E1; *omit* N¹·³⁻⁶
3.22 sea∧] N²⁻⁶,E1; ~ , N¹
4.9   game,] N²⁻⁶,E1; ~ ∧ N¹
4.11 offspring] N²⁻⁶,E1; ~ - ~ N¹
4.14 song. Over] E1; song, while over $N
4.14 corner∧] N²⁻⁵; ~ , N¹·⁶,E1
*4.18 the manner] *stet* $N
4.25 these lists] E1; this list $N
5.15 felt] E1; wished $N
5.19 "Cashier"] V; "cashier" $N, E1
6.5   confidence∧]   N²·⁶,E1; ~ , N¹·³·⁵
6.15 mysterious] E1; mystic $N
6.26 brain] E1; tired brain $N
6.27 whether] E1; whether or not $N
7.12 The girl] E1; She $N
7.26 moment∧] N²⁻⁶; ~ , N¹,E1
7.26 fine] E1; great $N
7.31.1 II] E1; PART II. N¹⁻³·⁵⁻⁶; *omit* N⁴
8.4   holding] E1; holding the basket for $N
8.5   came an idea of] E1; was born a little plan for $N
8.9   view,] N³⁻⁶, E1; ~ ∧ N¹⁻²
8.18–19 darkness] E1; solemn, mystic darkness $N
8.37 —inevitably] E1; ∧ brilliantly $N
9.3   more that she] E1; more she $N
9.4   emotions] E1; fine emotions $N
9.10 and] E1; *omit* $N
9.10 the] E1; th' $N
9.22 ardently] E1; with great feeling $N

9.29 indignant] E1; angry $N
9.32 poem] E1; great poem $N
9.38–10.1 heartlessness] N²⁻⁶,E1; heartlessnes N¹
*10.2 crowd] *stet* $N
10.5 water∧] E1; ~ , $N
*10.7 lands] *stet* $N
10.14 cloud] E1; storm $N
10.15 associated long] E1; long associated $N
10.17 th'—house] E1; ~ ∧ ~ $N
10.21 Kingly] E1; Imperial $N
10.29 good-bye] N³,E1; good-by N¹·⁵⁻⁶; good ∧ bye N²; goodby N⁴
10.32 horse."] horse and they were gone." $N (horses N⁶)
10.35 incoherent] E1; incoherent in a chaotic rage $N
11.1 forced] E1; caused $N
11.3 the—revolver] E1; ~ ∧ ~ $N
11.8 Up town] N²⁻⁵; Uptown N¹·⁶,E1
11.10 arteries] E1; arteries and broken bones $N
11.16 Sorington] E1; Sorrington $N
11.19 struck] E1; struck his horse $N
11.22 suddenly] E1; all suddenly $N
11.24 aged legs] E1; gait $N
11.25 them] E1; his aged legs $N
*11.38 clinched] N⁴; clenched N¹⁻³·⁵⁻⁶,E1
12.12 understood] E1; pursued $N
*12.15 ¶ The dust] *stet* $N

ONE DASH—HORSES

[The copy-text is N¹: *Philadelphia Press*. Other texts collated are N²: *Kansas City Star*; N³: *Nebraska State Journal*; N⁴: *Buffalo Commercial*; N⁵: New Orleans *Daily Picayune*; NR: *New Review*; PM: *Pocket Magazine*; A1: *The Open Boat*, Doubleday & McClure, 1898; E1: *The Open Boat*, Heinemann, 1898. Since A1 and E1 are derived texts they are not ordinarily listed unless they are the source of emendations.]

13.0 omit] PM,NR; PART I. $N
13.7 et seq. José] NR; Jose $N, PM
13.14 "Si (no ¶)] NR; ¶ $N,PM
13.14 et seq. señor] NR; senor $N,PM
13.19 rein,] N²⁻⁵,PM,NR; ∼ ∧ N¹
13.20 tenderly∧] N².⁴⁻⁵,PM,NR; ∼ , N¹·³
13.25 sombre] N³⁻⁴,PM,NR; somber N¹⁻²·⁵
13.25 sky,] N²⁻⁵,PM,NR; ∼ ∧ N¹
14.16 ate,] N³⁻⁵,PM,NR; ∼ ∧ N¹⁻²
14.25 wall,] N²⁻⁵,PM,NR; ∼ ∧ N¹
15.11 "Damn (no ¶)] NR; ¶ $N,PM
*15.22 North] stet N¹⁻²
*15.31 quavering] NR; quivering $N,PM
15.31 Richardson (no ¶)] NR; ¶ $N,PM
15.36 waist] E1; wrist $N,PM, NR,A1
16.8 Suddenly∧] N²⁻³,PM; ∼ , N¹·⁴⁻⁵,NR
16.11 snake] N²⁻⁵,PM,NR; suake N¹
16.12 were black] N²⁻⁵,PM,NR; were as black N¹
16.16 They (no ¶)] NR; ¶ $N,PM
16.20 posed] N²⁻⁵,PM,NR; poised N¹
16.24 The (no ¶)] NR; ¶ $N,PM
16.26 fearful,] N²⁻⁵,PM,NR; ∼ ∧ N¹
16.37 or∧] N²⁻⁵,PM,NR; ∼ , N¹
17.10 tamale] N³; tomale N¹⁻²·⁵, PM; meal N⁴; tomate NR
17.17 of ferocity] E1; of singular ferocity $N,PM,NR,A1
17.18 He (no ¶)] NR; ¶ $N,PM
17.25 Richardson (no ¶)] NR (But he); ¶ $N,PM
*17.26–27 as rigidly] N²⁻⁴,PM; at rigidly N¹; as rigorously N⁵; omit NR
17.30; 18.23 The (no ¶)] NR; ¶ $N,PM
*18.3 this——,"] stet N¹+ (PM: ∼ —— ∧")

18.26 threats] E1; menace $N, PM,NR,A1
18.26 As] PM,NR,A1,E1; PART II. As $N
18.26 As (no ¶)] NR; ¶ $N,PM
18.34; 19.7 Richardson (no ¶)] NR; ¶ $N,PM
*18.35 vibrating and] E1; mystic and $N,PM,NR; omit A1
19.3 A (no ¶)] NR; ¶ $N,PM
19.23 hand,] N²⁻⁵,PM,NR; ∼ ∧ N¹
19.24 On (no ¶)] NR; ¶ $N,PM
19.24 threshold∧] N³⁻⁵,NR; ∼ , N¹⁻²,PM
19.31 José (no ¶)] NR; ¶ $N,PM
19.38 The (no ¶)] NR; ¶ $N,PM
20.26 Those (no ¶)] NR; ¶ $N,PM
20.28 of] N²⁻⁵,PM,NR; omit N¹
20.34 and that way] N²⁻³·⁵,PM, NR; and that N¹; omit N⁴
20.38 past,] N²⁻⁵,PM,NR; ∼ ∧ N¹
21.5 fabulous] E1; mystic $N, PM,NR,A1
21.15 spring,] N²⁻⁵,PM,NR; Spring ∧ N1 ·
21.16 forth∧] N²⁻⁵,PM,NR; ∼ , N¹
21.16 Sometimes (no ¶)] NR; ¶ $N,PM
21.18–19 the purple] N²⁻⁵,PM, NR; purple N¹
21.23 last,] N²⁻⁴,PM,NR; ∼ ∧ N¹·⁵
21.33 coins] E1; silver coins $N, PM,NR,A1
21.33 "Ride (no ¶)] NR; ¶ $N, PM
21.35 "Go (no ¶)] NR; ¶ $N,PM
22.1; 22.34 Richardson (no ¶)] NR; ¶ $N,PM
22.3 danger;] N²⁻⁵,PM,NR; ∼ , N¹
22.8,29; 23.6 José (no ¶)] NR; ¶ $N,PM
22.8 nevertheless∧] N²⁻⁵,PM,NR; ∼ , N¹
22.17 Richardson,] N²⁻⁵,PM,NR; ∼ ∧ N¹
22.23 But (no ¶)] NR; ¶ $N,PM
22.38 He (no ¶)] NR; ¶ $N,PM

23.6   turned] N²⁻⁵, PM,NR; truned N¹

23.7   his heels] N²⁻⁵,PM,NR; heels N¹

23.9   The (*no ¶*)] NR; ¶ $N,PM

24.4   two hundred] PM,NR; 200 $N

24.10   Then (*no ¶*)] NR; ¶ $N, PM

24.13   top speed] N².⁵, NR; topspeed N¹; ~ - | ~ N³; ~ - ~ N⁴,PM

24.26   rage.] N²⁻⁵,PM,NR; ~ : — N¹

24.26   "——!" (*no ¶*)] NR; ¶ $N, PM

24.28   ——!"] N²⁻⁵,PM,NR; ——! ∧ N¹

24.31   The (*no ¶*)] NR; ¶ $N,PM

24.32   Finally (*no ¶*)] NR; ¶ $N, PM

THE WISE MEN

[The copy-text is E1: *The Open Boat*, Heinemann, 1898. Texts collated are LB: *The Lanthorn Book* [1898]; LM *Ludgate Monthly*; A1: *The Open Boat*, Doubleday & McClure, 1898.]

26.0   A Detail of American Life in Mexico] A1; *omit* LB,LM,E1

26.3   credit] A1; great credit LB, LM,E1

*26.15 *et seq.* Kids] A1; kids LB, LM,E1

26.18   splendor] LB,A1; splendour LM,E1

26.19   "When (*no ¶*)] LB; ¶ LM,E1,A1

26.19   two] LB,A1; *omit* LM,E1

26.23   four-thirty] LB,A1; 4:30 LM,E1

*26.29   is] *stet* LM,E1

27.2–3   sidewalk] A1; ~ - ~ LM, E1

27.3   in] A1; of LM,E1

27.14   seats] LB,A1; chairs LM, E1

27.24   eyeing] LB,LM; eying E1, A1

27.29   —the very best—] A1; *omit* LB,LM,E1

27.36   finest] A1; best LB,LM,E1

27.38   out] A1; *omit* LB,LM,E1

28.1   parlor] LB,A1; parlour LM, E1

28.5   moustache] LB,A1 (mustache); moustaches LM,E1

28.11   set] A1; sat LB,LM,E1

*28.14   mean] *stet* LM,E1,A1

28.16   vest] A1; waistcoat LB, LM,E1

28.18   each] A1; every LB,LM,E1

28.27   chorus:] LB,A1; ~ , LM, E1

28.32   suddenly.] LB; ~ — E1; ~ : LM,A1

28.33   be,] A1; *omit* LB,LM,E1

28.36   Say, now] A1; Now LB, LM,E1

29.2   conference] A1; confidence LB,LM,E1

29.4   said:] LB,LM,A1; ~ — E1

29.7   much] A1; *omit* LB,LM,E1

29.7–8   or night] A1; *omit* LB, LM,E1

29.10–11   Some . . . afoot.] A1; Men noted it. LB,LM,E1

29.15   some] A1; *omit* LM,E1

29.15   -colored] A1; -coloured LM,E1

29.19   stretched] A1; led LB,LM, E1

29.20   endless elbows crooking] A1; countless crooked elbows LB,LM,E1

29.31   is] A1; is ever LB,LM,E1

29.33   'im] LB,A1; him LM,E1

29.34   understand—] LB,A1; ~ , LM,E1

29.37–38 meaningly] A1; meanfully LB,LM,E1
*29.38 thought he] *stet* LB,LM,
E1
30.1 said:] LB,LM,A1; ~ — E1
30.3 oh] LB,A1; O LM,E1
30.4 cried:] LB,LM,A1; ~ — E1
30.9 Bank] A1; Book LB,LM,E1
30.11 'im] LB,A1; him LM,E1
30.14 Nobody . . . this.] LB,A1;
Nobody gets in on this but us.
LM,E1
30.18 among] A1; through LB,
LM,E1
30.19–20 their . . . plot] A1;
omit LB,LM,E1
30.23 now] A1; *omit* LB,LM,E1
30.24 hot!] LM,LB; ~ ? E1,A1
30.33 race.] LM,LB; ~ ? E1,A1
30.35 now] LB,A1; *omit* LM,E1
31.1 said:] LB,LM,A1; ~ — E1
31.8 'round‸] LB; 'round' LM,E1;
‸ round ‸ A1
31.11 remarked:] LB,LM,A1;
~ — E1
31.11 "Freddie (*no* ¶)] LB,LM,
A1; ¶ E1
31.21 yard] LB,A1; yards LM;
yards' E1
31.23 "Say (*no* ¶)] LB,A1; ¶
LM,E1
31.25 'im] A1; him LB,LM,E1
31.25–26 He's an old man.] A1;
omit LB,LM,E1
31.28 though?] A1; ~ , LB,LM;
~ ! E1
31.28 daresn't] LB,A1; daren't
LM,E1
32.2 runner,] LB,LM,A1; ~ ‸ E1
32.5 meant] LB,LM; meant that
E1,A1
32.14 labored] LB,A1; laboured
LM,E1
32.18 partner‸] LB,LM; ~ , E1,
A1
*32.32 It's] *stet* LB,LM,E1
32.36 kind] LB,A1; kinds LM,E1
33.3 time] LB,A1; *omit* LM,E1
33.5 lights,] LB,A1; lights and
LM,E1

33.6 policemen] LB,LM,A1; policeman E1
33.8 arrangements] LB,A1; arrangement LM,E1
33.9 said:] LB,A1; ~ , LM,E1
33.14 until] LB,A1; till LM,E1
33.15 neighborhood] LB,A1;
neighbourhood LM,E1
33.15 evening] A1; *omit* LB,LM,
E1
*33.16 *calle*] A1; calle LB,LM,E1
*33.18 class] *stet* LB,LM,E1
33.19 derby] LB,A1; Derby LM,
E1
33.19 cutaway] LB,LM,A1; ~ - ~
E1
*33.22 pave] *stet* LB,E1,A1
33.23 odor] LB,A1; odour LM,E1
33.32 ¶ The Kids . . . Old] A1;
omit (*no* ¶) LB,LM,E1
34.12 said:] LM,A1; ~ — E1;
~ , LB
34.21 intensely:] LM,A1; ~ —
E1; ~ , LB
34.24 derndest‸] LB,LM; ~ , E1,
A1
34.34 vest] A1; waistcoat LB,
LM,E1
34.37 seems] A1; seemed LB,
LM,E1
34.37 great] A1; *omit* LB,LM,E1
35.1–2 gesticulating and] A1;
omit LB,LM,E1
35.3 principals, the Kids, . . .
them,] LB,A1 (them‸); ~ —
~ ~ ‸ . . . ~ — LM,E1
35.13 broad‸] LB,A1; ~ , LM,E1
35.16 cried:] LB,A1; ~ , LM,
E1
35.18 S-s-sh] LB,A1; S-s-h LM,
E1
35.22 wagered:] LB,A1; ~ , LM,
E1
35.23 was] LB; were LM,E1,A1
35.28 cried:] A1; ~ , LM,E1; ~ .
LB
35.29 The (*no* ¶)] LB; ¶ LM,E1,
A1
35.29 afterward] A1; afterwards
LB,LM,E1

35.30 shouted:] LB,A1; ~ , LM,
E1
35.31 other] A1; *omit* LB,LM,E1
35.33 "The (*no* ¶)] LB,A1; ¶
LM,E1
35.34 City] A1; city LB,LM,E1
35.37 broad fine] A1 (broad,);
fine broad LB,LM,E1
36.1 Old World] A1; old world
LB,LM,E1
*36.3 buskins] *stet* LM,E1,A1
36.7 rows] A1; roads LB,LM,E1
36.13 off] A1; *omit* LB,LM,E1
36.22 fool!] A1; ~ . LB; ~ , LM,
E1
36.22 A] A1; And LB; and LM,
E1
36.23 darkness] A1; deep gloom
LB,LM,E1
36.28 again:] LM,A1; ~ . LB;
~ — E1
36.28 replied:] LM,A1; ~ . LB;
~ — E1
36.30 more] LB,LM,A1; a more
E1
36.32 throng] LB,A1; crowd
LM,E1
36.33 thickly packed] LB,LM,A1;
~ - ~ E1
36.35 bawling:] LB, A1; ~ , LM,
E1
36.36 profound gloom] A1; distance LB,LM,E1
37.2 barbaric] A1; *omit* LB,LM,
E1
37.4 toward] LB,A1; towards
LM,E1
37.5 maniac] A1; oiled LB,LM,
E1

37.9 You cuss . . . buttons,] A1
(Durn); *omit* LB,LM,E1
37.9 did you] A1; Did anybody
LB,LM,E1
37.12 "Say . . . anything!"] A1;
omit LB,LM,E1
37.14 'im] LB,A1; him LM,E1
37.16 great] A1; *omit* LB,LM,
E1
37.22 falling] LB,LM,A1; fallen
E1
37.23 stammer:] LB, LM,A1;
~ — E1
37.23 "Say (*no* ¶)] LB,A1; ¶ LM,
E1
37.23 can't that] LB,A1; ~ — ~
LM,E1
37.24 old man] LB,A1; ~ — ~
LM,E1
37.25 gasp:] LB,LM,A1; ~ — E1
37.26 Later (*no* ¶)] LB; ¶ LM,
E1,A1
37.29 that.] LB,LM; ~ ? E1,A1
*37.39 jeer] A1; jibe LB,LM,E1
37.39 "What's (*no* ¶)] LB,A1; ¶
LM,E1
*38.3 hollo, Benson!] A1; hello!
Benson, LM,E1; hello, Benson,
LB
38.12,14 said:] LB,LM,A1; ~ —
E1
38.13 said:] LB,A1; ~ , LM;
~ — E1
38.15 defiantly:] LB,LM,A1;
~ — E1
38.20 remarked:] LB,A1; ~ ,
LM,E1

THE FIVE WHITE MICE

[The copy-text is the Huntington MS. Texts collated are W: New York
World; E1: *The Open Boat*, Heinemann, 1898; A1: *The Open Boat*, Doubleday & McClure, 1898. MS 'dont' for 'don't', 'cant' for 'can't', 'didnt' for
'didn't', and 'it's' for 'its' have been silently emended throughout.]

39.1 cocktail] W,A1; ~ - ~ MS,
E1
39.13 driving,] E1,A1; ~ ∧ MS

39.20 Freddie,] W,E1,A1; ~ ∧
MS
39.29 epidemic] W,E1,A1; epe-
demic MS

40.1   honor] A1; honour MS,E1
40.12   supposititious] W,E1,A1; supposititous MS
40.33   deserts,] E1,A1; ~ ‸ MS, W
41.1   blew] W,E1,A1; blow MS
*41.1   in] stet MS
41.3   stony] W,E1,A1; stoney MS
41.23   received] E1,A1; recieved MS
41.39   scatheless] W,A1; unscathed MS,E1
42.9–13;50.4–8   In MS each line is preceded by a double quote, removed in W, E1, and A1
42.9   chance,] W,E1,A1; ~ ‸ MS
42.10   pants,] W,E1,A1; ~ ‸ MS
42.11   sin,] W,E1,A1; ~ ‸ MS
42.12   if you] W,E1,A1; if MS
*42.19   All of the] stet MS
42.20–21   bottom-up] W,A1; bottom-down MS,E1
43.8   circus-box] W,A1; theatre-box MS,E1
43.28 et seq.   'Frisco] W,A1; Frisco MS,E1
43.36   I've] W,E1,A1; Ive MS
*44.1   They] stet MS
*44.3–6   "Oh . . . feet."] stet MS
44.7   Kid] W,A1; kid MS,E1
*44.23   comic, foolish, wise] W,A1; ~ ‸ ~ ‸ ~ MS; ~ , ~ - ~ E1
44.35   rooms,] W,E1,A1; ~ ‸ MS
*45.1   Comere] stet MS
45.3–4   Indians] W,E1,A1; indians MS
*45.11   'round] V; around MS,E1; round W,A1
45.13   Cer'ly] W; Cerly MS,E1; Ce'r'ly A1

45.27   astonishment,] E1,A1; ~ ‸ MS
45.37   suddenness] E1,A1; suddeness MS
46.3   calle] A1; calle MS,E1
46.4   scraping] E1,A1; scrapeing MS
46.19   is as] W,E1,A1; is a MS
46.23   ain'] W,A1; ain't MS (aint),E1
46.24,26   N'York Kid] W,A1; N'York kid MS,E1
46.26   shut] W,A1; shup MS,E1
47.7 et seq.   señor] E1,A1; senor MS,W
47.17   "Yes!"] E1,A1; "~"! MS
47.29   unplaced,] E1,A1; ~ ‸ MS
47.32   stupefied] E1,A1; stupified MS
48.11   perpendicular] W,E1,A1; perpindicular MS
48.26   Eastern] W1,A1; eastern MS,E1
49.13   inconceivable] W,E1,A1; inconcievable MS
49.36   manoeuver] V; manoever MS; manœuvre W,E1; manœuver A1
50.4–6   chance, . . . pants, . . . sin,] W,E1,A1; ~ ‸ . . . ~ ‸ . . . ~ ‸ MS
50.10   pierced] W,E1,A1; peirced MS
50.10   unwieldy] W,E1,A1; unweildly MS
50.18   repose,] W,E1,A1; ~ ‸ MS
50.21   sufficient] E1,A1; sufficent MS
51.19   high] W,A1; omit MS,E1

A MAN AND SOME OTHERS

[The copy-text is Cy: Century. Texts collated are E1: The Open Boat, Heinemann, 1898; and A1: The Open Boat, Doubleday & McClure, 1898.]

53.27–28   mysterious and devilish] E1; mystic and sinister Cy
54.14   geet E1; git Cy,A1
54.30   cent‸] V; ~ . Cy,E1,A1

57.7   two] E1; three Cy,A1
57.13   Strange . . . strange] A1; Mystic . . . mystic Cy,E1
61.5   uncanny] E1; mystic Cy,A1

THE OPEN BOAT

[The copy-text is Sc: *Scribner's Magazine*. Other texts collated are E1: *The Open Boat*, Heinemann, 1898; and A1: *The Open Boat*, Doubleday & McClure, 1898.]

*69.38   doubtlessly] *stet* Sc,E1
70.29   expanse,] E1,A1; ~ ; Sc
71.17   bailing.] A1; ~ : Sc,E1
*72.25,28; 73.2 light-house] V;
    lighthouse Sc,E1,A1
73.3,13   Captain] A1; captain
    Sc,E1`
*74.5–7   The man . . . shadow]
    stet Sc
75.5   white—] A1; ~ , Sc,E1
75.5   trees_∧] E1,A1; ~ , Sc
75.20   Billie."] A1; Billie," said
    the captain. SC; Billie," said
    he. E1
75.35   impudently] E1; *omit* Sc,
    A1
76.5   dunes] E1; low dunes Sc,A1
77.17   clouds.] A1; ~ : Sc,E1

77.26   Captain] A1; captain Sc,
    E1
*79.27   those] V; these Sc,E1,A1
79.35,39   it!] A1; ~ . Sc,E1
81.23; 84.25 gods_∧] E1,A1; ~ ,
    Sc
85.23   hand,] E1,A1; ~ _∧ Sc
*85.24   never more shall see] A1;
    shall never see Sc,E1
85.28   it] A1; the fact Sc,E1
85.33   the breaking] E1; breaking
    Sc,A1
89.21   wave] E1,A1; waves Sc
89.32; 91.26 Captain] A1; captain Sc,E1
90.5   so mixed] E1; mixed, Sc,A1
91.6   Holland] E1; Algiers Sc,A1
91.8   possible?"] E1,A1; ~ ? _∧ Sc

FLANAGAN AND HIS SHORT FILIBUSTERING ADVENTURE

[The copy-text is McC: *McClure's Magazine*. Texts collated are ILN: *Illustrated London News*; E1: *The Open Boat*, Heinemann, 1898; A1: *The Open Boat*, Doubleday & McClure, 1898. Both E1 and A1 are derived texts and thus are noted only in special circumstances of philological interest.]

93.7   men_∧] ILN; ~ , McC
*93.12   afterward] A1; afterwards
    McC,ILN,E1
93.21   tongue_∧] ILN; ~ , McC
94.2   himself_∧] ILN; ~ , McC
94.27   office_∧] ILN; ~ , McC
94.30   came_∧ . . . stood_∧] ILN;
    ~ , . . . ~ , McC
95.7   floor_∧] ILN; ~ , McC
95.17   ice-house] ILN; icehouse
    McC
95.25   *Thunder Voice*] A1; "Thunder Voice" McC; *Thunder-Voice* ILN,E1
95.28   acquaintance_∧ . . . another_∧] ILN; ~ , . . . ~ , McC
95.35   moments_∧] ILN; ~ , McC
95.38   red_∧] ILN; ~ , McC
96.4   grey moustache] ILN; gray
    mustache McC

96.6   bridge_∧] ILN; ~ , McC
96.13   *et seq. Foundling*] ILN;
    "Foundling" McC
97.10   Savannah_∧] ILN; ~ , McC
97.15   water_∧] ILN; ~ , McC
97.27–28   night_∧ . . . *Foundling*_∧] ILN; ~ , . . . ~ , McC
98.1   masts_∧ . . . darkness_∧] ILN;
    ~ , . . . ~ , McC
98.14   guns_∧] ILN; ~ , McC
98.20–21   open_∧ . . . sea_∧] ILN;
    ~ , . . . ~ , McC
98.21   grey] ILN; gray McC
98.27–28   direction_∧] ILN; ~ ,
    McC
99.5   floundered] ILN; foundered
    McC
99.8   "Hell!" said he] ILN; He
    said a strong word McC
99.28   gently_∧] ILN; ~ , McC

99.33 languid₀] ILN; ~ , McC
100.6 captain₀] ILN; ~ , McC
100.10 afterward] A1; afterwards McC,ILN,E1
100.20 soundly₀] ILN; ~ , McC
100.34 stokers₀ . . . doors₀] ILN; ~ , . . . ~ , McC
101.6 paused₀] ILN; ~ , McC
101.21 shore₀] ILN; ~ , McC
101.27 again₀] ILN; ~ , McC
101.36 grinned₀] ILN; ~ , McC
*101.37 said he] A1; he said McC,ILN,E1
102.13 The (no ¶)] ILN,E1; ¶ McC,A1
102.38 all] E1; omit McC,ILN, A1
102.39 second boat came aboard] E1; last boat went shoreward McC,ILN,A1
*103.5–6 engine-rooms] ILN,A1; engine-room McC,E1
103.11 deep₀] ILN; ~ , McC
*103.20 into]ILN; in McC
103.25 loud₀] ILN; ~ , McC
103.38 pilot-house] ILN; ~ ₀ ~ McC
104.11 tall₀] ILN; ~ , McC

104.17 starboard₀] ILN; ~ , McC
104.19 saw₀ . . . past₀] ILN; ~ , . . . ~ , McC
104.25 by God,] ILN (~ ~ !), E1; now, McC,A1
105.14 "Hell . . . Flanagan.] ILN; omit McC
105.23 night₀] ILN; ~ , McC
105.24–25 water₀ . . . glamour₀] ILN; ~ , . . . ~ , McC
105.28 folded₀] ILN; ~ , McC
105.30 dejectedly] E1; slowly McC,ILN,A1
105.32 Finally₀ . . . night₀] ILN; ~ , . . . ~ , McC
106.37 grey] ILN; gray McC
107.3 The terrified . . . gestures.] E1; omit McC,ILN,A1
107.9,10 Voice] ILN; voice McC
107.11 deck₀] ILN; ~ , McC
107.14 sank₀] ILN; ~ , McC
107.16 two] E1; three McC, ILN,A1
*107.20 head] stet McC,A1
107.23 beach₀] ILN; ~ , McC
108.2 beautifully] E1; delightfully McC,ILN,A1

THE BRIDE COMES TO YELLOW SKY

[The copy-text is McC: *McClure's Magazine*. Other texts collated are Ch: *Chapman's Magazine*; E1: *The Open Boat*, Heinemann, 1898; A1: *The Open Boat*, Doubleday & McClure, 1898. However, the two book texts are derived and are not noted except for special reasons.]

*109.8 coach] stet McC
*110.5 trains] stet McC
111.3–4 waiters₀ . . . suits₀] Ch; ~ , . . . ~ , McC
111.9 patronage₀ . . . deference₀] Ch; ~ , . . . ~ , McC
111.10 yet₀ . . . coach₀] Ch; ~ , . . . ~ , McC
111.15 that₀] Ch; ~ , McC
111.28 them₀] Ch; ~ , McC
112.2 would] Ch; could McC
112.5–6 glee, reproach] Ch; glee, and reproach McC
112.7 toward] Ch; towards McC

112.8 band₀ . . . painfully₀] Ch; ~ , . . . ~ , McC
112.34 porter₀] Ch; ~ , McC
113.4 cadence₀] Ch; ~ , McC
113.5 stopped₀] Ch; ~ , McC
113.23 et seq. Weary Gentleman] Ch; " ~ ~ " McC
113.27 et seq. bar-keeper's] Ch; barkeeper's McC
113.27 board-walk] Ch; ~ ₀ ~
114.3 great₀] Ch; ~ , McC
114.21 morose] E1; solemn McC,Ch,A1

114.32   But₍₎] Ch; ~ , McC
115.13–14   but₍₎ . . . precaution₍₎]
Ch; ~ , . . . ~ , McC
115.21   But,] Ch; "But," McC
115.21   interrupted:]   Ch; ~ ,
McC
116.32   heavy₍₎] Ch; ~ , McC
117.24   head₍₎] Ch; ~, McC
118.11–12   still, calm] Ch; still
McC

118.21   two hundred] Ch; 200
McC
118.31   this] Ch; his McC
119.7   "Tried (no ¶)] Ch; ¶ McC
*119.20   the glory of the marriage]
stet McC
120.7   drooping₍₎] Ch; ~ , McC
120.10   —is this] Ch; omit McC

DEATH AND THE CHILD

[The copy-text is E1: *The Open Boat*, Heinemann, 1898. Other texts collated are BW: *Black and White*; HW: *Harper's Weekly*; A1: *The Open Boat*, Doubleday & McClure, 1898.]

121.7   grass,]   BW,HW,A1; ~ ₍₎
E1
121.21   ships,]   BW,HW,A1; ~ ₍₎
E1
121.23   air] BW,HW,A1; the air
E1
121.30   Then, too,] BW,HW,A1;
~ ₍₎ ~ ₍₎ E1
122.1   all,] BW,HW,A1; ~ ₍₎ E1
122.6–7   countenances₍₎]   BW,
HW,A1; ~ , E1
*122.16   moments] stet BW,HW,
E1
122.33   universities.] HW,A1;
~ ! BW,E1
122.39–123.1   words₍₎ . . . fugi-
tives₍₎] BW,HW,A1; ~ , . . .
~ , E1
123.12   northwest] V; ~ - ~ BW,
E1; ~ - | ~ HW,A1
123.23   clock—] BW,HW,A1; ~ ,
E1
*123.30   this kind] A1; his kind
BW,HW,E1
*123.36   an explosion] stet BW,
HW,E1
*124.11   with] HW,A1; by BW,E1
124.11   thought,] BW,HW,A1;
~ ₍₎ E1
124.17   honor] HW,A1; honour
BW,E1
124.18   fight,] BW,HW,A1; ~ —
E1

124.31   meantime₍₎] BW,HW,A1;
~ , E1
124.37   sides] BW,HW,A1; side
E1
*125.6   But₍₎] BW,HW; ~ ,   E1;
omit A1
125.15   ardor] HW,A1; ardour
BW,E1
125.17   shouted:] BW,HW,A1;
~ , E1
125.18   road₍₎] BW,HW,A1; ~ ,
E1
*125.31   gesticulation] stet HW,E1
125.35   grimy] BW,HW,A1; gri-
mey E1
125.38   clamored] HW,A1; clam-
oured BW,E1
126.6   him] BW,HW,A1; them E1
126.20   lieutenant,] BW,HW,A1;
~ ₍₎ E1
126.21   -shaped] HW,A1; -shape
BW,E1
126.21   soldiers₍₎] BW,HW,A1; ~ ,
E1
126.27   At (no ¶)] HW,A1; ¶
BW,E1
126.39   levee] HW,A1; levée BW,
E1
*127.6   ¶ The] stet E1
127.14   odor] HW,A1;   odour
BW,E1
*127.15   all] stet BW,HW,E1
127.17   on₍₎] BW,HW; ~ , E1,A1

127.26 mountain,] BW,HW,AI; ~∧ EI

127.28; 128.12 -colored] HW,AI; -coloured BW,EI

127.29 darkness,] BW,HW,AI; ~∧ EI

128.10 cleaned] BW,HW,AI; clean EI

129.5 commonness∧] BW,HW,AI; ~ , EI

129.27 art;] BW,HW,AI; ~ : EI

129.28 beauty,] HW,AI; ~∧ BW,EI

130.1 them∧] BW,HW; ~ , EI, AI

130.14 beware,] BW,HW; ~ ; EI; ~∧ AI

130.34 reflected, too,] BW,HW, AI; ~∧ ~∧ EI

131.8 tree∧] BW,HW,AI; ~ , EI

131.11 pain∧] BW,AI; ~ , HW, EI

131.12 vale∧] BW,HW; ~ , EI, AI

131.25 Nevertheless,] BW,HW, AI; ~∧ EI

*131.31 moved] HW,AI; curved BW,EI

131.31 around] BW,HW,AI; round EI

132.9 only] BW,HW,AI; omit EI

132.18 et seq. bandoleers] HW, AI; bandoliers BW,EI

132.25 Or∧] BW,HW,AI; ~ , EI

132.34 Exchange—] BW,HW,AI; ~ ; EI

133.7 gasps;] HW; ~ : BW; ~ , EI; ~ — AI

133.20 off.] HW; ~ : BW,AI; ~ — EI

133.35 course,] BW,HW,AI; ~∧ EI

134.18 rumor] HW,AI; rumour BW,EI

134.39 preoccupation] BW,HW, AI; pre-occupation EI

135.2 manner,] BW,HW,AI; ~∧ EI

*135.15 sheep] stet BW,EI

135.32 could] BW,HW,AI; can EI

136.3 picture;] BW,HW,AI; ~ , EI

136.6 The (no ¶)] BW,HW,AI; ¶ EI

136.6 line, . . . course,] BW, HW,AI; ~∧ . . . ~∧ EI

*136.12 connected] stet BW,HW, EI

*136.25 fine] BW,HW,AI; omit EI

137.3 up] BW,HW,AI; omit EI

137.4 soldiers,] BW,HW,AI; ~∧ EI

137.12 once] BW,HW,AI; omit EI

137.13 and, . . . impatiently,] BW,HW,AI; ~∧ . . . ~∧ EI

137.16 mass,] BW,HW,AI; ~∧ EI

137.22 motions;] BW,HW; ~ , EI; ~ . AI

137.34 sir! No] BW,HW,AI; sir! no EI

137.35 had had] BW,HW,AI; had EI

138.14 said:] BW,AI; ~ — EI; ~ , HW

138.26 him,] BW,HW,AI; ~∧ EI

138.34 cartridge-belt] BW,HW, AI; ~∧ ~ EI

139.3 unhumanly] HW,AI; inhumanly BW,EI

139.31 struck. But] HW,AI; ~ ; but BW; ~ , but EI

139.32 silken, sliding,] BW,HW, AI; ~∧ ~∧ EI

140.15 plain, indeed,] BW,HW, AI; ~∧ ~∧ EI

140.29 formulæ] BW,HW,AI; formula EI

140.30 -colored] HW,AI; -coloured BW,EI

141.2 eyes, too,] BW,HW,AI; ~∧ ~∧ EI

141.3 sad,] BW,HW,AI; ~∧ EI

141.5 silence,] BW,HW,AI; ~∧ EI

141.19 wee] BW,HW,AI; omit EI

THE BLUE HOTEL

[The copy-text is CW: *Collier's Weekly*. The other text collated is A1: *The Monster*, Harper's, 1899.]

143.15 god-like] V; god-|like CW; godlike A1
146.36 fight!"] A1; ~ !_∧ CW
147.8 house!] A1; ~ . CW
148.23 Scully,] V; ~ ; CW,A1
157.14 fragments] A1; framentsg CW
160.13 swiftly] A1; swifty CW

160.30 agony-masks] V; ~ . | ~ CW; ~ _∧ ~ A1
161.2 of] A1; o | CW
161.10 Let] A1; Letf CW
163.9 girls,] A1; ~ _∧ CW
165.29 a glass] A1; glass CW
165.30 drank] A1; drink CW
167.11 wife_∧] A1; ~ , CW

TWELVE O'CLOCK

[The copy-text is PMM: *Pall Mall Magazine*. The other text collated is E2: *The Monster*, Heinemann, 1901.]

171.0 I] E2; *omit* PMM
171.22 *et seq.* humor] V; humour PMM,E2
172.1 An'] E2; ~ _∧ PMM
172.10 Organize. . . . Organize] V; Organise. . . . Organise PMM,E2
173.3 -colored] V; -coloured PMM,E2
173.20 patronized] V; patronised PMM,E2
173.26 house,] E2; ~ _∧ PMM
174.16 victimized] V; victimised PMM,E2

174.17 civilization] V; civilisation PMM,E2
176.4 toward] E2; towards PMM
176.23 agin] E2; again PMM
176.32,36 damn] V; dam PMM, E2
176.36 it's] E2; its PMM
177.6 torment] *stet* PMM,E2
177.18 through] E2; though PMM
177.29 fer] V; for PMM,E2

MOONLIGHT ON THE SNOW

[The copy-text is FL: *Frank Leslie's Monthly Magazine*. The other text collated is E2: *The Monster*, Heinemann, 1901.]

179.0 I] E2; CHAPTER I. FL
179.1 *et seq.* War Post] V; Warpost FL; Warpost E2
179.20 fifteen thousand dollars] E2; $15,000 FL
179.21 titles_∧] E2; ~ , FL
179.23 insane_∧] E2; ~ , FL
180.14–15 and_∧ . . . gasps_∧] E2; ~ , . . . ~ , FL
180.30 theatres] E2; theaters FL
180.38 tin-horns] E2; ~ _∧ ~ FL

180.39 Crowdger's] E2; Crowdgers FL
*180.39 Corners] V; Corner FL, E2
181.15 law_∧] E2; ~ , FL
181.23.1 II] E2; CHAPTER II. FL
182.5 "So (*no* ¶)] E2; ¶ FL
182.6 *et seq.* Bobbie] E2; Bobby FL
182.20 Damned] E2; D—d FL

182.21 Crowdger's] E2; Cowd-
gers FL
182.34 damned] E2; d—d FL
182.36–37 but∧unfortunately∧]
E2; ∼ , ∼ , FL
183.6 Finally∧] E2; ∼ , FL
183.14–15 stood∧ . . . hawing∧]
E2; ∼ , . . . ∼ , FL
183.19 et seq. Mister] E2; Mr.
FL
183.22 Simpson?] E2; ∼ ! FL
183.24 Then∧] E2; ∼ , FL
183.31 you—admit] E2; ∼ ∧ ∼
FL
184.2 "Yes." "All right."] E2;
" ∼ ," " ∼ ∼," FL
184.9 ahead——] E2; ∼ . FL
184.11 course. We] E2; ∼ ∧ we
FL
184.23.1 III] CHAPTER III. FL
184.29 bright∧] E2; ∼ , FL
184.33 cold∧] E2; ∼ , FL
185.5 You . . . Simpson.] E2;
omit FL
*185.8 stage coach] stet FL
185.10 dusty∧] E2; ∼ , FL
185.10 rickety] E2; ricketty FL
185.21 At (no ¶)] E2; ¶ FL
186.3 Tom] E2; Jack FL

186.11 and∧ . . . see∧] E2; ∼ ,
. . . ∼ , FL
186.12 here∧ . . . scoundrels∧]
E2; ∼ , . . . ∼ , FL
186.15 you∧ no doubt∧] E2; ∼ ,
no ∼ , FL
186.17 haughtily.] E2; ∼ : FL
186.21 father.] E2; ∼ : FL
186.25 slowly.] E2; ∼ : FL
186.26 acquaintance∧] E2; ∼ ,
FL
187.0 IV] E2; CHAPTER IV. FL
187.2 cowboys∧] E2; ∼ , FL
187.27 large∧] E2; ∼ , FL
188.4 here] E2; omit FL
188.21.1 V] E2; CHAPTER V. FL
189.6 an'] E2; and FL
189.9 himself.] E2; ∼ : FL
189.15 But∧ . . . instant∧] E2;
∼ , . . . ∼ , FL
189.21,30 goin'] E2; going FL
189.22 "Only (no ¶)] E2; ¶ FL
189.24 performance.] E2; ∼ ?
FL
189.29 Post.] E2; ∼ : FL
189.35 reg'lar] E2; regular FL
190.33 air∧] E2; ∼ , FL
191.4 An'] E2; And FL
191.6 hell] E2; h—— FL

A POKER GAME

[The copy-text is TMs: the Barrett original typescript. The other text collated is E1: Last Words, Digby, Long, 1902.]

192.9 the∧ more] E1; ∼ , ∼ TMs
192.12 on] TMs (original); in
TMs (Cora's alteration)
192.13 consummated] E1; con-
sumated TMs
192.19 Old∧] E1; ∼ , TMs
193.4 actor,] E1; ∼ ∧ TMs
193.7 et seq. Mr.] E1; ∼ ∧ TMs
193.10 There,] E1; ∼ . TMs
193.10 he.] V; ∼ ∧ TMs; ∼ , E1
193.11–12 actor∧ presently,] V;
∼ , ∼ ∧ TMs; ∼ , ∼ , E1
193.19–20 shoulder,] E1; ∼ ∧
TMs

194.2 Thereupon] E1;
There-upon TMs
194.4–5 leisurely] E1; leisurly
TMs
194.5 occurred] E1; occured
TMs
194.12 can't] E1; cant TMs
194.23 boy,"] E1; ∼ ∧∧ | TMs
194.24 exuberantly,] E1; ∼ ∧
TMs
194.25 losing] E1; loosing TMs

WORD-DIVISION

1. End-of-the-Line Hyphenation in the Virginia Edition

[NOTE: No hyphenation of a possible compound at the end of a line in the Virginia text is present in the copy-texts except for the following readings, which are hyphenated within the line in these copy-texts. Hyphenated compounds in which both elements are capitalized are excluded.]

3.28	never-|ending		128.36	sheep-|herding
12.9	swift-|flying		139.26	blood-|marked
17.35	blanket-|covered		150.5	met-tro-|*pol*-is
23.36	silver-|trimmed		151.31	card-|board
33.18	self-|satisfied		154.23	wide-|mouthed
43.17	hedge-|hogs		155.34	board-|whacking
57.20	sheep-|herder		156.5	torture-|chamber
59.12	to-|night		164.35	-o-|oh
60.29	grass-|blades		165.15	disease-|stricken
75.32	sea-|water		166.1	highly-|nickeled
93.27	hundred-|thousand-		172.5	hell-|bent-
95.22	to-|see-		173.32	glassy-|eyed
98.17	search-|light		176.25	Square-|X
102.28	stoke-|room		177.1	left-|hand
104.1	engine-|room		179.9	serene-|browed
106.18	sword-|play		181.2	cow-|punchers
107.11	fire-|room		182.37	real-|estate
127.29	tender-|eyed		183.33	well-|known

2. End-of-the-Line Hyphenation in the Copy-Texts

[NOTE: The following compounds, or possible compounds, are hyphenated at the end of the line in the copy-texts. The form in which they have been transcribed in the Virginia text, listed below, represents the practice of the individual copy-texts as ascertained by other appearances or by parallels, or—failing that—by the known characteristics of Crane as seen in his manuscripts.]

13.6	sun-shot		27.21	bar-tenders
16.11	round-faced		56.17	bartenders
19.31	lemon-colored		59.18	to-night
20.37	forelimb		61.15	knee-joints
22.4	outpost		70.30	wind-riven
26.31	flip-flapping		71.25	bead-like

71.32	jack-knife	118.29	maroon-colored
73.8	sea-weed	119.37	Sunday-school
73.19	iron-bound	125.24	blood-stains
74.38	double-watch	136.22	wide-eyed
75.11	life-saving	140.33	hill-side
75.19; 81.16	light-house	141.20	grass-blade
79.31	life-crew	143.15	god-like
82.16	oarsman	146.13	tenderfoot
86.26	life-saving	148.27	white-faced
89.37	life-belt	149.10	half-turned
94.15	custom-house	150.4	school-house
95.9	outgoing	150.31	upright
97.11	northeast	152.4	light-haired
98.29	war-stores	154.20	fire-wheel
100.15	overboard	155.10	downstairs
103.2	oncoming	158.21	mid-current
109.30	lay-out	161.36	blood-stains
112.35	muscle-bound	172.25	rattlesnake
113.22	twenty-one	189.34	law-abidin'
116.11	armor-plate	190.34	snow-squall
117.7	door-ways		

3. *Special Cases*

[NOTE: In the following the compound is hyphenated at the end of the line in the copy-text and in the Virginia Edition.]

190.4 to-|morrow (i.e., to-mor-   193.34 green-|clothed
    row)   (i.e., green-clothed)

HISTORICAL COLLATION

THE PACE OF YOUTH

[N¹: Dayton *Daily Journal*; N²: *Kansas City Star*; N³: *Nebraska State Journal*; N⁴: New York *Press*; N⁵: *Minneapolis Tribune*; N⁶: San Francisco *Examiner*; E1: *The Open Boat*, Heinemann, 1898.]

3.4   tarrier] terror N³
3.16–24   A soft . . . slowly.] *omit* N⁴
3.28   in a] the N³
3.28   never-] neer- N⁵
3.31   and] *omit* N⁶
4.10   arise] rise N⁵
4.12   orchestrion] orchestra N³
4.13   with its] with a N⁵
4.14   song. Over] song, while over $N
4.17   man] man who N²
4.18   the manner] a manner E1
4.24–26   affixing . . . childhood] *omit* N⁴
4.25   sort of] sort of a N²

4.25   these lists] this list $N
4.28   on his platform] *omit* N⁴
4.29   shyly] *omit* N⁴
4.30   great] greatest N³
4.33   it] *omit* N²
4.34–37   Even . . . father.] *omit* N⁴
4.35   discerned] discovered N³
4.38   shining] *omit* N⁴
5.2   her] he N⁵
5.3–9   At . . . netting.] *omit* N⁴
5.15   that] *omit* N²
5.15   felt] wished $N
5.21   a tender] the tender E1
5.22–6.32   The love affair . . . joy.] *omit* N⁴

5.38 of] *omit* N³
6.1 at] of N⁶
6.8 an] some N⁵
6.13 for] for their N⁵
6.15 incomprehensible] incomparable N²
6.15 mysterious] mystic $N
6.17–36 They . . . participate.] *omit* N⁶
6.18 that] *omit* N³
6.20 affair] affairs N³
6.26 brain] tired brain $N
6.27 whether] whether or not $N
6.31 in] *omit* N⁵
6.31 thought] thought that N⁵
6.33 there] here N⁵
6.39 clattered] chattered N⁵
7.4 obvious] *omit* N⁴
7.6–9 He was . . . dreaming.] *omit* N⁴
7.12 The girl] She $N (*no* ¶ N⁴)
7.12 cast down her eyes] cast her eyes down N⁴
7.13–14 She . . . father.] *omit* N⁴
7.13 withstand] understand N³; stand N⁶
7.17,27 "I've (*no* ¶)] ¶ E1
7.17 speakin'] speaking N⁴
7.24–25 He . . . Stimson.] *omit* N⁴
7.26 fine] great $N
7.29–31 Through . . . submission.] *omit* N⁴
7.31.1 N⁴ synopsizes: Stimson was the owner of a merry-go-round. His daughter Lizzie sold the tickets and a young man collected them and looked after the juvenile riders. This young fellow found time to glance at the pretty cashier often enough until he had won her affections. One day Stimson caught him casting amorous glances at the cashier and forthwith threatened to discharge him if he did not attend to business more strictly.
7.32–34 Stimson . . . submission,] *omit* N⁴

7.35 behind the silvered netting] *omit* N⁴
7.35 there] *omit* N⁴
8.4 ¶ The] *no* ¶ N⁴
8.4 holding] holding the basket for $N
8.5–6 Into . . . Stimson.] *omit* N⁴
8.5 came an idea of] was born a little plan for $N
8.11–28 The electric . . . silver.] *omit* N⁴
8.14 sometimes] sometime N³
8.18 vanished] vanish N³
8.18–19 darkness] solemn, mystic darkness $N
8.29 two] *omit* N⁵
8.30–31 He . . . coward.] *omit* N⁴
8.31 stop on] stop at N⁵
8.37 "Oh (*no* ¶)] ¶ E1
8.37 —inevitably] ˄brilliantly $N
9.2 for love a] love for N⁵
9.2–6 an admiration . . . them] *omit* N⁴
9.3 more that she] more she $N
9.4 emotions] fine emotions $N
9.9 their] her N²
9.10 "Won't (*no* ¶)] ¶ E1
9.10 come] *omit* N⁵
9.10 and] *omit* $N
9.10 the] th' $N
9.11 The (*no* ¶)] ¶ E1
9.11 man] woman E1
9.14 at] *omit* N³
9.14 this] the N³
9.22 ardently] with great feeling $N
9.24 "You (*no* ¶)] ¶ E1
9.29 indignant] angry $N
9.30 "Oh (*no* ¶)] ¶ E1
9.32 poem] great poem $N
9.33 in] in in N³
9.37 ¶ They] *no* ¶ N⁴
9.37–10.3 If . . . stolid.] *omit* N⁴
10.2 crowd] crowds E1
10.6 of] or N⁴
10.7 lands] bands E1
10.8 the dull] a dull E1
10.11 cage] stage N⁵

10.13   ¶ He] *no* ¶ E1
10.13   He . . . grenadiers.] *omit*
        N⁴
10.13   "Where (*no* ¶)] ¶ N⁴,E1
10.14   cloud] storm $N
10.15   associated long] long associated $N
10.16   "They've (*no* ¶)] ¶ E1
10.16   round] 'round N²
10.17   th'—house] ~ ₍ₐ₎ ~ $N
10.21–24 Kingly . . . children.]
        omit N⁴
10.21   Kingly] Imperial $N
10.25   ¶ He] *no* ¶ N⁴,E1
10.28   away—] ~ . E1
10.32   horse."] horse and they
        were gone." $N± (horses N⁶)
10.33   dreadful] terrible N⁵
10.33   "Get (*no* ¶)] ¶ E1
10.34   d——,] *omit* N⁴,E1
10.35   incoherent] incoherent in a
        chaotic rage $N
11.1   forced] caused $N
11.2   a shrill] with a shrill E1
11.3   the—revolver] ~ ₍ₐ₎ ~ $N
11.6   was] were E1
11.8   "Up (*no* ¶)] ¶ E1
11.9   The (*no* ¶)] ¶ E1
11.10   arteries] arteries and broken bones $N

11.10   a large number of] several
        N³
11.15   poise] pose E1
11.16   Sorington] Sorrington $N
11.18   the full] a full N²
11.19   struck] struck his horse $N
11.22   suddenly] all suddenly $N
11.22   animated] animate N²
11.24–25 aged . . . them] gait
        and spread his aged legs $N
11.32   impassive] passive N³
11.35   he] *omit* N⁵
11.35   "Go (*no* ¶)] ¶ E1
11.38   clinched] clenched N¹⁻³,⁵⁻⁶,
        E1
12.1   from] from the N²
12.4   bobbing, bobbing] bobbing,
        bobbing, bobbing N⁴
12.6–14 He . . . earth.] *omit* N⁴
12.7   the . . . the] a . . . a E1
12.12   understood] pursued $N
12.15   ¶ The] *no* ¶ E1
12.16   The (*no* ¶)] ¶ E1
12.16–17 a suggestion] the suggestion N²
12.20   "No (*no* ¶)] ¶ E1
12.20   Stimson (*no* ¶)] ¶ E1
12.25   the sudden] a sudden E1

ONE DASH—HORSES

[N¹: *Philadelphia Press*; N²: *Kansas City Star*; N³: *Nebraska State Journal*;
N⁴: *Buffalo Commercial*; N⁵: New Orleans *Daily Picayune*; NR: *New Review*; PM: *Pocket Magazine*; E1: *The Open Boat*, Heinemann, 1898; A1:
The Open Boat, Doubleday & McClure, 1898.]

13.0   ONE DASH—HORSES] AN
        ADVENTURE IN MEXICO. |
        "ONE DASH—HORSES." N²;
        ONE DASH WITH HORSES N⁵;
        HORSES NR,E1
13.7,29 in] into N⁴
13.28   on] in N⁵
13.28   the] his NR,E1
14.10   of the room] *omit* NR,E1
14.16   the] a N³
14.20   then] the N³
14.21   into] in N⁴

14.22   a Mexican] the Mexican
        NR,E1
14.37   rhythmical] rythmetical N⁴
15.10   treble] trouble N³
15.11   Damn] D—— PM,A1
15.12   muttered Richardson] he
        muttered NR,E1
15.18   further] farther A1
15.18   of the opinion] of opinion
        NR,E1
15.23   kill] not kill N²
15.26   spurs] spur N³

15.28 Look out] Lookout N³
15.31 quavering] quivering $N, PM,A1
15.36 waist] wrist $N,PM,NR,A1
16.6 detail] details N²
16.12 were black] were as black N¹
16.15 thrummed] drummed N³
16.18 the folds of] omit NR,E1
16.20 posed] poised N¹
16.31 in . . . manner] very drunkenly NR,E1
16.32 little] omit PM,A1
16.37 idiot.] ~ ? NR,E1
17.5–6 a hatred . . . them] omit N²,⁴
17.10 tamale] tomale N¹⁻²,⁵,PM, A1,E1; tomate NR; meal N⁴
17.17 of ferocity] of singular ferocity $N,PM,NR,A1
17.19 shuddering] shudderingly N⁴
17.23 I am] I'm PM,A1
17.25 Richardson] But he NR,E1
17.25–26 impassively] passively N⁵
17.26 however] omit NR,E1
17.26 clinched] clenched E1
17.26–27 as rigidly] omit NR,E1; at rigidly N¹; as rigorously N⁵
17.28 chords] cords N³
17.36 now] omit N³
18.5 its] the N²
18.19 night] the night NR,E1
18.20,25 was] were NR,E1
18.20 toward] towards NR,E1
18.22 the knife] a knife NR,E1
18.23 the] his N³
18.26 threats] menace $N,PM, NR,A1
18.26 N¹⁻⁴: SYNOPSIS. | Richardson and his Mexican servant, Jose, arrive, as evening falls, at a Mexican hamlet, where they put up at a small inn. The saddles are brought in and both lie down to sleep. They are awakened by the music of a dance in the adjoining room, and Richardson overhears two Mexicans quarreling as to his robbery,

and possible murder. One of them, a fat round-faced fellow, enters the room with a torch, followed by several companions. Finding Richardson on the alert, revolver in hand, they beat his servant, hoping to provoke him to an attack. He remains calm. Just then the voices [N²: voice] of the girls are heard calling the men to the dance, and the Mexicans gradually withdraw. (Text from N¹.)

18.28 because . . . hide] omit N⁴
18.31 Richardson] he NR,E1
18.35 vibrating and] mystic and $N,PM,NR; omit A1
18.37–38 occasionally mumbled] mumbled now and again NR, E1
19.2 clang] bang N⁵
19.6 become] fallen NR,E1
19.7 Richardson . . . dawn.] He felt the effect of this cold dawn in his blood. NR,E1
19.11 saddles . . . held two] omit N⁴
19.12 held] had NR,E1
19.13 his] a N²
19.13 toward] towards N⁵
19.16–17 lineman] linesman NR, E1
19.24 toward] towards N³
19.24 Richardson] he NR,E1
19.30 and] omit N⁵
19.32 around] round NR,E1
19.33; 20.23 animal] beast NR,E1
19.33–34 evidently] omit NR,E1
19.38 at this time] omit NR,E1
20.1–2 for the horse] for his horse N²; omit NR,E1
20.3 stirring] omit N⁴
20.4 nor] nothing NR,E1
20.7 The fingers of Richardson] The American's fingers NR,E1
20.12 wretched] omit N³
20.16 men] riders NR,E1
20.22 forward. The] forward as the N⁵
20.25 breathe] breath N³⁻⁴

20.27   of the village] *omit* NR,E1
20.34   and that way] *omit* N⁴
20.34   ² way] *omit* N¹
21.3   as] *omit* N²⁻³
21.5   fabulous] mystic $N,PM, NR,A1
21.7   bended] bent A1
21.8   the . . . charger] his charger's flanks NR; his charger's sides E1
21.11   when] where N⁵
21.12   certainly] *omit* NR,E1
21.14   to them that he was] himself NR,E1
21.18–19   the purple] purple N¹
21.23   drew] draw N²
21.33   two] *omit* N³
21.33   coins] silver coins $N,PM, NR,A1
22.1   Richardson] But Richardson NR,E1
22.3   and] *omit* NR,E1
22.4   servant] panic-stricken servant NR,E1
22.4   an] *omit* N³,NR,E1
22.9   in] to N²
22.21   from] form N³
22.25   requires for] takes NR,E1
22.26   As a matter of truth] *omit* NR,E1
22.29   his bridle] the bridle E1

22.30   around] about NR,E1
22.30   the saddle] his saddle N³
22.33   resembled] resemble PM, NR,E1,A1
23.7   his heels] heels N¹
23.9   madly to] madly at N⁵
23.11   sort of a] sort of N³·⁵
23.27   a little] the little N²
23.35   little of . . . much of] little . . . much N⁵
23.37   bobbed] bobbed up N⁵
23.39   of the party] *omit* NR,E1
24.5   to profoundly] profoundly to NR,E1
24.15   around] round NR,E1
24.16   somewhat] something NR, E1
24.16   now] *omit* NR,E1
24.28   —!—!—!—!] —!—!—! N³
24.28   These (*no* ¶)] ¶ N³
24.28   lines] dashes NR,E1
24.32   —!—!—!] —!—!—!—! N³
24.33   sprang] sprung N³
24.37   again gulped] gulped again NR,E1
24.38–39   one of . . . rurales] a favourite method NR,E1
25.1   evidently] *omit* NR,E1
25.2   while] *omit* NR,E1
25.10   shining] shinning N⁵

THE WISE MEN

[LB: *The Lanthorn Book* [1898]; LM: *Ludgate Magazine*; E1: *The Open Boat*, Heinemann, 1898; A1: *The Open Boat*, Doubleday & McClure, 1898.]

26.0   A Detail of American Life in Mexico] *omit* LB,LM,E1
26.3   credit] great credit LB,LM, E1
26.10   Mexico,] ~ — LM
26.19   two] *omit* LM,E1
26.23   four-thirty] 4:30 LM,E1
26.29   is] are LB,A1
27.2–8   On the sidewalk . . . furious sunshine.] *omit* LB
27.3   in] of LM,E1
27.14   seats] chairs LM,E1
27.18   broad] *omit* LB

27.19–23   "He allowed . . . eh?"] *omit* LB
27.29   —the very best—] *omit* LB,LM,E1
27.36   finest] best LB,LM,E1
27.38   out] *omit* LB,LM,E1
28.5   moustache]   moustaches LM,E1
28.11   set] sat LB,LM,E1
28.14   mean] means LB
28.16   vest] waistcoat LB,LM,E1
28.18   each] every LB,LM,E1
28.23   Anton'] Anton LM

28.33 be,] *omit* LB,LM,E1
28.36 Say,] *omit* LB,LM,E1
29.2 conference] confidence LB, LM,E1
29.7 didn't] did not LB,A1
29.7 much] *omit* LB,LM,E1
29.7–8 or night] *omit* LB,LM,E1
29.10–11 Some . . . afoot.] Men noted it. LB,LM,E1
29.14–18 The sunlight . . . air spaces.] *omit* LB
29.15 some] *omit* LM,E1
29.19 stretched] led LB,LM,E1
29.20 endless elbows crooking] countless crooked elbows LB, LM,E1
29.22 At (*no* ¶)] ¶ A1
29.23 ¶ "Sit] *no* ¶ A1
29.31 is] is ever LB,LM,E1
29.33; 30.11 'im] him LM,E1
29.36 The (*no* ¶)] ¶ A1
29.37–38 meaningly] meanfully LB,LM,E1
29.38 thought] thought that A1
30.9 Bank] Book LB,LM,E1
30.14 Nobody but us gets in on this.] Nobody gets in on this but us. LM,E1
30.15 They (*no* ¶)] ¶ A1
30.18 among] through LB,LM,E1
30.19–20 their faces ashine with a plot] *omit* LB,LM,E1
30.23 now] *omit* LB,LM,E1
30.35 now] *omit* LM,E1
31.1 They (*no* ¶)] ¶ A1
31.10 During (*no* ¶)] ¶ A1
31.21 yard] yards LM; yards' E1
31.25 'im] him LB,LM,E1
31.25–26 He's an old man.] *omit* LB,LM,E1
31.28 daresn't] daren't LM,E1
32.3 cinch] clinch LM
32.5 meant] meant that E1,A1
32.8 know] know that A1
32.12 and] *omit* LB
32.32 It's] is it A1
32.36 kind] kinds LM,E1
32.37 bets] bets that LB,A1
33.3 time] *omit* LM,E1
33.5 lights,] lights and LM,E1
33.6 policemen] policeman E1

33.8 arrangements] arrangement LM,E1
33.14 until] till LM,E1
33.15 evening] *omit* LB,LM,E1
33.18 class] classes A1
33.22 pave] pavé LM
33.31–32 with?" . . . Colonel] bet?" with Colonel LB
33.32 The Kids . . . . Old] *omit* LB,LM,E1
34.18 back] backs A1
34.24 derndest] durndest A1
34.34 vest] waistcoat LB,LM,E1
34.37 seems] seemed LB,LM,E1
34.37 great] *omit* LB,LM,E1
35.1–2 gesticulating and] *omit* LB,LM,E1
35.3 principals, . . . them,] ~ — . . . ~ — LM,E1
35.15 The group (*no* ¶)] ¶ A1
35.16 Suddenly (*no* ¶)] ¶ A1
35.18 S-s-sh] S-s-h LM,E1
35.20 into] in A1
35.21 men] man LM
35.23 was] were LM,E1,A1
35.27 Once (*no* ¶)] ¶ A1
35.29 afterward] afterwards LB, LM,E1
35.30 smoke!ᴧ ᴧWell . . . blowed!ᴧ ᴧThunder] ~ !" " ~ . . . ~ !" " ~ A1
35.31 other] *omit* LB,LM,E1
35.37 broad fine] fine broad LB, LM,E1
36.3 buskins] buckskins LB
36.7 rows] roads LB,LM,E1
36.13 off] *omit* LB,LM,E1
36.22 A] And LB; and LM,E1
36.23 darkness] deep gloom LB, LM,E1
36.28 Everybody (*no* ¶)] ¶ A1
36.30 more] a more E1
36.32 throng] crowd LM,E1
36.36 profound gloom] distance LB,LM,E1
37.2 barbaric] *omit* LB,LM,E1
37.4 toward] towards LM,E1
37.5 maniac] oiled LB,LM,E1
37.7 toward] towards LM,E1
37.9 You cuss . . . buttons,] *omit* LB,LM,E1

37.9   Dern] Durn A1
37.9   did you] Did anybody LB,
     LM,E1
37.12 "Say . . . anything!"] omit
     LB,LM,E1
37.14 'im] him LM,E1
37.14 These (no ¶)] ¶ A1
37.16 great] omit LB,LM,E1
37.22 falling] fallen E1
37.23-24 Say—can't—can't that
     old—old man run!] Say, can't—

can't—that old—old—man run!
     LM,E1
37.26 Who's] Whose LM
37.28 Hell] Smoke A1
37.39 jeer] jibe LB,LM,E1
37.39 "What's (no ¶)] ¶ LM,E1
38.2   Damn] Hang LM
38.3   hollo, Benson!] hello, Ben-
     son, LB; hello! Benson, LM,E1
38.18 Hammigan] Hammihan LB

The Five White Mice

[MS: Huntington autograph; W: New York *World*; E1: *The Open Boat*,
Heinemann, 1898; A1: *The Open Boat*, Doubleday & McClure, 1898. The
listing of MS alterations follows this section.]

39.0   THE] omit W
39.6   ironical] ironclad W
39.8-14 From . . . helpers.] omit
     W
39.31-40.7 They . . . picnic.]
     omit W
40.1   too] omit E1
40.3   bended] bent A1
40.12 supposititious] supposititous
     MS
40.13 -like] omit W
40.15 mellow organ-tones] organ-
     mellow tones E1
40.19 for dinner] for dinners E1
40.22 within] in E1
40.28 shake] stake A1
40.31 An (no ¶)] ¶ W
40.32 Madres] Madre W
41.1   blew] blow MS
41.1   in] on W,A1
41.2   hand] hands W
41.5   performances] performance
     E1,A1
41.8   "Not (no ¶)] ¶ W
41.9   There (no ¶)] ¶ W
41.14-26 into the middle . . .
     upon it.] omit W
41.39 scatheless] unscathed MS,
     E1
42.2   shoulder] shoulders E1
42.12 if you] if MS
42.15-16 From . . . ace.] omit W

42.18 vanquished] vanished W
42.19 of] omit E1
42.20 his] the E1
42.20-21 bottom-up] bottom-down
     MS,E1
42.23 "Oh (no ¶)] ¶ W,E1
42.24 Instantly (no ¶)] ¶ E1
42.26 "Maybe (no ¶)] ¶ E1
42.30 fifty dollars] $50 W
42.33 genial] general W,A1
43.1   everyone] every one W,E1,
     A1
43.1   "Why (no ¶)] ¶ W,A1
43.6-7 Why . . . chump.] omit W
43.8   circus-box] theatre-box MS,
     E1
43.13 suddenly] omit E1
43.20-25 He presented . . . advo-
     cate.] omit W
43.28 the other Kid—] omit W
43.30 "Where (no ¶)] ¶ W
43.31 a] omit A1
44.1   They] They've W,A1
44.3-6 "Oh . . . feet!"] "Oh . . .
     time!" "Let . . . go." "Damn
     . . . circus." "Get . . . feet?"
     "What . . . for?" "Get . . .
     feet!" A1
44.4   'em] 'm A1
44.8   As (no ¶)] ¶ A1
44.12-20 In . . . dead.] omit W
44.20 At (no ¶)] ¶ W

44.23 foolish, wise] ~ - ~ E1
44.25 upon] on E1
44.26 discuss] discussing W
44.33 wobbled] wabbled W
45.1 Comere] Com'ere E1; Come 'ere W,A1
45.2 Hellokid] Hello, Kid W
45.7 Comonangetadrink] Com-onan' | getadrink W
45.7 The (no ¶)] ¶ E1,A1
45.11 'round] around MS,E1; round W,A1
45.23 a glower] glower W
45.24 cab] a cab W
45.26–29 He . . . friend.] omit W
45.32 Comonangetadrink] Come-aagetadrink W
45.33–46.17 "Oh . . . stage.] omit W
46.18 burrowing] barrowing W
46.23 ain'] ain't MS(aint),E1
46.24–25 mos' proper,] mos' proper shober E1
46.25 but he's] he's W
46.26 Shut] Shup MS,E1
46.27 Benson (no ¶)] ¶ W
46.28 twirled] whirled W
47.4 yellow] omit E1
47.7 want] want to E1

47.8–36 Benson . . . wave.] omit W
47.38 also] omit E1
48.6 This] The A1
48.9 bended] bent A1
48.13–20 He . . . collision.] omit W
48.30 fortifications] fortification W
48.33 times] time W
49.2 financing] financiering W
49.7–11 The . . . swearing.] omit W
49.14 impression] expression W
49.19–21 It . . . unknown.] omit W
50.1–8 It . . . chance."] omit W
50.13 his weapon] the weapon W
50.17 arose] rose W
50.20–25 Perhaps . . . light.] omit W
50.29 steps] step W
50.35 bloody] bloody a A1
51.10–13 He . . . it.] omit W
51.19 high] omit MS,E1
51.29 from whence] where A1
51.35 Frishco] 'Frisco W,A1
51.36–52.2 He . . . Kid?] omit W

THE FIVE WHITE MICE

Alterations In The Manuscript

39.2 swiftly] *after* 'whirling' *was written* 'rap' *but then deleted and* 'like' *interlined with a caret, inscription then continuing with* 'a top'; 'swiftly' *was interlined after* 'top' *when* 'like a top' *was deleted*
39.3 cheap watch.] *interlined above deleted* 'bit of mechanism'
39.8 From] *originally continuous text but a paragraph sign inserted*
39.9 tray] *preceded by deleted* 'orders'
39.9 rooms] *preceded by deleted* 'r'

39.9 across] *interlined with a caret above deleted* 'over'
39.10–11 city, . . . siesta,] *originally* 'city's life at the high noon' *but deleted except for* 'city' *and* ', awakening from its siesta,' *interlined*
39.13 roar] *preceded by deleted* 'loud'
39.21 support,] *interlined above deleted* 'help'
39.21 the] *interlined with a caret*
39.26 at] *preceded by a deleted illegible letter that may be the start of* 'no'
39.26 Occasionally] *preceded by deleted* 'Soo'

39.29 an] *interlined with a caret*

39.30 had] *interlined above deleted 'were'*

40.3 heads] *interlined above deleted 'eyes'*

40.5 at] *written over 'in'*

40.6 the] *interlined with a caret*

40.8 over the] *interlined above deleted 'in the'*

40.9–10 Casa Verde.] *originally 'the saloon.' which was deleted and 'Maison Cafe Verde' interlined; then 'Maison Cafe' was deleted and 'the Casa' written preceding it*

40.10 became] *interlined above deleted 'were'*

40.18 for] *interlined with a caret*

40.29 ²it!] *following quote mark deleted*

40.32 rays] *preceded by deleted 'glimmering'*

40.33 the dice] *'the' interlined*

40.36 burlesquing] *'u' after 'q' interlined*

41.2 the] *preceded by deleted 'it'*

41.3 paused.] *interlined with a caret above deleted 'waited.'*

41.12 the] *interlined with a caret*

41.15 the] *interlined above deleted 'that'*

41.15 exemption] *interlined with a caret above deleted 'safety'*

41.18 flashes] *preceded by one or two deleted illegible letters, the first of which may be 'b'*

41.32 narrowed eventually] *interlined with a caret above deleted 'narrowly'*

41.33 in] *interlined with a caret*

41.36 fate] *preceded by deleted 'he'*

41.39 others,] *interlined above deleted 'crowd'*

42.11 Gold] *interlined above deleted 'Dust'*

42.17 had] *interlined with a caret*

42.17 accomplished] *interlined above deleted 'achieved'*

42.19 of] *squeezed in later*

42.20 For] *'F' written over 'H'*

42.24 presiding] *interlined above deleted 'presided'*

42.25 every man] *interlined with a caret*

42.26 Maybe] *followed by a deleted comma*

42.26 he] *interlined with a caret after deletion of 'the Kid.' following 'repeated' and the addition of a period*

42.28 is,] *comma inserted after deletion of exclamation and of quote marks*

42.35 With] *preceded by deleted 'He'*

42.35 manner] *'m' written over 'a' (query 'air'?)*

42.39 all] *interlined with a caret*

43.1 rang the voice] *interlined above deleted 'could be heard the'*

43.1 Freddie] *interlined with a caret above deleted 'Teddie'*

43.1 berating] *followed by deleted period*

43.2 was the] *'the' interlined*

43.4 know the first thing] *interlined with a caret above deleted 'anything'*

43.6 drillin'] *preceded by deleted 'you'*

43.6 you,] *followed by deleted 'if'*

43.7 my] *interlined above deleted 'his'*

43.7 a] *interlined with a caret*

43.9 about] *interlined above deleted 'over'*

43.13 would] *preceded by deleted 'wh'*

43.13 jeer] *interlined above deleted 'thrust'*

43.14 at the Kid] *interlined with a caret*

43.14 Five] *preceded by deleted 'Th'*

43.15 On] *'Afterward' was interlined with a caret before 'On' with its 'O' reduced to 'o', and then 'Afterward' was deleted and three underlines placed below altered 'O'*

43.15 others] *preceded by deleted* 'the'

43.18 banter] *followed by deleted* 'retorted'

43.20 case] *interlined with a caret*

43.23 His companions] *interlined with a caret above* 'They'

43.25 convincing] *interlined with a caret*

43.29 Kid] *interlined with a caret*

43.31 ²that] *interlined with a caret*

44.4 time?] *question mark altered from period*

44.5 for?] *question mark altered from period*

44.12 ²the] *interlined with a caret*

44.15 surpasses] 'es' *written over* 'ing'

44.17 agreement] *interlined with a caret above deleted* 'con' *ending with the upstroke of a* 't'

44.20 not] *interlined with a caret*

44.22 until late] *interlined with a caret*

44.23 at the comic] *interlined above deleted* 'until late' *that had followed a deleted period after* 'laughing'

44.25 Frisco] *interlined above deleted* 'other'

44.28 pealed] *interlined above deleted* 'sounded'

44.28 rooms] 's' *added and another period attached*

44.35 rooms] 's' *added*

45.1 Comere] *originally* 'Com' ere'; *then an* 'h' *interlined and deleted, followed by the deletion of the apostrophe and the joining of* 'm' *and* 'e'

45.4 His] *preceded by deleted* 'A'

45.9 Kid?] *question mark altered from period*

45.18 abruptly] *interlined above deleted* 'sternly'

45.31 and] *interlined with a caret*

45.33 along,] *interlined with a caret above deleted* 'on,'

45.38 in] *interlined above deleted* 'with'

45.39 tumbling] *preceded by deleted* 'f'

46.1 reasons] *preceded by deleted* 'other'

46.2 kerb] *interlined above deleted* 'curb'

46.14 the] *preceded by deleted* 'a'; *followed by* 'tale' *interlined above deleted* 'story'

46.15 even] *originally interlined with a caret before* 'didnt' *but then deleted and interlined with a caret after it*

46.16 swore.] *period inserted and following* 'deeply.' *deleted*

46.21 shadows.] *period deleted and final* 's' *and period added*

46.23 load'] *apostrophe added when final* 'ed' *deleted*

46.30 long] *preceded by deleted* 'very'

46.30 opinion] *interlined above deleted* 'impression'

46.32 dogs.] *period altered from exclamation point*

46.38 There] 'T' *written over an almost completed* 'A'

47.3–4 vacantly] *interlined above deleted* 'vacously'

47.5 Kid] *interlined with a caret*

47.8 gentle] *interlined above deleted* 'mild'

47.13 a light.] *interlined above deleted* 'matches.'

47.18 the left] 'the' *formed by deleting final* 'ir' *of* 'their'

47.26 were] *followed by deleted* 'to'

47.29 an unplaced] *originally interlined with a caret after* 'forgotten' *but then moved by a line to a caret after* 'of'; *a comma before interlined* 'an' *was not deleted after the change of position*

47.39 black] *followed by deleted* 'rubber'

48.6 and] *interlined above deleted* 'to'

48.12 sight] *interlined above individually deleted* 'th side'

48.20 straight] *preceded by deleted* 'thrilling'

48.24 two] *interlined above deleted* 'one'

48.28 first] *preceded by deleted* 'it'

48.32 laconically] *interlined with a caret*

49.8 without] 'out' *interlined with a caret*

49.9 For . . . comrade] *interlined with a caret; following* 'H' *of* 'He' *altered to* 'h'

49.8–9 swearing.] *originally the sentence ended here with a period; then the period was deleted and after a comma was added* 'for the sake of his dead comrade.' *which was then deleted and a period placed above the comma*

49.13 inconceivable] *originally* 'inconceevable' *but the first* 'e' *altered to* 'i'

49.23 him] *first interlined after* 'came' *but then deleted and interlined with a caret after* 'upon'

49.23 lightning] *preceded by deleted* 'summer'

49.24 not] *interlined with a caret by another hand*

49.33 been] *interlined with a caret*

49.35 it was possible to] *interlined with a caret above deleted* 'he could'

49.36 manoeuver] *Crane started to form a* 'u' *after* 'o' *but then mended it to* 'e' *and wrote* 'manoever'

49.37 ¹he] *preceded by deleted* 'he'

50.1 ¹a] *interlined with a caret*

50.2–3 In . . . duty.] *the start interlined above deleted* 'He ceased to breath.' *and then continued squeezed in on the line below*

50.5 corduroy] *preceded by a deleted illegible letter, just possibly a* 'C'

50.8 house] *interlined with a caret by another hand above deleted* 'temple'

50.10 unwieldy] *originally* 'unweeldy' *but the second* 'e' *altered to* 'i'

50.11 He] *preceded by deleted* 'Th'

50.13 fatally] *interlined with a caret by another hand above deleted* 'fattaly'

50.20 Perhaps] *preceded by deleted* 'B'

51.1 consideration] 'd' *written over* 't'

51.8 him] *interlined above deleted* 'them'

51.18 a tone of cynical] *interlined above deleted* 'smiling mockery'

51.21 scowled] *preceded by deleted* 'frowned'

A MAN AND SOME OTHERS

[Cy: *Century*; E1: *The Open Boat*, Heinemann, 1898; A1: *The Open Boat*, Doubleday & McClure, 1898.]

53.27–28 mysterious and devilish] mystic and sinister Cy,A1

54.14 geet] git Cy,A1

55.34 county] country E1

57.7 two] three Cy,A1

57.13 Strange . . . strange] Mystic . . . mystic Cy,E1

59.32 afterwards] afterward A1

60.17 you better] you'd better A1

61.5 uncanny] mystic Cy,A1

62.21 corse] corpse A1

64.16,18 a'] a E1

THE OPEN BOAT

[Sc: *Scribner's Magazine*; E1: *The Open Boat*, Heinemann, 1898; A1: *The Open Boat*, Doubleday & McClure, 1898.]

68.0   A . . . Commodore] *omit* A1
69.2   command] commanded E1
69.10   " 'A . . . south,'] "ᴧ ~ . . . ~ ‚ᴧ A1
69.38   doubtlessly] doubtless A1
71.9   mind] minds A1
72.6   ¶ They] *no* ¶ A1
74.21   apropos] *à propos* E1
75.20   Billie."] ~ ‚" said the captain. Sc; ~ ‚" said he. E1
75.21   " 'A . . . north,'] "ᴧ ~ . . . ~ ‚ᴧ A1
75.25   was] were A1
75.35   impudently] *omit* Sc,A1
76.5   dunes] low dunes Sc,A1
79.9   Toward] Towards E1

79.27   those] these Sc,E1,A1
81.30   "'Keep . . . up,'] "ᴧ ~ . . . ~ ‚ᴧ A1
82.13   warmed] warm A1
82.29   awakening] awaking A1
84.18–19   with the thing] *omit* E1
84.19   awaken] awake A1
85.24   never . . . see] shall never see Sc,E1
85.28   it] the fact Sc,E1
85.33   the breaking] breaking Sc, A1
89.21   wave] waves Sc
90.5   so] *omit* Sc,A1
90.6   that] so that A1
91.6   Holland] Algiers Sc,A1
91.40   toward] towards E1

FLANAGAN AND HIS SHORT FILIBUSTERING ADVENTURE

[McC: *McClure's Magazine*; ILN: *Illustrated London News*; E1: *The Open Boat*, Heinemann, 1898; A1: *The Open Boat*, Doubleday & McClure, 1898.]

93.12   pow-wow] "pow-wow" ILN, E1
93.12   afterward] afterwards McC,ILN,E1
93.16   of] from ILN,E1
94.12   the] *omit* ILN,E1
94.14; 95.17   was] were ILN,E1
94.21   silent,] ~ ᴧ ILN,E1; ~ - A1
97.24, 26   toward] towards ILN,E1
98.26   which] *omit* ILN,E1
98.29   coal] coals ILN,E1
99.5   floundered] foundered McC, A1
99.8   "Hell!" said he] He said a strong word McC,A1
99.19   and feeling] feeling ILN, E1
99.30   providentially] providently E1
99.35   in] on ILN,E1
99.36   separate] separating ILN, E1

100.10   afterward] afterwards McC,ILN,E1
100.35   walked] walked on ILN,E1
101.16   anyone] any one E1,A1
101.24   stoke-hole] stoke-hold ILN,E1
101.26   I'll] it'll ILN,E1
101.37   said he] he said McC,ILN, E1
102.13   to] *omit* ILN; from E1
102.25   for you] *omit* ILN,E1
102.28   gong] gang ILN
102.38   all] *omit* McC,ILN,A1
102.39   second boat came aboard] last boat went shoreward McC, ILN,A1
103.5   everyone] every one E1,A1
103.5–6   engine-rooms] engine-room McC
103.11   black] *omit* ILN,E1
103.20   into] in McC,A1
104.2   anybody] everybody ILN,E1

104.6 board] board of the *Found-*
    ling ILN,E1
104.24 northward] northwards
    ILN,E1
104.25 by God] now McC,A1
105.14 "Hell . . . Flanagan.] *omit*
    McC,A1
105.24 lit] lighted A1
105.25 the] *omit* ILN,E1
105.29 condition] conditions
    ILN,E1
105.30 dejectedly] slowly McC,
    ILN,A1
106.4 sir] ~ ? ILN,E1
106.8 toward] towards E1
106.13 Afterward] Afterwards
    ILN,E1
106.14 her] *omit* ILN,E1
106.26–28 He . . . voyages.] *omit*
    ILN,E1
106.38 inferno] Inferno ILN,E1

107.3 The . . . gestures.] *omit*
    McC,ILN,A1
107.4 and] *omit* ILN,E1
107.9, 10 Voice] voice McC,A1
107.16 two] three McC,ILN,A1
107.20 head] hand ILN,E1
107.26 plashed] splashed ILN,E1
107.29–30 High . . . evening.]
    omit ILN,E1
107.31–32 music . . . dreams]
    music came faintly to the people
    among the palms ILN,E1
108.2 beautifully] delightfully
    McC,ILN,A1
108.2–3 donned wraps and] *omit*
    ILN,E1
108.8 opportunity] the opportunity
    ILN,E1
108.8–10 The . . . deep.] *omit*
    ILN,E1
108.11 dear,] ~ ? ILN; ~ ! E1

THE BRIDE COMES TO YELLOW SKY

[McC: *McClure's Magazine*; Ch: *Chapman's Magazine*; E1: *The Open
Boat*, Heinemann, 1898; A1: *The Open Boat*, Doubleday & McClure, 1898.]

109.8 coach] train Ch,E1
110.5 trains] train Ch,E1
110.7 He (*no* ¶)] ¶ Ch,E1
110.25 infrequently] unfrequently
    Ch,E1
110.31 To (*no* ¶)] ¶ Ch,E1
110.39 A (*no* ¶)] ¶ Ch,E1
111.4 glowing] dazzling Ch,E1
111.10 plain] palpable Ch,E1
112.2 would] could McC,A1
112.3 on] upon Ch,E1
112.5 glee,] glee, and McC,A1
112.7 toward] towards McC
112.29 "We're (*no* ¶)] ¶ Ch,E1
113.6 none] no one Ch,E1
113.11 As (*no* ¶)] ¶ Ch,E1
113.21 Southern] Southron Ch,E1
114.13 "Scratchy (*no* ¶)] ¶ Ch,E1
114.14 The (*no* ¶)] ¶ Ch,E1
114.17 "All (*no* ¶)] ¶ Ch,E1
114.18 in] *omit* Ch,E1
114.21 morose] solemn McC,Ch,
    A1

114.21 "Say (*no* ¶)] ¶ Ch,E1
114.22 His (*no* ¶)] ¶ Ch,E1
115.6 around] round E1
115.12 upon] on Ch,E1
115.14 "Will (*no* ¶)] ¶ Ch,E1
115.21 But,] "But," McC,A1
115.26 Wow] Whow E1
116.10 fittings] fillings Ch
116.11 armor-plate] plate armour
    Ch,E1
116.20 "I (*no* ¶)] ¶ Ch,E1
116.25 yowls] yells Ch,E1
116.27 "Here (*no* ¶)] ¶ Ch,E1
117.4 sledding] sledging Ch,E1
117.13 sank, straightened and
    sank] sank Ch,E1
117.19 revolvers] revolver Ch,E1
118.12 calm] *omit* McC,A1
118.19 North] north Ch,E1
118.31 this] his McC,A1
119.10 toward] towards Ch,E1
119.12 goin'] going Ch,E1

119.20 the marriage] their mar-
    riage Ch,E1
119.21 environment]   environ-
    ments Ch
119.21 "You (*no* ¶)] ¶ Ch,E1
119.25 "Don't (*no* ¶)] ¶ Ch,E1
119.28 His (*no* ¶)] ¶ Ch,E1

119.33 you] you'd Ch,E1
119.36 "If (*no* ¶)] ¶ Ch,E1
120.6   Married?] ~ ! Ch,E1
120.6   Seemingly] seeming Ch,E1
120.10 —is this] *omit* McC,A1
120.15 Potter (*no* ¶)] ¶ Ch,E1

DEATH AND THE CHILD

[BW: *Black and White*; HW: *Harper's Weekly*; E1: *The Open Boat*, Heinemann, 1898; A1: *The Open Boat*, Doubleday & McClure, 1898.]

121.0   Death] The Death BW
121.23 air] the air E1
122.16 moments] times A1
122.24 only been expressed] been
    expressed only A1
122.27 "Ah (*no* ¶)] ¶ HW
123.13 very] *omit* HW,A1
123.21 toward] towards BW
123.30 dwell] dwelt A1
123.30 this] his BW,HW,E1
123.36 an explosion] one explo-
    sion A1
124.5   "Well (*no* ¶)] ¶ BW
124.5   now have] have now HW
124.11 with] by BW,E1
124.14 was] were HW
124.31 meantime] mean time HW
124.31 had changed] was changed
    A1
124.37 sides] side E1
125.5   knew∧ . . . confronted,] ~ ;
    . . . ~ ∧ A1
125.6   titanic] Titanic BW
125.6   But] *omit* A1
125.31 gesticulation]   gesticula-
    tions BW,A1
126.6   him] them E1
126.8   peasant] peasants HW
126.21 -shaped] shape BW,E1
126.24 brave.   Else] ~ : ~ BW;
    ~ , ~ HW,A1
126.27 At (*no* ¶)] ¶ BW,E1
127.1   aghast,] ~ ∧ HW,A1
127.4   He (*no* ¶)] ¶ HW,A1
127.6   ¶ The] *no* ¶ BW,HW,A1
127.15 all] *omit* A1
127.17 Further] Farther A1

128.10 cleaned] clean E1
128.16 every one] everyone BW
128.28 it nearer] it near HW,A1
129.9   known] known that A1
129.10 all ∧ tender] ~ - ~ BW
129.14 straggle] struggle A1
130.14-15 and so . . . misery]
    omit A1
130.21 He (*no* ¶)] ¶ HW
130.30 toward] towards BW
130.37 all] all the A1
131.16 infamous] informous BW
131.25 down] firmly down BW
131.25 onward] on A1
131.31 moved] curved BW,E1
131.31 around] round E1
132.9   only] *omit* E1
132.24 condition] conditions A1
132.34 Stock Exchange] stock ex-
    change HW,A1
133.20 He turned (*no* ¶)] ¶ HW
133.22 "Pardon (*no* ¶)] ¶ A1
133.23 The (*no* ¶)] ¶ HW,A1
133.25 Peza (*no* ¶)] ¶ HW,A1
133.25 "Yes (*no* ¶)] ¶ HW
134.1   He (*no* ¶)] ¶ BW
135.5   concluded] concluded that
    HW,A1
135.6   a] an A1
135.8   afterward] afterwards BW,
    HW
135.15 sheep] steep HW,A1
135.32 could] can E1
135.34 mountains] mountain HW
136.12 connected] concerted A1
136.16 meantime] mean time HW
136.16 in] into BW

136.23   "Yes (no ¶)] ¶ HW,A1
136.23   it is] it's BW
136.24   They (no ¶)] ¶ HW,A1
136.25   fine] omit E1
136.28   Peza (no ¶)] ¶ HW,A1
136.35   toward] towards BW,HW
137.3   up] omit E1
137.9   man] men A1
137.12   once] omit E1
137.21   Officers (no ¶)] ¶ HW,A1
137.22   motions] motion A1
137.23; 138.1,24,24,30 toward] towards HW
137.26   every one] everyone BW
137.35   had had] had E1
138.25   the corner] a corner HW, A1

138.31   "Yes (no ¶)] ¶ HW,A1
139.3   unhumanly]   inhumanly BW,E1
139.4   at] in BW
139.8   clammy] clumsy A1
139.26   swollen] swoollen BW
140.4   readjustment]   readjustments HW
140.6   trenches] benches BW
140.7   toward] towards HW
140.20   indication]   indications BW
140.29   formulæ] formula E1
141.6   fearless] fearless and A1
141.19   wee] omit E1

THE BLUE HOTEL

[CW: *Collier's Weekly*; A1: *The Monster*, Harper's, 1899.]

143.19 *et seq.* toward] towards A1
143.33 *et seq.* Afterward] Afterwards A1
148.4,23 'way] away A1
150.38   shouted] cried A1
151.24   arisen] risen A1
154.2   and] but A1

154.27   purposes] purpose A1
158.3   git] go A1
158.24   further] farther A1
162.34   now] omit A1
165.29   a glass] glass CW
165.30   drank] drink CW

TWELVE O'CLOCK

[PMM: *Pall Mall Magazine*; E2: *The Monster*, Heinemann, 1901.]

171.18   -F] -P E2
171.18,19 up] omit E2
171.26   their] there E2
172.16   mornin'] morin' E2
172.24   odd] old E2
173.26   th'] the E2
173.32   glassy-] glass- E2

174.6   to one] one to E2
174.11   an'] and E2
176.4   toward] towards PMM
177.10   statues] two statues E2
177.26   or] nor E2
177.29   fer] for PMM,E2

Proof Corrections in E2

[The reading to the left of the bracket is that in the present text. To the right of the bracket E2(u) indicates the original state of the proof and E2(c) the ink proof correction. All of these corrections appear in the E2 final text.]

171.2,7 *me.*] ~ . E2(u); ~ ! E2 (c)
171.18 -F] -F E2(u); -P E2(c)
171.18,19 up] up E2(u); *deleted* E2(c)
171.26 their] their E2(u); there E2(c)
172.10 Organize: that's] Organise; that's E2(u); Organise. That's E2(c)
172.16 "Mornin' . . . voices.] *omitted* E2(u); "Morin' . . . voices. E2(c)

174.6 to one] to one E2(u); one to E2(c)
176.4 toward] towards E2(u); toward E2(c)
176.23 agin] again E2(u); agin E2(c)
177.10 statues] statues E2(u); two statues E2(c)
177.19 his two] the two E2(u); his two E2(c)
177.26 or] or E2(u); nor E2(c)
177.28 hand.] ~ ∧ E2(u); ~ . E2(c)

MOONLIGHT ON THE SNOW

[FL: *Frank Leslie's Monthly Magazine*; E2: *The Monster*, Heinemann, 1901.]

179.18 couldn't] could not E2
180.9 *et seq.* 'round] round E2
180.17 "It's (*no ¶*)] ¶ E2
180.23 a] *omit* E2
180.28 "Yes (*no ¶*)] ¶ E2
180.39 Corners] Corner FL,E2
181.19 were] *omit* E2
181.27 East] east E2
182.1 "Come (*no ¶*)] ¶ E2
182.10 "Oh (*no ¶*)] ¶ E2
182.20 Damned] D—d FL
182.21,22 Corners] Corner E2
182.28 "I (*no ¶*)] ¶ E2
182.34 damned] d—d FL
183.8 on occasion] on state occasions E2
183.19,29 "Mister (*no ¶*)] ¶ E2
183.21 respectful] respectable E2
183.22 "Yes (*no ¶*)] ¶ E2
183.37 in every way] *omit* E2
184.4,8 "Well (*no ¶*)] ¶ E2
184.10 "Why (*no ¶*)] ¶ E2
184.11 course. We] course we FL
184.15 Gawd's] Gawd E2
184.16 mout'] mouth E2
184.28 store's] stores' E2
185.1 "I (*no ¶*)] ¶ E2
185.5 You . . . Simpson.] *omit* FL
185.8 stage] *omit* E2
185.9 "The (*no ¶*)] ¶ E2
185.21 "Driver (*no ¶*)] ¶ E2
185.33 the] *omit* E2

186.3 Tom] Jack FL
186.9 "You (*no ¶*)] ¶ E2
186.21 "Why (*no ¶*)] ¶ E2
187.2 had been] were E2
187.20 had] was E2
187.24 sick] ill E2
187.31 Corners] Corner E2
187.34 up] up in E2
188.4 ther'd] the'd E2
188.4 here] *omit* FL
188.6 a] *omit* E2
188.6 "Look (*no ¶*)] ¶ E2
188.12 Corners] Corner E2
188.27 back] aback E2
188.29 sheriff] the sheriff E2
189.6 an'] and FL
189.8 "Gentlemen (*no ¶*)] ¶ E2
189.10 "Why (*no ¶*)] ¶ E2
189.21,30 goin'] going FL
189.29 jest] just E2
189.32 cons-ti-tuted] con-sti-tuted E2
189.35 reg'lar] regular FL
189.36 fightin'] fighten E2
190.6 outsider] outsiders E2
190.7 the] their E2
190.11 their—] ~ ∧ E2
190.19; 191.1 "Well (*no ¶*)] ¶ E2
191.2 fer] for E2
191.4 An'] And FL
191.6 hell] h—— FL

Proof Corrections in E2

[The reading to the left of the bracket is that in the present text. To the right of the bracket E2(u) indicates the original state of the proof and E2(c) the ink proof correction. All of these corrections appear in the E2 final text.]

179.24 hoarded] horded E2(u);
    hoarded E2(c) *in pencil*
180.39; 182.21,22; 187.31; 188.12
    Corners] Corners E2(u); Cor-
    ner E2(c)
183.17 times] time E2(u); times
    E2(c)

187.2 had been] *omit* E2(u);
    were E2(c)
187.3 thugs] things E2(u); thugs
    E2(c)
187.20 had] had E2(u); was
    E2(c)

A POKER GAME

[TMs: Barrett typescript; E1: *Last Words*, Digby, Long, 1902.]

192.12 on] on TMs; in TMs *altera-*
    tion by Cora
194.4 diamonds] diamond E1

194.8 these] those E1
194.15 roar of horror] fear, horror
    E1